DYNAMICS

EDUARD C. PESTEL

PROFESSOR OF MECHANICS
DIRECTOR OF INSTITUTE OF MECHANICS
TECHNISCHE UNIVERSITÄT HANNOVER

WILLIAM T. THOMSON

PROFESSOR OF ENGINEERING
CHAIRMAN OF MECHANICAL ENGINEERING
UNIVERSITY OF CALIFORNIA, SANTA BARBARA

McGRAW-HILL BOOK COMPANY

NEW YORK   ST. LOUIS   SAN FRANCISCO
TORONTO   LONDON   SYDNEY

DYNAMICS

Library of Congress Catalog Card Number 67-30053

49521

1234567890 HDMM 7543210698

TO OUR PATIENT WIVES
ANNELIESE AND PATRICIA

A large number of books on mechanics have been published in the past decades—some of them excellent—so that we who venture to add to their number feel bound to offer some explanation. But before doing so, we should like to assure the reader that the effort to write another text in this classic field was undertaken only after thorough soul searching concerning our own conviction that we would make a worthwhile contribution to the textbook literature on applied mechanics.

During our long activity as teachers we have time and again observed that students, when first confronted with statics, kinematics, and dynamics, are troubled not so much by the manipulations of mathematics as by difficulties encountered in the understanding of the fundamental concepts, in translating mechanics problems into mathematical form as well as in the interpretation of the physical content of mathematical equations.

For this reason we adopted the basic philosophy that axiomatics, new concepts, and definitions should be taught first, using mathematical tools and notations with which students are familiar. For example, in the volume on statics, we start with the essential properties of a force and lead the student directly to the vector properties of the statical moment and couple. The "free-body principle" is then formulated with the concept of equilibrium. Throughout the two volumes, the application of simple concepts which avoid lengthy analysis is demonstrated. For example, complicated mechanisms and plane and space trusses are simply analyzed by reasoning advanced graphically as a consequence of the equilibrium of concurrent forces.

Although we make liberal use of graphical representation in order to convey concepts and ideas most vividly to the reader, we refrain, with very few exceptions, from including graphical methods in our text. We do not believe they further the understanding as well as the application of the science of mechanics. On the other hand, the presentation and derivation of the theorems in vector notation are straightforward, and students are guided by the few rules of vector algebra, without having to memorize all the special steps involved in most graphical methods.

The experienced reader will remember that vector notation was accepted in introductory texts in engineering mechanics in this country only after some hesitation; now, however, it seems fashionable to force the issue of notation to extremes. Attempts are being made to replace symbolic vector notation by indicial notation in order to prepare students at the very beginning for the later use of tensors. We deplore this development, because it induces students to place the importance of notation over that of conceptual understanding. This results in a most unwelcome attitude, not only toward mechanics, but also toward other equally important fields of science. Besides, how many students eventually progress to advanced continuum mechanics, where tensor notation may be required? On the other hand, symbolic vector notation conveys, in our opinion, the mechanical concept most vividly, and we do not believe this to be so with index notation.

Here, the rules of subscripts tend to distract beginners from the far more important mechanics aspect of the problem at hand.

On the basis of the pedagogic notion that learning is a process of induction rather than deduction, we usually treat a special case before attempting the presentation of the general problem. Only in situations where the general problem does not pose any difficulties of understanding do we deviate from this approach. Each new development of the theory is supported by one or more illustrative examples that bring to life the somewhat abstract ideas that make up the theory of mechanics. These examples were chosen mainly for their didactic value and in such simple form that they are sufficient to illustrate the theory without the necessity of handling rather involved algebra.

After this brief discussion of the didactic procedure used in this text, we turn to the contents of this two-volume text. Although there are, of course, numerous ways to present the field of rigid-body mechanics to beginners, we chose to follow the traditional historical development. Thus the first volume is devoted to statics, which is chiefly concerned with the conditions under which material bodies remain in a state of rest, called equilibrium. It was this part of mechanics that was extensively developed before Isaac Newton laid the foundation for the branch of mechanics that is usually called dynamics. The first volume is based on the concept of the free-body technique. However, a thorough introduction to the method of virtual work is included. Hereby the student is confronted with a procedural approach as well as with concepts that will be most useful in all branches of rigid-body and continuum mechanics, which cannot be grasped by him in its full import too early during his introduction to mechanics. Here he also gains a thorough understanding of the problem concerning the stability of equilibrium, which will be most helpful when he later studies this topic in the theory of elasticity.

The second volume is concerned with kinematics and dynamics. Kinematics deals with the geometry of motion of material bodies, thus offering the concepts and the mathematical tools for the description of their motion without concern with the agents that bring it about. In dynamics, on the other hand, we treat the relation between the motion of material bodies and its causes. Here we learn to deal with a great variety of technically important topics: satellite motion, vibration problems, impact of colliding bodies, rocket propulsion, gyroscopes, etc. In this volume, with the exception of a few sections in Chapters 4, 5, and 6, the free-body technique is used throughout, because we believe that only in this way are students led to a deep insight into the interplay between the forces and the motion of bodies. This insight is easily lost when students are made to rely too early on analytic procedures that yield the equations of motion through a mathematical mechanism and often induce beginners to ignore the relations between cause and effect, so vital especially for the engineer.

In the choice of problems we were led solely by didactic reasons. Although this viewpoint also requires the selection of engineering problems that stir the interest as well as the imagination of students, we could not persuade ourselves to discard certain standard problems that have been proved to be of unfailing pedagogic value. This sense of value also guided us in the derivation of the various theorems that form the skeleton of our science. We always placed the requirement that our development be suggestive, lucid, and conceptually potent before the desire to offer the shortest and most elegant approach. Frequently, however, we believe we were able to reconcile both views.

We hope the two-volume text will inspire many students to travel the long road from the roots of mechanics to a level of working knowledge where they are well prepared to pursue advanced studies in the various special topics in this and related fields of science and engineering. It is our firm conviction that an equally broad as well as thorough basic training in mechanics must serve as a unifying foundation at a time when, with technology advancing in all fields, the application of mechanics finds itself in such diverging areas that the unhealthy temptation to specialize at too early a date is an ever-present danger in today's science and engineering education.

During the several years in which the two volumes were written, many individuals assisted with their development. We acknowledge our indebtedness especially to Dr. H. Waller, Dr. B. Dirr, and Dr. J. Wittenburg of the Technische Universität Hannover. We are also grateful to our reviewers Dr. Thomas Kane of Stanford University and Dr. Thomas Caughey of the California Institute of Technology, who offered many invaluable suggestions. Finally we express our gratitude to Frau H. Otto, who typed and retyped the manuscript many times.

EDUARD C. PESTEL

WILLIAM T. THOMSON

CONTENTS

INTRODUCTION

MECHANICS.   CONCEPT AND SCOPE

Mechanics treats the laws of motion of material bodies, including the conditions for their state of rest as a special case of motion, and of the application of these laws to problems in engineering, astronomy, and other applied sciences.   Motion is defined as the change of position in time.   However, in the field of mechanics, not only the concepts of space and time are involved, but also the question of what is moving.   For example, in our discussions we are concerned with the motion of rigid bodies and with systems of such bodies interacting with one another either by means of material agents, such as rigid rods or elastic springs, or because of gravitational attraction or other field forces.

Since any rigid body may always be regarded as composed of material particles of infinitesimally small dimension or of material points, the mechanics limited in this sense is called *point mechanics*, in contrast to *continuum mechanics*, which is concerned with deformable bodies, ranging from elastic to fluid and gaseous materials.

The immediate engineering applications of rigid-body mechanics are too numerous to be listed here.   It may suffice to point out that there is no field in engineering that can be mastered without a thorough understanding of mechanics.   To mention only a glamorous topic, the mapping of a satellite's trajectory, the navigation of the rocket and its stabilization by platforms of gyroscopes, the structure and the engine of the rocket—all these fundamental problems in space travel are, first, problems of mechanics.

BASIC LAWS

Point mechanics is based on the three axioms formulated by Newton[1] in 1687 in his epochal work[2] "Philosophiae naturalis principia mathematica":

I   Every body continues in its state of rest, or of uniform motion in a right line, unless it is compelled to change that state by forces impressed upon it.

II   The change of motion is proportional to the motive force impressed, and is made in the direction of the right line in which that force is impressed.

III   To every action there is always an opposed and equal reaction; or the mutual actions of two bodies upon each other are always equal, and directed to contrary parts.

These axioms constitute the essential extract of the experimental experience and phenomenological evidence available in Newton's age.   As they

[1] Isaac Newton (born 1642 in Woolsthorpe, England; died 1727 in London).
[2] English translation of the Latin original by Andrew Motte (1729).   Republished by the University of California Press.

were appreciably expanded at the end of the nineteenth century, a revision of Newton's empirical laws became inevitable.   However, in engineering applications, except those dealing with nuclear and fast-moving-electron phenomena, they are still valid without reservation.   Newton stated his laws for particles (material points).   The question as to how far his axioms are directly applicable to extended rigid bodies, and in what way they serve as a point of departure for the theory of general motion of rigid bodies and systems of such bodies, constitutes a major concern of this text.

IDEALIZATIONS AND ABSTRACTIONS

Most readers remember the anecdote about the Greek mathematician Archimedes of Syracuse,[1] who in 216 B.C. was asked by his king, Hiero, a very suspicious man—like all who live by the suppression of others—to find out whether his goldsmith had worked into the king's crown all the gold given to him or whether he had set some of it aside for less royal customers. When, after intensive thinking, Archimedes exclaimed his famous $εὕρηκα$, the history of theoretical physics began, not so much because he had dis-covered the law of buoyancy, but because of the reasoning by which he had solved the problem.   His approach consisted in abstracting from the crown all that was purely circumstantial, regarding it solely as a chunk of metal made up of two alloys in a proportion that he had to know.[2]   Here we find the origin of the general procedure in dealing with problems in the field of physics.   After pinpointing, in the maze of accidental and circumstantial phenomena, what is essential for the solution of the problem at hand, the "real thing" is replaced by a hypothetical substitute that embodies these essential features.   For only after such a simplifying idealization of the "real thing" are we able to carry out a purposeful qualitative investigation of the problem and finally, if needed, its quantitative analysis.

One of the basic idealizations in point mechanics is the *rigid body*, which is defined by the assumption that any two points in this body do not change their distance from each other.   A specialization of this concept is the *material point*, that is, a body whose spatial dimensions are vanishingly small. Using the concept of the material point we may also define a rigid body as a system of material points whose mutual distances remain constant.   In this instance it is immaterial in point mechanics whether we have a finite number

[1] Born 287 B.C. in Syracuse, Sicily; died 212 B.C. in the same place.
[2] To appreciate this intellectual feat, we have to consider that Archimedes' procedure was quite foreign to the way of "natural philosophical" thinking as established by Aristotle (born 384 B.C. in Stageira, Greece; died 322 B.C. in Chalkis, Greece). ·After Archimedes' death, at the hand of a Roman soldier during the conquest of Syracuse, his method was forgotten.   Instead, the Aristotelian philosophy of physics continued to dominate the thinking of all those interested in the study of natural phenomena for the following eighteen centuries.   This was responsible for the utter sterility of the physical sciences until the era of Galilei (born 1564 in Pisa, Italy; died 1642 in Arcetri, Italy).   It is somehow symbolic that Newton was born in the year that Galilei died.

of material points or whether they fill space continuously as infinitesimal mass elements.

Here it is well to mention that, in general, different idealizations are used for the same "real thing" when problems of different nature are being considered. If, for example, we investigate the motion of the earth about the sun, both the sun and the earth may be considered material points; however, if dynamic problems involving the earth's rotation about its polar axis are studied, the earth can no longer be regarded as a single material point.

The choice of the substitute system is affected by the purpose of the investigation. For example, when the trajectory of a rocket is the object of our study, then the actually very flexible structure of the rocket, with all its fuel and consisting of more than 100,000 parts, is considered a solid rigid body, and the results of such calculations are quite satisfactory despite this drastic simplification. On the other hand, when the important topic of the rocket's vibrations during the takeoff period is under investigation, then far more detailed substitute systems are necessary. Here the complexity of the substitute system depends on the frequency range in which we are interested. For low frequencies the idealization of the rocket as an elastic rod carrying a number of point masses may suffice, but for frequencies in the acoustic range the rocket structure must be treated as an extremely complicated elastic body (see Figs. I.1 and I.2).

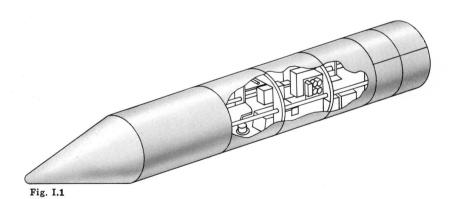

Fig. I.1

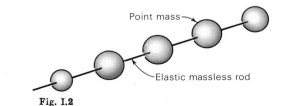

Point mass

Elastic massless rod

Fig. I.2

Finally, even the beginner should realize that the choice of the substitute system completely prejudices the solution of the problem under consideration. It is, therefore, most important that the student practice the "art" of idealization from the very beginning of his occupation with the science of mechanics. In doing so, he will gradually acquire the ability to detect the essence of a problem. The more skilled he is in the formulation of the substitute system, the more likely he is to obtain realistic solutions at rather small mathematical expense.

SPACE AND TIME

We describe the positions and motions of material bodies in spatial dimensions based on our daily experience; that is, in refined scientific language, we consider space a three-dimensional homogeneous and isotropic continuum. Hence we proceed with the conviction that we are able to measure the distance between two points by comparison with a certain scale with any desired accuracy and that we shall find such a distance the same whenever, wherever, and in whatever direction it is measured. Furthermore, this means that we assume space to be independent of the events taking place in it.

Concerning the concept of time we assume that, for example, a sun dial affords us the possibility of defining the quantity that we call time. Now, if, in addition, we were able to decide whether two events took place simultaneously, then we could apply such a time scale to all events in order to determine their duration and to relate them to a certain zero event. Here, too, we take it for granted that our time scale is affected neither by the events nor by the space in which their time flow is studied.

These definitions of time and space are in accordance with experimental evidence only so long as the speed of the objects under study is small compared with the speed of light. As soon as this prerequisite is violated, a thorough revision of our concepts of time and space becomes necessary, a revision that formed the beginning of Einstein's (born 1879 in Ulm, Germany; died 1955 in Princeton, N.J.) theory of relativity.

DIMENSIONS, MEASURES, AND UNITS

It is customary in engineering mechanics to use length, time, and force as basic *dimensions*, but in general physics the concept of mass replaces that of force.[1] The reasons for this deviation are rather obvious. First, if, as is usual in engineering mechanics, we follow the historical development, then statics is the first subject in this field. Here the mass of a material body is encountered only in the form of the body's weight, which, by means of our muscular sense, is defined as a force. Second—and this is perhaps

---

[1] It may be interesting to note that the Primus Mathematicorum, C. F. Gauss (born 1777 in Braunschweig, Germany; died 1855 in Göttingen, Germany), who introduced the cgs system of units, thought for some time of choosing force instead of mass as the third basic dimension.

the most important reason—engineers are interested mainly in the interaction of structural components and in the strains and stresses that occur within them. Hence, force is predominant in their mechanical considerations, and thus we develop the concept of force in the first chapter of "Statics" completely independent of the concept of mass.

When we wish to describe a physical quantity for further processing in numerical form, it is necessary to state its measure and the dimensional *unit* in which it is measured, because such quantity is not a "pure" number but has a dimension[1] that is expressed in a certain unit.   The basic dimensional units in engineering mechanics are compiled in Table I.1.   For further

Table I.1

Force	1 lb = 16 oz
Length	1 ft = 12 in.
Time	1 sec (1 mean solar day = 86,400 sec)

discussion of the various systems of units the reader is referred to textbooks on physics.

Hence a length L is completely described as

$$L = 5 \text{ ft}$$

where the number 5 is the measure and ft denotes the dimensional unit *foot*. We can therefore consider L the product of measure and dimensional unit. Such products are referred to as the numerical quantities Q.   The dimensional unit of any such numerical quantity is denoted by the following symbolism:[2]

$$\text{Dimensional unit of } Q = [Q]$$

For example, in the case of length L measured in feet we write

$$[L] = \text{ft}$$

or in the case of a force F measured in pounds

$$[F] = \text{lb}$$

or in the case of a time duration t expressed in seconds

$$[t] = \text{sec}$$

[1] The original concept of geometric dimensions was extended to physical quantities first by J. B. J. Fourier (born 1768 in Auxerre, France; died 1830 in Paris) and later in complete fashion by J. C. Maxwell (born 1831 in Edinburgh, Scotland; died 1879 in Cambridge, England).

[2] For the sake of brevity we often use a different notation, for example, weight W [lb] instead of weight W ([W] = lb).

SECONDARY DIMENSIONAL UNITS

We consider two numerical quantities Q_1 and Q_2. We then define their product Q_1Q_2 as a numerical quantity expressed in the dimensional unit $[Q_1] \cdot [Q_2]$. Equally their quotient Q_1/Q_2 is to be taken as a numerical quantity of dimension $[Q_1]/[Q_2]$. In this way we obtain, besides the basic dimensional units, the so-called derived or secondary dimensional units. For example, we consider a point that travels along a certain path, thereby traversing the distance Δl within the time interval Δt. Then we call the quotient of these two numerical quantities $\Delta l/\Delta t$ the average velocity of the point during the time interval Δt. Since

$$[\Delta l] = [L] \qquad \text{and} \qquad [\Delta t] = [t]$$

the dimension of the velocity is $[L]/[t]$, for example,

$$\frac{[L]}{[t]} = \frac{\text{ft}}{\text{sec}}$$

LAW OF DIMENSIONAL HOMOGENEITY

The addition of two or more numerical quantities is possible only if their dimensional units are equal:

$$[Q_1] = [Q_2] = \cdots \qquad \text{so that} \qquad [Q_1 + Q_2 + \cdots] = [Q_1] = [Q_2] = \cdots$$

Hence it follows immediately that an equation between numerical quantities can exist only if the numerical quantities on both sides of the equation are expressed in the same dimensional units:

$$Q_1 = Q_2$$
only if
$$[Q_1] = [Q_2]$$

The last equation gives expression to the law of dimensional homogeneity, which must always be carefully obeyed when we establish equations for the mathematical formulation of physical phenomena. Only when this is done is the equation valid for all systems of units. Experience shows that the danger of violating this law is greatest when experimental data plotted in a diagram as a curve are transformed into an approximate functional relationship.

DIMENSIONAL UNIT 1

For the purpose of "dimensional algebra" it is necessary to introduce the dimensional unit 1 for all nondimensional quantities. That this is so is seen from the example of an angle defined as length of arc/radius and thus of dimension $[L]/[L] = 1$. The beginner must also know that mathematical operations, beyond mere addition, subtraction, division, and multiplication, concerning numerical quantities are permissible only if these numerical quantities are nondimensional.   For example, the equation

$$y = C \sin x$$

makes sense only if $[y] = [C]$ and $[x] = 1$, since, if we develop $\sin x$ into a series, we have

$$\sin x = x - \frac{x^3}{3!} + \frac{x^5}{5!} - \cdots$$

which satisfies the law of dimensional homogeneity only if

$$[x] = [x^3] = [x^5] = \cdots$$

Hence we must have $[x] = 1$.

KINEMATICS
OF A
PARTICLE

1.1 GENERAL CONSIDERATIONS

Kinematics deals with the motion of bodies in space without taking its causes into account. In this chapter we limit our discussion to the motion of a single particle and utilize the concepts of space and time in accordance with our daily experience; that is, geometric relations of motion in space are described with the aid of euclidean geometry, and time is considered independent of the state of motion of the observer.

In kinematics we deal with the three basic concepts of position, velocity, and acceleration. Hence, we have to define them as well as devise mathematical means for their description.

First, the kinematic properties of a moving point are defined only with respect to a certain *reference body* or *reference frame*.[1] For example, when we define the velocity of an airplane, we must state whether it is its velocity relative to the ambient air as reference body (airspeed) or whether it is its velocity relative to the earth as reference frame (ground speed) that we are concerned with. As another example, in medieval astronomy the paths of the planets were defined relative to the center of the earth until Copernicus and Kepler showed that a much simpler mathematical description was possible when the motion of the planets was defined with respect to the center of the sun as reference body. In mechanical engineering an important problem is the study of the flow of fluids through the rotating parts of turbines, pumps, compressors, and the like. It is often advantageous to use the rotor of such machines as the reference body in order to define the kinematic properties of the flowing liquid or gaseous particles.

Next, let us describe these kinematic quantities. Once we have chosen a suitable reference body, it becomes necessary to use a particular *coordinate system* for the mathematical description of the position, velocity, and acceleration of the point under observation from the reference body. An infinity of different coordinate systems is available. They can be cartesian, cylindrical, spherical, and the like, having an infinity of different points of origin and different orientations, fixed or moving with respect to the reference body. In most simple situations we employ a coordinate system tied to the reference body.

Often, however, it may be convenient to describe the motion of a particle by means of a coordinate system moving with respect to the reference

[1] Throughout the text we use both terms to define the same concept.

frame.[1]   Then it becomes necessary to (1) determine the motion of the
coordinate system with respect to the reference body and (2) derive the
relationships for the mathematical description of the kinematic properties
of the particle, as defined with respect to the reference body, in the moving
coordinates, using the information gained in step 1.   Solely for didactic
reasons this part of point kinematics is not discussed until Chap. 5,
Relative Motion.

The choice of the coordinate system is just as important as that of the
reference body for a convenient mathematical description of the kinematic
properties of a moving point.   From a more general point of view of mechanics, there is, however, an important qualitative difference when choosing
the reference body and, then, the coordinate system, because Newton's first
two laws hold only in a certain class of reference bodies.   So, when confronted
with the choice of a reference body in dealing with a problem in mechanics,
we always have to ask whether the reference body under consideration is such
that Newton's laws are valid at least to a satisfactory degree of accuracy
or not.   On the other hand, in the choice of the coordinate system we are
led solely by reasons of mathematical convenience.

1.2 BASIC CONCEPTS

The position of a point P with respect to a reference body K is defined by the
position vector $\overline{OP} = \mathbf{r}$.   It can be described, for example, in terms of the
cartesian coordinate system shown in Fig. 1.2-1 as

$$\mathbf{r} = x\mathbf{i} + y\mathbf{j} + z\mathbf{k} \qquad \blacktriangleleft \quad (1.2\text{-}1)[2]$$

This position vector can also be expressed by means of the unit vector $\mathbf{1}_r$
along $\mathbf{r}$ as

$$\mathbf{r} = r\mathbf{1}_r \qquad \blacktriangleleft \quad (1.2\text{-}2)$$

where
$$r = \sqrt{x^2 + y^2 + z^2} \qquad \blacktriangleleft \quad (1.2\text{-}3)$$

The direction of the unit vector $\mathbf{1}_r$ needs to be identified in terms of the
fixed x, y, z coordinate axes.   We can establish this relationship by equating
the vector $\mathbf{r}$ in the two representations (1.2-1) and (1.2-2):

$$\mathbf{1}_r = \frac{\mathbf{r}}{r} = \frac{x}{r}\mathbf{i} + \frac{y}{r}\mathbf{j} + \frac{z}{r}\mathbf{k} \qquad (1.2\text{-}4)$$

$$\mathbf{1}_r = \mathbf{i} \cos \alpha + \mathbf{j} \cos \beta + \mathbf{k} \cos \gamma \qquad (1.2\text{-}5)$$

where α, β, and γ are the angles between $\mathbf{r}$ and the positive x, y, z coordinate

---

[1] In Chap. 6, especially, we shall see that the choice of a coordinate system not tied to the reference frame
often becomes imperative for the description not only of the kinematic but, even more so, of the dynamic
properties of moving bodies.

[2] Important equations in each section are indicated by ◀.

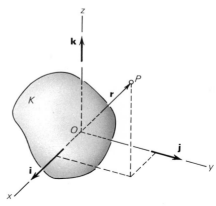

Fig. 1.2-1

axes, respectively, and $\cos \alpha = x/r$, $\cos \beta = y/r$, and $\cos \gamma = z/r$ are the direction cosines defining the orientation of **r**.

We now study the motion of a particle P with respect to a reference body K to which we tie a cartesian coordinate system defined by the unit vectors **i**, **j**, and **k**. The path of P is then described by the position vector

$$\mathbf{r}(t) = x(t)\mathbf{i} + y(t)\mathbf{j} + z(t)\mathbf{k} \tag{1.2-6}$$

The velocity of P with respect to K at a time t is defined by the time rate of change of the position vector:

$$\mathbf{v} = \lim_{\Delta t \to 0} \frac{\mathbf{r}(t + \Delta t) - \mathbf{r}(t)}{\Delta t} = \lim_{\Delta t \to 0} \frac{\Delta \mathbf{r}}{\Delta t} = \frac{d\mathbf{r}}{dt} = \dot{\mathbf{r}} \tag{1.2-7}$$

Substituting for **r** from Eq. (1.2-6) and recognizing that the directions defined by **i**, **j**, and **k** do not change with t, we obtain[1]

$$\mathbf{v} = \dot{x}\mathbf{i} + \dot{y}\mathbf{j} + \dot{z}\mathbf{k} \qquad \blacktriangleleft \tag{1.2-8}$$

or
$$\mathbf{v} = v_x\mathbf{i} + v_y\mathbf{j} + v_z\mathbf{k}$$

The third fundamental kinematic concept, acceleration, was hardly given any attention before Newton discovered its intimate relationship with force. Acceleration is the time rate of change of the velocity:

$$\mathbf{a} = \lim_{\Delta t \to 0} \frac{\Delta \mathbf{v}}{\Delta t} = \frac{d\mathbf{v}}{dt} \tag{1.2-9}$$

By introducing the velocity in terms of the displacement vector from Eqs.

---

[1] For the differentiation of the vector r(t), we made use of the rule that a vector is differentiated in terms of its components with respect to the parameter time, as long as the directions of the coordinates remain constant.

(1.2-7) and (1.2-8), the acceleration of the point P with respect to the reference body K is also obtained as the second derivative of the displacement vector:

$$\mathbf{a} = \frac{d^2\mathbf{r}}{dt^2} = \ddot{x}\mathbf{i} + \ddot{y}\mathbf{j} + \ddot{z}\mathbf{k} \qquad \blacktriangleleft \quad (1.2\text{-}10)$$

or $\qquad \mathbf{a} = a_x\mathbf{i} + a_y\mathbf{j} + a_z\mathbf{k}$

ILLUSTRATIVE EXAMPLE 1.2-1
The path of a point P with respect to a reference body K is described by the position vector

$$\mathbf{r}(t) = x(t)\mathbf{i} + y(t)\mathbf{j} + z(t)\mathbf{k}$$

with $x(t) = 1t$ ft, $y(t) = 1t$ ft, and $z(t) = 2t^2$ ft ($[t]$ = sec).[1]   Determine the velocity and acceleration of the point with respect to K.
SOLUTION: Referring to Eq. (1.2-8), the velocity of the point P is

$$\mathbf{v} = 1\mathbf{i} + 1\mathbf{j} + 4t\mathbf{k} \qquad \text{ft/sec}$$

and according to Eq. (1.2-10) we have as its acceleration

$$\mathbf{a} = 4\mathbf{k} \qquad \text{ft/sec}^2$$

which is constant, whereas the velocity is changing linearly with time in the z direction.

PROBLEMS
1.2-1   A vector extends from the point $(-2,1,-3)$ to $(1,3,5)$.   Determine its length.
1.2-2   The position of a particle at $t = 0$ is given as $(1,-2,1)$.   If at time t it is observed to be at $(-3,5,4)$, express its displacement in the form $\Delta\mathbf{r} = x\mathbf{i} + y\mathbf{j} + z\mathbf{k}$.
1.2-3   The position of a particle at time t is given with respect to a fixed coordinate system as $(3,5,8)$.   Determine the direction cosines of the position vector.
1.2-4   In Prob. 1.2-3, determine the unit vector pointing to the particle.
1.2-5   Given the displacement vectors

$$\mathbf{r}_1 = 3\mathbf{i} + 2\mathbf{j} - \mathbf{k}$$
$$\mathbf{r}_2 = 2\mathbf{i} + \mathbf{j} + 3\mathbf{k}$$
$$\mathbf{r}_3 = -\mathbf{i} + 2\mathbf{k}$$

Determine their sum, and give the unit vector along the resultant displacement.
1.2-6   Given the coordinates of the points a and b as a $(1,2,3)$, b $(3,1,1)$.   Find $\mathbf{r} = \mathbf{a} \times \mathbf{b}$, and give the direction cosines of $\mathbf{r}$.
1.2-7   A vector $\mathbf{r}$ is 20 units long and makes an angle of 60° with the x axis and 45° with the z axis.   State all possibilities for expressions of $\mathbf{r}$ in the form $x\mathbf{i} + y\mathbf{j} + z\mathbf{k}$.
1.2-8   Determine the angle between the two vectors

$$\mathbf{r}_1 = \mathbf{i} + 3\mathbf{j} + 2\mathbf{k}$$
$$\mathbf{r}_2 = 5\mathbf{i} + 2\mathbf{j} + 3\mathbf{k}$$

1.2-9   Find the angle between the vectors

$$\mathbf{r}_1 = 2\mathbf{i} - \mathbf{j} + \mathbf{k}$$
$$\mathbf{r}_2 = 4\mathbf{i} - 2\mathbf{k}$$

[1] In this and many of the following illustrative examples the reader must remember that the numbers are numerical quantities.   For example, in $z = 2t^2$ ft the number 2 is of the dimension of ft/sec².

1.2-10 Find the angle between the lines ab and ac where a, b, c have coordinates a (2,5,−3), b (3,−2,4), and c (−1,1,2) respectively.

1.2-11 The vector $r_1 = 2i − 2j + 2k$ is perpendicular to the vector $r_2 = xi − 2j − 3k$. Determine x.

1.2-12 Find the component of the vector $r_1 = 3i − 2j + 4k$ parallel to $r_2 = 1i + 5j − 2k$.

1.2-13 A satellite is tracked by a radar station on the surface of the earth. Placing the x, y, z coordinates through the radar station in the E-N plane and along the normal to the horizontal E-N plane respectively, the direction cosines of the satellite at time t are (0.120, 0.207, and 0.973). If the distance of the satellite at t, as measured by the radar, is 180 miles, determine its rectangular coordinates.

1.2-14 A particle is observed to be in position (6,14,12). Determine its direction cosines and compare them with a second set measured from a parallel coordinate system with origin at (2,3,5).

1.2-15 A particle is observed to move from (5,1,4) to (2,7,10) in time t. If an observer moves during the same time from (0,0,0) to (−1,2,2), determine the position vectors as seen by the observer at times $t = 0$ and t.

1.2-16 Determine the unit vector in the direction of the position change as viewed by the observer in Prob. 1.2-15.

1.3 MOTION ALONG A STRAIGHT LINE OR RECTILINEAR MOTION

Straight-line motion is the simplest form of motion. However, it deserves special attention because of its great importance in engineering and science. Just think of the motion of the pistons in an automobile engine, the free fall of a body on earth, the motion of an elevator, and the like.

MOTION AS A FUNCTION OF TIME

Straight-line motion is a special case of general three-dimensional motion, and it is possible to choose a cartesian coordinate system so that the position vector $\mathbf{r} = \overline{OP}$ coincides with the x axis:

$$\mathbf{r}(t) = x(t)\mathbf{i} \tag{1.3-1}$$

Since one coordinate, namely, $x(t)$,[†] suffices to determine the position of point P, we say that P has one degree of freedom.[1] It is easily seen that in this case the velocity $\mathbf{v}$ and the acceleration $\mathbf{a}$ are vectors also in line with the position vector $\mathbf{r}$. They are obtained by consecutive differentiations of Eq. (1.3-1):

$$\mathbf{v} = \frac{d\mathbf{r}}{dt} = \dot{x}\mathbf{i} = v_x\mathbf{i} \tag{1.3-2}$$

$$\mathbf{a} = \frac{d\mathbf{v}}{dt} = \ddot{x}\mathbf{i} = a_x\mathbf{i} \tag{1.3-3}$$

Frequently the acceleration a_x of a particle is given, and then its velocity and

---

[†] The reader is warned against identifying the coordinate $x(t)$ with the path $s(t)$ through which the point has traveled, because for motions where the velocity changes its direction, we have $x \neq s$ (see Illustrative Example 1.3-1).

[1] Any particle whose motion is confined to a line, straight or curved, has one degree of freedom.

displacement are found by integration, with due consideration of the initial conditions, that is, the velocity $\dot{x}(0)$ and the position $x(0)$ at time $t = 0$:

$$\dot{x}(t) = \dot{x}(0) + \int_0^t a_x \, dt \qquad \blacktriangleleft \quad (1.3\text{-}4)$$

$$x(t) = x(0) + \int_0^t v_x \, dt \qquad \blacktriangleleft \quad (1.3\text{-}5)$$

For the case of straight-line motion, the relationship between the position, velocity, and acceleration versus time can easily be represented graphically. Figure 1.3-1 is such a representation for a certain motion where a particle P

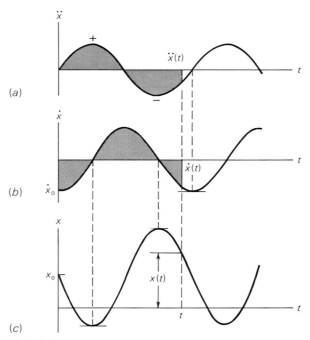

(a)

(b)

(c)

Fig. 1.3-1

with initial displacement $x(0) = x_0$ and initial velocity $\dot{x}(0) = \dot{x}_0$ moves along the x axis with acceleration $\ddot{x}(t)$, a known function of time. The integration of the acceleration then yields

$$\dot{x}(t) = \dot{x}(0) + \int_0^t \ddot{x}(t) \, dt$$

whereas the integration of the velocity results in the displacement equation

$$x(t) = x(0) + \int_0^t \dot{x}(t)\, dt$$

The integrals $\int_0^t \ddot{x}(t)\, dt$ and $\int_0^t \dot{x}(t)\, dt$ are represented by the shaded areas of Fig. 1.3-1a and b respectively. The kinematic meaning of the geometric relations between extrema, zeros, and points of inflection of the curves in Fig. 1.3-1 is found by suitable interpretation of Eqs. (1.3-2) and (1.3-3).

MOTION AS A FUNCTION OF DISPLACEMENT

We frequently encounter a problem where the acceleration is given as a function of the displacement, that is, $\ddot{x} = f(x) = \ddot{x}(x)$. In such case we can eliminate dt from the equations $\dot{x} = dx/dt$ and $\ddot{x} = d\dot{x}/dt$ by their division and obtain

$$\dot{x}\, d\dot{x} = \ddot{x}(x)\, dx \qquad \blacktriangleleft \quad (1.3\text{-}6)$$

Integration of Eq. (1.3-6) yields

$$\tfrac{1}{2}(\dot{x}^2 - \dot{x}_1{}^2) = \int_{x_1}^{x} \ddot{x}(x)\, dx \qquad \blacktriangleleft \quad (1.3\text{-}7)$$

where $\dot{x}_1$ is the velocity of the particle at position x_1.

For the special case where $\ddot{x} = \ddot{x}_0 = \text{const}$, Eq. (1.3-7) yields

$$\tfrac{1}{2}(\dot{x}^2 - \dot{x}_1{}^2) = \ddot{x}_0(x - x_1)$$
$$\dot{x}^2 = \dot{x}_1{}^2 + 2\ddot{x}_0(x - x_1) \qquad (1.3\text{-}8)$$

PHASE PLANE

It is often of interest to know the velocity $\dot{x}$ as a function of x. The function $\dot{x} = f(x)$ is graphically displayed by the so-called phase curve in the phase plane where the coordinates are velocity and displacement. The phase curve shown in Fig. 1.3-2 corresponds to the example of Fig. 1.3-1 and is constructed by plotting the values of the velocity and displacement taken at equal times from Fig. 1.3-1b and c. In this particular case the phase curve is closed, since the function $x(t)$ is periodic. In the general case of

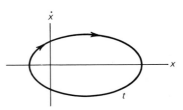

Fig. 1.3-2

nonperiodic functions the curve is not closed. The student should prove that phase curves always intersect the x axis normally and that the points on the curve progress in a clockwise direction with increasing time.

ILLUSTRATIVE EXAMPLE 1.3-1

A point P moves along the x axis according to the equation

$$x(t) = \tfrac{1}{4} - 1t + 1t^2 \qquad 0 \le t \le 1 \text{ sec}$$

where x is measured in feet, when t is given in seconds. Determine the displacement of the particle and the distance traveled by the particle between $t = 0$ and $t = 1$ sec. Plot the phase curve.

SOLUTION: By differentiating, the velocity and acceleration are

$$\dot{x}(t) = -1 + 2t \qquad \text{ft/sec}$$
$$\ddot{x}(t) = 2 \text{ ft/sec}^2$$

We call attention to the fact that the distance s traveled by P along the path is equal to the integral of the absolute value of the velocity, which may differ from the displacement that defines the position of the particle. This is the case when the velocity changes its sign during the considered time interval, and the integral must then be divided into more than one interval. For example, the distance traveled by P during the time $t = 0$ to $t = 1$ sec is

$$s(1) - s(0) = \int_0^1 |\dot{x}|\, dt = \int_0^{1/2} (1 - 2t)\, dt + \int_{1/2}^1 (2t - 1)\, dt = \tfrac{1}{4} + \tfrac{1}{4} = \tfrac{1}{2} \text{ ft}$$

(note that the velocity changes its sign at $t = 0.5$ sec—see Fig. 1.3-3b), whereas the integral of the velocity yields

$$x(1) - x(0) = \int_0^1 \dot{x}\, dt = \int_0^1 (2t - 1)\, dt = (t^2 - t)\Big]_0^1 = 0$$

The absolute value of the velocity and the distance s traveled by P are shown in Fig. 1.3-3a and b by the dashed curves. If we eliminate the time between the displacement and velocity equations, we obtain

$$x = \tfrac{1}{4}\dot{x}^2 \qquad \text{ft}$$

Thus, the phase-plane plot is a parabola, as shown in Fig. 1.3-4. The phase curve can also be found directly from Fig. 1.3-3a and b by picking off the values x and $\dot{x}$ for equal times.

ILLUSTRATIVE EXAMPLE 1.3-2

An airplane coming in for a landing touches the ground at 130 mph and decelerates to 20 mph in 3,200 ft of runway. Assuming constant deceleration, determine its value and the time t required.

SOLUTION: Since the velocity is given for two positions x_1 and x_2 that are 3,200 ft apart, we use Eq. (1.3-8), which is based on the differential relationship $\ddot{x}\, dx = \dot{x}\, d\dot{x}$—see Eq. (1.3-6). This equation, when integrated for constant acceleration $\ddot{x} = \ddot{x}_0$, leads to

$$\ddot{x}_0(x_2 - x_1) = \tfrac{1}{2}(\dot{x}_2^2 - \dot{x}_1^2) \qquad \text{see Eq. (1.3-8)}$$

Multiplying the data given in miles per hour by $\tfrac{88}{60}$ to obtain them in feet per second, we have

$$\ddot{x}_0 = \frac{(20^2 - 130^2)(\tfrac{88}{60})^2}{2 \times 3{,}200} = -5.55 \text{ ft/sec}^2$$

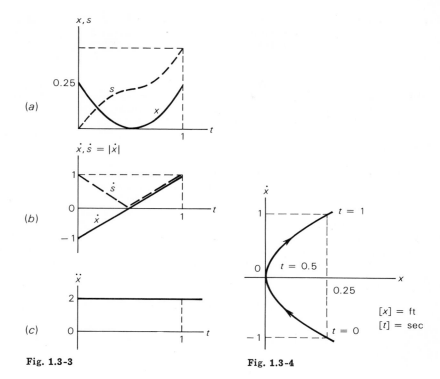

$x, s = |\dot{x}|$

(a)

(b)

(c)

Fig. 1.3-3

$\dot{x}$

$t = 1$

$t = 0.5$

0.25

$t = 0$

$[x] = $ ft

$[t] = $ sec

Fig. 1.3-4

The required time is found from the velocity equation (1.3-4) $\dot{x}_2 - \dot{x}_1 = \ddot{x}_0 t$:

$$t = \frac{(20 - 130)(\text{88}\!\%_0)}{-5.55} = 29.1 \text{ sec}$$

PROBLEMS

1.3-1　The speed with which a parachutist lands on the ground is generally about 32 ft/sec. Determine the height from which a man without a parachute would have to jump in order to have the same landing speed.

1.3-2　In a vertical takeoff the engines exert a thrust that gives the rocket a constant acceleration of $2.0g$ for 40 sec. What velocity is attained at this time, and what is its height?

1.3-3　The position of a particle moving along the x axis is given by the equation $x = 16t - 4t^2$, where x is in feet and t in seconds. (a) Plot x, $\dot{x}$, and $\ddot{x}$ as functions of t from $t = 0$ to 4 sec. (b) Determine the displacement of the particle during the time interval $t = 1$ to 4 sec. (c) What is the distance traveled during this time?

1.3-4　In Prob. 1.3-3 determine the equation $x = f(\dot{x})$, and plot the phase-plane curve for $t = 0$ to 4 sec.

1.3-5   A particle moves along the x axis with an acceleration of -3 ft/sec². If it starts at the origin with an initial velocity of 9 ft/sec, determine the equations for x, $\dot{x}$, and $\ddot{x}$, and plot these curves for the time interval $t = 0$ to $t = 5$ sec.

1.3-6   In Prob. 1.3-5 determine the displacement of the particle at $t = 4$ sec and the distance traveled up to this time.

1.3-7   Plot the phase-plane curve for Prob. 1.3-5.

1.3-8   The acceleration of a particle moving along the x axis is given as $\ddot{x} = 2t - 4$ ft/sec². When $t = 0$, the particle is at the origin with a velocity of 10 ft/sec in the positive x direction. Determine the equations for $\dot{x}$ and x, and plot $\ddot{x}$, $\dot{x}$, and x versus t for $t = 0$ to $t = 6$ sec.

1.3-9   A point moves according to the equation $y = y_0 + a \sin \omega t$. Plot the phase-plane diagram.

1.3-10   A particle starts from rest and moves along a straight line in accordance with the equation $\dot{x} = 4t - t^2$, where the units are feet and seconds. Plot $\ddot{x}$, $\dot{x}$, and x versus t for $t = 0$ to $t = 5$ sec. Determine (a) the maximum displacement, (b) the average velocity during the first 4 sec, and (c) the acceleration at $t = 2$ sec.

1.3-11   A particle starts with an initial velocity of 20 ft/sec at $x = 0$ and is accelerated according to the equation $\ddot{x} = 24 - 6t^2$ ft/sec². Plot $\ddot{x}$, $\dot{x}$, and x versus t for 5 sec starting from $t = 0$. Determine the average speed and the average velocity during the time interval $t = 2$ to $t = 5$ sec.

1.3-12   Figure P 1.3-12 shows the acceleration of an automobile that starts from rest and is given a uniformly increasing acceleration, reaching 12 ft/sec² in 6 sec. The brakes are then suddenly applied, and the car is brought to a stop in the next 9 sec with a uniform deceleration of 4 ft/sec². Express $\ddot{x}$, $\dot{x}$, and x as functions of time for each phase of the motion, and plot the corresponding graphs.

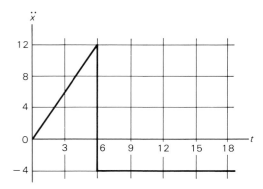

Fig. P 1.3-12

1.3-13   A rocket tested on a horizontal track starts from rest and accelerates according to the curve shown in Fig. P 1.3-13. Represent the curve by two straight lines, and determine the velocity attained and the distance covered to burnout at time $t = 45$ sec.

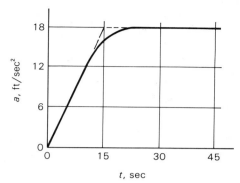

Fig. P 1.3-13

1.3-14 From a tower of height H a ball is thrown vertically upward with initial velocity v_0. Determine the maximum height h_{max}, the corresponding time t_{max}, and the time t_g for it to reach the ground.

1.3-15 What is the height H_1 of the tower in Prob. 1.3-14 for which the time during the downward motion is equal to $2t_{max}$?

1.3-16 On June 2, 1966, Surveyor I made a successful soft landing on the moon. During the final phase, the vernier engines held the descent at a constant velocity of 5 ft/sec between the heights of 40 and 13 ft. The engines were then shut off, and the spacecraft was in free fall. Determine the velocity at which Surveyor landed on the surface (lunar $g \approx 5.3$ ft/sec^2). How many seconds did it take for the last 40 ft?

1.3-17 The velocity of a train traveling with constant acceleration is observed at two stations A and C as follows:

Station	x, miles	v, mph
A	0	23.4
C	1.50	40.0

Determine the velocity v_B at an intermediate station B that is $\frac{1}{2}$ mile from A.

1.3-18 A train can attain its maximum speed of 60 mph in 4 min and then stop in a distance of $\frac{1}{2}$ mile. Assuming that acceleration and deceleration are uniform, find the least time required for the train to go between two stations $8\frac{1}{2}$ miles apart. Draw the velocity-time diagram.

1.3-19 An electric train starting from rest attains a speed of 80 ft/sec with constant acceleration in 1 min, travels for another minute at this speed, and then decelerates to a full stop with constant deceleration in 1,200 ft. Plot v versus t. How far has it traveled, and how long did it take?

1.3-20   An electric train can start from rest with an acceleration of 1 mph/sec until it acquires a normal speed of 60 mph and decelerates at a rate of 2 mph/sec, when the brakes are applied.   Draw the curve for velocity versus time when the train starts from station A and stops at station B, where the distance between A and B is 2 miles.   Determine the time required.

1.3-21   A local train has a normal speed of 70 mph between stations.   When putting on brakes, it can decelerate at a rate of 2 mph/sec, and when starting out, it can accelerate at a rate of 1 mph/sec.   (a) Calculate the time lost in making a stop of 1 min.   (b) Plot $\ddot{x}$, $\dot{x}$, and x versus time for the entire period between stations. (c) Calculate the minimum distance between stations for which the train can just reach 70 mph before putting on the brakes.

1.3-22   An automobile starts from rest and attains a speed of 75 mph with constant acceleration, maintains this speed for 10 sec, and then with the brakes applied, comes to a stop with constant deceleration.   If the deceleration is twice that of the acceleration and the total distance traveled is 2,400 ft, determine the time elapsed.

1.3-23   Figure P 1.3-23 shows the velocity-time curve for a typical sounding rocket, where the peak point represents burnout.   Determine the altitude at intervals of 25 sec, and plot the altitude-time curve from the velocity curve (use Simpson's rule for the powered phase).

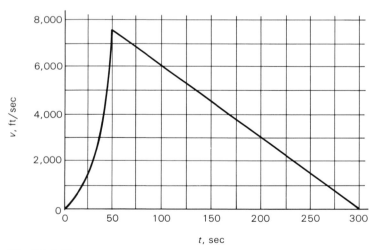

Fig. P 1.3-23

1.3-24   A simple harmonic motion has an amplitude of 10 in.   When the displacement is 6 in., the velocity is 24 in./sec.   Determine the acceleration at this position.

1.3-25   The velocity of a point moving along the x axis is given as $\dot{x} = \pi \cos (\pi t/2)$ in./sec. Calculate the distance traveled by the point during the first 3 sec.

1.3-26   At a street intersection, car A passes the stop line at 15 mph with a constant acceleration of 1 mph/sec.   Car B starts from zero velocity at the stop line and moves with a velocity of $10\sqrt{t}$ mph, where t is measured in seconds.   Find the time for car B to overtake car A.

1.3-27   In Prob. 1.3-26 how far has each car traveled when B overtakes A, and what are their velocities?

1.3-28   Water is dripping from a faucet at a rate of one drop per second.   Determine (a) the distance between the first and second drops as a function of time, (b) the distance between the first and third drops.

1.3-29   In Prob. 1.3-28 set up the equation for the distance between the first and the nth drops.

1.3-30   The position of a particle is defined for any time t by the relation

$$x = 1t^3 - 6t^2 + 3t - 10$$

where x is expressed in feet and t in seconds.   Determine the position, velocity, and acceleration, and plot them against time for $0 \leq t \leq 5$ sec.

1.3-31   With initial conditions $v_0 = 40$ ft/sec and $x_0 = 0$, the acceleration of a particle moving along a straight line is $a_x = -10$ ft/sec^2.   Determine the velocity, position, and the total distance traveled when $t = 6$ sec.   Plot its phase-plane trajectory.

1.3-32   A particle starts from the origin $x = 0$ with negligible velocity $x_0 = \epsilon$ and accelerates according to the equation $\ddot{x} = 12x^{1/3}$.   Determine its displacement x as a function of time t.   What is the dimension of the numerical quantity 12?

1.4   PLANE MOTION OF A POINT

As another special case we study the plane motion of a point.   Since the path of a point P is confined to a plane, it has two degrees of freedom.[1] We describe the motion in cartesian and polar coordinates, as well as a combination of both.

(A) CARTESIAN COORDINATES

Letting the plane in which the motion takes place coincide with the xy plane, we have $z \equiv 0$.   Thus,

$$\mathbf{r}(t) = x(t)\mathbf{i} + y(t)\mathbf{j} + 0\mathbf{k}$$
$$= x(t)\mathbf{i} + y(t)\mathbf{j} \tag{1.4-1}$$

Since the unit vectors $\mathbf{i}$, $\mathbf{j}$, and $\mathbf{k}$ do not change their direction with time, we have as the velocity vector

$$\mathbf{v}(t) = \dot{x}(t)\mathbf{i} + \dot{y}(t)\mathbf{j} \tag{1.4-2}$$

and correspondingly as the acceleration vector

$$\mathbf{a}(t) = \ddot{x}(t)\mathbf{i} + \ddot{y}(t)\mathbf{j} \tag{1.4-3}$$

ILLUSTRATIVE EXAMPLE 1.4-1

A ball is thrown from a tower of height H with the initial velocity $\mathbf{v}_0$ at an angle α measured above the horizontal, as shown in Fig. 1.4-1.   The acceleration vector is (air resist-

[1] Any particle whose motion is confined to a surface, plane or curved, has two degrees of freedom.

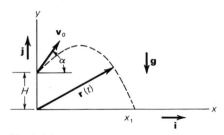

Fig. 1.4-1

ance being neglected)

$$\mathbf{a} = \mathbf{g} = 0\mathbf{i} - g\mathbf{j} \qquad (a)$$

Calculate (a) the path of the ball, (b) the point x_1 where the ball hits the ground at time t_1.
SOLUTION: In view of Fig. 1.4-1, we can formulate the given initial conditions as follows:

$$\mathbf{v}(0) = \mathbf{v}_0 = (v_0 \cos \alpha)\mathbf{i} + (v_0 \sin \alpha)\mathbf{j} \qquad (b)$$
$$\mathbf{r}(0) = \mathbf{r}_0 = 0\mathbf{i} + H\mathbf{j} \qquad (c)$$

With these initial conditions, the integration of the given acceleration vector $\mathbf{a} = -g\mathbf{j}$ with respect to time yields the velocity:

$$\mathbf{v}(t) = \int_0^t \mathbf{a}\, dt + \mathbf{v}_0 = (v_0 \cos \alpha)\mathbf{i} + (-gt + v_0 \sin \alpha)\mathbf{j} \qquad (d)$$

and one more integration yields the position of the ball:

$$\mathbf{r}(t) = \int_0^t \mathbf{v}\, dt + \mathbf{r}_0 = (v_0 \cos \alpha)t\mathbf{i} + [-\tfrac{1}{2}gt^2 + (v_0 \sin \alpha)t + H]\mathbf{j} \qquad (e)$$

Thus, we have found the path of the ball in parametric form, t being the parameter.
   In order to answer the first question, that is, to find $y = y(x)$, we have to eliminate the parameter, time t.   Writing $\mathbf{r}(t) = x(t)\mathbf{i} + y(t)\mathbf{j}$, we recognize from Eq. (e) that

$$x(t) = (v_0 \cos \alpha)t \qquad (f)$$
$$y(t) = H - \tfrac{1}{2}gt^2 + (v_0 \sin \alpha)t \qquad (g)$$

Hence we have from Eq. (f)

$$t = \frac{x}{v_0 \cos \alpha}$$

and substituting this relationship in Eq. (g), we find

$$y(x) = H - \tfrac{1}{2}g\frac{x^2}{v_0^2 \cos^2 \alpha} + x \tan \alpha \qquad (h)$$

which establishes the path as a parabola.
   From the coordinates chosen (see Fig. 1.4-1) we see that the point where the ball hits the ground is described by the position vector

$$\mathbf{r}(t_1) = x_1\mathbf{i} + 0\mathbf{j}$$

Letting the time at which this occurs be $t = t_1$, the condition $y(t_1) = 0$ yields, in view of

Eq. (g),

$$t_1{}^2 - \frac{2v_0 \sin \alpha}{g} t_1 - \frac{2H}{g} = 0$$

which has the solution, considering that $t_1 > 0$,

$$t_1 = \frac{v_0 \sin \alpha}{g} + \sqrt{\frac{2H}{g} + \left(\frac{v_0 \sin \alpha}{g}\right)^2} \qquad (i)$$

Substituting this expression for t_1 in Eq. (f), we obtain

$$x_1 = x(t_1) = \frac{1}{2} \frac{v_0{}^2}{g} \sin 2\alpha + v_0 \cos \alpha \sqrt{\frac{2H}{g} + \left(\frac{v_0 \sin \alpha}{g}\right)^2} \qquad (j)$$

(B) POLAR COORDINATES

In polar coordinates we define the position of a moving point P by the vector

$$\mathbf{r} = r(t)\mathbf{1}_r \qquad \blacktriangleleft \qquad (1.4\text{-}4)$$

where $\mathbf{1}_r$ is a unit vector always directed along $\mathbf{r}$ and making an angle $\theta(t)$ with the x axis, as shown in Fig. 1.4-2. Here we are already faced with the

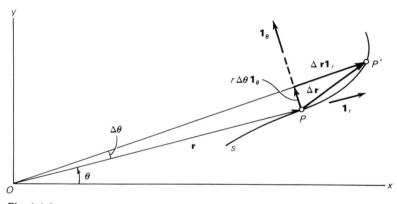

Fig. 1.4-2

situation that the velocity and acceleration of the particle, though defined with respect to the reference frame K, in which the x, y axes are fixed, are described by the coordinates r and θ, whose unit vectors $\mathbf{1}_r$ and $\mathbf{1}_\theta$ change their direction with respect to the reference frame K.

To determine the velocity of P as it moves along the curve s, we differentiate $\mathbf{r}$, using the product rule and recognizing that $\mathbf{1}_r$ changes in direction:

$$\dot{\mathbf{r}} = \dot{r}\mathbf{1}_r + r\dot{\mathbf{1}}_r \qquad (1.4\text{-}5)$$

In interpreting this equation, let P move to P' in the short time interval Δt. Considering $\Delta \theta$ to be small, we may resolve the vector $\Delta \mathbf{r}$ into the components $\Delta r \mathbf{1}_r$† and $r \cdot \Delta \theta \cdot \mathbf{1}_\theta$, where $\mathbf{1}_\theta$ is a unit vector normal to $\mathbf{1}_r$. Then the limiting value of $\Delta \mathbf{r} / \Delta t$ as $\Delta t \to 0$ is

$$\dot{\mathbf{r}} = \mathbf{v} = \lim_{\Delta t \to 0} \frac{\Delta r}{\Delta t} = \lim_{\Delta t \to 0} \left(\frac{\Delta r}{\Delta t} \mathbf{1}_r + r \frac{\Delta \theta}{\Delta t} \mathbf{1}_\theta \right) = \dot{r} \mathbf{1}_r + r \dot{\theta} \mathbf{1}_\theta \quad \blacktriangleleft \quad (1.4\text{-}6)$$

Comparing Eqs. (1.4-5) and (1.4-6), we arrive at

$$\dot{\mathbf{1}}_r = \dot{\theta} \mathbf{1}_\theta \qquad (1.4\text{-}7)$$

where $\dot{\theta}(t)$ is the angular velocity of the position vector $\mathbf{r}$, that is, the angle traversed by the vector in unit time. This relationship for the derivative of the unit vector $\mathbf{1}_r$, which is evident from Fig. 1.4-3, can also be deduced by

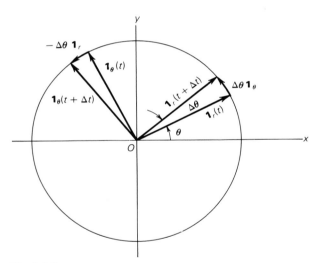

Fig. 1.4-3

writing $\mathbf{1}_r$ in the form

$$\mathbf{1}_r = (\cos \theta) \mathbf{i} + (\sin \theta) \mathbf{j}$$

and differentiating:

$$\dot{\mathbf{1}}_r = [(-\sin \theta) \mathbf{i} + (\cos \theta) \mathbf{j}] \dot{\theta}$$

Since $\mathbf{1}_\theta = -\sin \theta \, \mathbf{i} + \cos \theta \, \mathbf{j}$, we arrive at the result

$$\dot{\mathbf{1}}_r = \dot{\theta} \mathbf{1}_\theta$$

† Note that $|\Delta \mathbf{r}| = |\mathbf{r}(t + \Delta t) - \mathbf{r}(t)| \neq \Delta r = r(t + \Delta t) - r(t)$.

Likewise the differentiation of $\mathbf{1}_\theta$ with respect to time yields

$$\dot{\mathbf{1}}_\theta = -\dot{\theta}\mathbf{1}_r \qquad (1.4\text{-}8)$$

a result that is also apparent from Fig. 1.4-3.

For the acceleration of the point P, we differentiate Eq. (1.4-6), recognizing again that both $\mathbf{1}_r$ and $\mathbf{1}_\theta$ rotate together with $\mathbf{r}$ at a rate $\dot{\theta}$:

$$
\begin{aligned}
\ddot{\mathbf{r}} &= \ddot{r}\mathbf{1}_r + \dot{r}\dot{\mathbf{1}}_r + (\dot{r}\dot{\theta} + r\ddot{\theta})\mathbf{1}_\theta + r\dot{\theta}\dot{\mathbf{1}}_\theta \\
&= \ddot{r}\mathbf{1}_r + \dot{r}\dot{\theta}\mathbf{1}_\theta + (r\ddot{\theta} + \dot{r}\dot{\theta})\mathbf{1}_\theta - r\dot{\theta}^2\mathbf{1}_r \\
&= (\ddot{r} - r\dot{\theta}^2)\mathbf{1}_r + (2\dot{r}\dot{\theta} + r\ddot{\theta})\mathbf{1}_\theta
\end{aligned}
$$

or

$$\ddot{\mathbf{r}} = (\ddot{r} - r\dot{\theta}^2)\mathbf{1}_r + \frac{1}{r}\frac{d}{dt}(r^2\dot{\theta})\mathbf{1}_\theta \qquad \blacktriangleleft \quad (1.4\text{-}9)$$

We have thus expressed the acceleration in terms of the radial and transverse components, which are

$$a_r = \ddot{r} - r\dot{\theta}^2 \qquad (1.4\text{-}10)$$

$$a_\theta = r\ddot{\theta} + 2\dot{r}\dot{\theta} = \frac{1}{r}\frac{d}{dt}(r^2\dot{\theta}) \qquad (1.4\text{-}11)$$

Again the reader is reminded that the velocity and acceleration of the particle, as described by polar coordinates in Eqs. (1.4-6) and (1.4-9), respectively, are defined with respect to the reference frame K to which the x, y axes are tied.

For the special case where the point P moves along a circular path with center O, Eqs. (1.4-6) and (1.4-9) reduce to ($r = r_0$ and $\dot{r} = \ddot{r} = 0$) (see

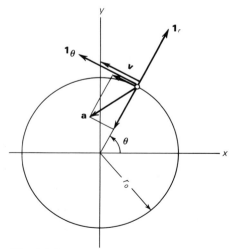

Fig. 1.4-4

Fig. 1.4-4)

$$\mathbf{v} = r_0\dot\theta\mathbf{1}_\theta \qquad (1.4\text{-}6a)$$
$$\mathbf{a} = -r_0\dot\theta^2\mathbf{1}_r + r_0\ddot\theta\mathbf{1}_\theta \qquad (1.4\text{-}9a)$$

ILLUSTRATIVE EXAMPLE 1.4-2

The slotted arm B of Fig. 1.4-5 rotates with the angular velocity θ about 0 so that the roller A is forced to slide over the fixed cam C. The shape of the cam is such that

$$\overline{OA} = r(t) = e - b\cos\theta \qquad e > b \qquad (a)$$

Calculate the acceleration of the center of A, first, with respect to the cam C and, second, with respect to the slotted arm B.

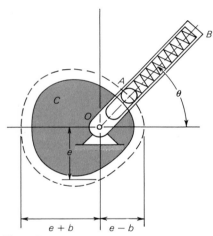

Fig. 1.4-5

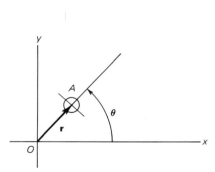

Fig. 1.4-6

SOLUTION: (1) We tie an x, y coordinate system (see Fig. 1.4-6) to the cam C and describe the center of the roller A by the polar coordinates r and θ. The acceleration is given by Eq. (1.4-9):

$$\mathbf{a}(t) = (\ddot r - r\dot\theta^2)\mathbf{1}_r + (2\dot r\dot\theta + r\ddot\theta)\mathbf{1}_\theta \qquad (b)$$

From Eq. (a) we have

$$\dot r = b\dot\theta\sin\theta \qquad (c)$$

and

$$\ddot r = b\dot\theta^2\cos\theta + b\ddot\theta\sin\theta \qquad (d)$$

Substitution of Eqs. (c) and (d) in Eq. (b) yields

$$\mathbf{a}(t) = [\dot\theta^2(2b\cos\theta - e) + b\ddot\theta\sin\theta]\mathbf{1}_r + [(e - b\cos\theta)\ddot\theta + 2b\dot\theta^2\sin\theta]\mathbf{1}_\theta \qquad (e)$$

(2) With respect to the slotted arm B we have only straight-line motion of the center of the roller A.

Therefore, with $r = e - b\cos\theta$ the acceleration relative to the arm B is

$$\ddot r = b\dot\theta^2\cos\theta + b\ddot\theta\sin\theta$$

(c) CURVILINEAR COORDINATES

Let us denote the path traversed by the point by s.   We then observe that, in general, the change $\Delta \mathbf{r}$ in the position vector $\mathbf{r}$ is not identical to the path Δs of the point during the interval Δt.   However, by writing $\mathbf{v}$ in the form

$$\mathbf{v} = \lim_{\Delta t \to 0} \frac{\Delta \mathbf{r}}{\Delta s} \frac{\Delta s}{\Delta t} = \frac{d\mathbf{r}}{ds} \frac{ds}{dt} \qquad (1.4\text{-}12)$$

it is evident from Fig. 1.4-7 that the limiting value of $\Delta \mathbf{r}/\Delta s$ is a unit vector $\mathbf{1}_\tau$ along the tangent to the path pointing in the direction of the path, as

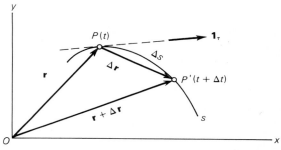

Fig. 1.4-7

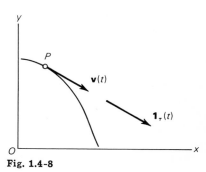

Fig. 1.4-8

shown in Fig. 1.4-8, and thus

$$\frac{ds}{dt} = v \qquad (1.4\text{-}13)$$

is the magnitude of the velocity vector. Hence we may write

$$\mathbf{v} = \frac{ds}{dt}\,\mathbf{1}_\tau = v\mathbf{1}_\tau \qquad (1.4\text{-}14)^1$$

where both the magnitude of the velocity and also the direction of the tangential unit vector are functions of time. Remember again that $\mathbf{v}$ is defined with respect to reference frame K, in which the x, y axes are fixed.

Let us now gain further insight into the nature of the acceleration vector as it is obtained by differentiating the velocity vector with respect to time as presented in Eq. (1.4-14):

$$\mathbf{a} = \frac{d\mathbf{v}}{dt} = \dot{v}\mathbf{1}_\tau + v\dot{\mathbf{1}}_\tau \qquad (1.4\text{-}15)$$

It is clear that the first term of this equation represents a vector in the tangential direction $\mathbf{1}_\tau$. However, what is the meaning of the second term?

In order to find out, first write the identity

$$\dot{\mathbf{1}}_\tau = \frac{d\mathbf{1}_\tau}{dt} = \frac{d\mathbf{1}_\tau}{ds}\frac{ds}{dt} = v\,\frac{d\mathbf{1}_\tau}{ds} \qquad (1.4\text{-}16)$$

Then consider that any infinitesimal sector ds of a curve may be approximated by an infinitesimally short circular arc of radius ρ, called the radius of curvature of the curve at the point s under consideration (see Fig. 1.4-9).

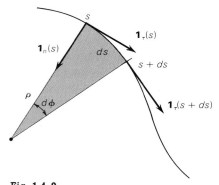

Fig. 1.4-9

The infinitesimal change of the tangential unit vector in going from s to $s + ds$ is depicted in Fig. 1.4-10 as

$$d\mathbf{1}_\tau = \mathbf{1}_\tau(s + ds) - \mathbf{1}_\tau(s)$$

¹ Note that unit vectors defining directions are free vectors.

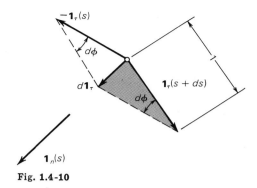

Fig. 1.4-10

Comparison of Figs. 1.4-9 and 1.4-10 then reveals that, considering that the infinitesimal shaded triangles are similar,

$$\frac{|d\mathbf{1}_\tau|}{|\mathbf{1}_\tau|} = \frac{ds}{\rho} \tag{1.4-17}$$

and furthermore that $d\mathbf{1}_\tau$ points in the direction of $\mathbf{1}_n$, the so-called principal normal unit vector, which is normal[1] to $\mathbf{1}_\tau$. Both $\mathbf{1}_\tau$ and $\mathbf{1}_n$ are in the plane of motion.[2] Thus we may write

$$\frac{d\mathbf{1}_\tau}{ds} = \frac{1}{\rho}\,\mathbf{1}_n \tag{1.4-18}$$

and hence in view of Eq. (1.4-16)

$$\dot{\mathbf{1}}_\tau = \frac{v}{\rho}\,\mathbf{1}_n \tag{1.4-19}$$

Substituting Eq. (1.4-19) into Eq. (1.4-15), we obtain (see Fig. 1.4-11)

$$\mathbf{a} = \dot{v}\mathbf{1}_\tau + \frac{v^2}{\rho}\,\mathbf{1}_n = \mathbf{a}_\tau + \mathbf{a}_n \qquad \blacktriangleleft \tag{1.4-20}$$

We then see that the tangential component $\mathbf{a}_\tau = \dot{v}\mathbf{1}_\tau$ takes care of the change in the magnitude of the velocity without regard to the change in its direction.

[1] The fact that $\dot{\mathbf{1}}_\tau$ and thus also $d\mathbf{1}_\tau$ are normal to $\mathbf{1}_\tau$ can also be shown, as follows, by formal reasoning. Because $\mathbf{1}_\tau \cdot \mathbf{1}_\tau = 1$, we have, by differentiation, $2(\mathbf{1}_\tau \cdot \dot{\mathbf{1}}_\tau) = 0$; that is, the scalar product of the unit vector and the derivative of the unit vector is zero. The scalar product of two finite vectors can be zero only if they are perpendicular to each other. Thus the time derivative of a unit vector is normal to the unit vector itself.

[2] In the general case of three-dimensional motion Figs. 1.4-9 and 1.4-10 reveal that $\mathbf{1}_\tau$ and $\mathbf{1}_n$ are in the plane of the approximating infinitesimal arc. In differential geometry this plane is called the osculating plane, which can also be defined as follows. Take three points on the curve, which obviously define a plane. As the points merge into one, the plane, in the limit, becomes the osculating plane for the curve in the particular point.

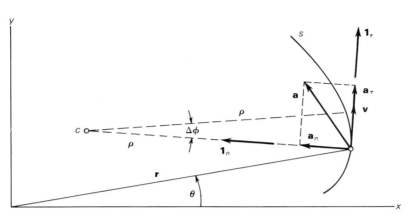

Fig. 1.4-11

The normal component $\mathbf{a}_n = (v^2/\rho)\mathbf{1}_n$, on the other hand, depends only on the square of the velocity and the curvature of the path and not on the change of speed.[1] It is sometimes useful to know that $\mathbf{a}_n$ can be found from the two equations

$$\mathbf{a}_n = \mathbf{a} - \mathbf{a}_\tau$$

and
$$\mathbf{a}_\tau = (\mathbf{a} \cdot \mathbf{1}_\tau)\mathbf{1}_\tau$$

The radius of curvature ρ[†] in Eq. (1.4-20), expressed in rectangular coordinates, is

$$\rho = \left| \frac{\left[1 + \left(\dfrac{dy}{dx}\right)^2\right]^{3/2}}{\dfrac{d^2y}{dx^2}} \right| \tag{1.4-21}$$

In polar coordinates the radius of curvature is

$$\rho = \left| \frac{\left[r^2 + \left(\dfrac{dr}{d\theta}\right)^2\right]^{3/2}}{r^2 + 2\left(\dfrac{dr}{d\theta}\right)^2 - r\dfrac{d^2r}{d\theta^2}} \right| \tag{1.4-22}$$

Another useful expression for $\mathbf{a}_n$ is quickly derived, considering that Fig.

---

[1] This resolution into the tangential and normal components is due to Christian Huygens (1629–1695), a Dutch contemporary of Newton's (1642–1727).

[†] G. B. Thomas, Jr., "Calculus and Analytic Geometry," 3d ed., p. 589, Addison-Wesley Publishing Company, Inc., Reading, Mass., 1960.

1.4-10 shows that

$$d\mathbf{1}_r = d\phi\mathbf{1}_n$$

or

$$\frac{d\mathbf{1}_r}{dt} = \dot{\mathbf{1}}_r = \frac{d\phi}{dt}\mathbf{1}_n = \dot{\phi}\mathbf{1}_n$$

Hence from Eqs. (1.4-15) and (1.4-20) we have

$$\mathbf{a}_n = v\dot{\phi}\mathbf{1}_n = \frac{v^2}{\rho}\mathbf{1}_n \qquad \blacktriangleleft \quad (1.4\text{-}23)$$

where $\dot{\phi}$ is the time rate by which the velocity vector $\mathbf{v}$ changes its direction. In fast-moving vehicles this quantity can easily be measured by means of gyroscopic instruments.

ILLUSTRATIVE EXAMPLE 1.4-3
After burnout a ballistic missile attains a maximum height of $0.320R$ (R = radius of earth), where the velocity is 12,600 mph.   Determine the radius of curvature of the trajectory at this point.
SOLUTION: At the highest point of the trajectory the tangential component of the acceleration is zero, whereas the normal acceleration is found, from the inverse-square law (see Illustrative Example 2.1-2), to be

$$g = \left(\frac{R}{1.32R}\right)^2 g_0$$

where g_0 = acceleration of gravity at the earth's surface.   Equating this to the normal acceleration as given by Eq. (1.4-20), we obtain

$$\left(\frac{1}{1.32}\right)^2 g_0 = \frac{v^2}{\rho}$$

$$\rho = \frac{1.32^2 \times (12,600 \times {}^{88}\!/_{60})^2}{32.2} = 18.5 \times 10^6 \text{ ft}$$

$$= 3,500 \text{ miles}$$

(D) PLANE MOTION IN CARTESIAN AND POLAR COORDINATES
This section is introduced solely to illustrate the simultaneous employment of two coordinate systems.   Considering, for example, the motion of a point P fixed in a body rolling along a straight line, it is advantageous to use cartesian and polar coordinates simultaneously, where the cartesian coordinate system is tied to the reference frame K.

ILLUSTRATIVE EXAMPLE 1.4-4
A wheel of radius r_0 rolls with angular velocity $\theta(t)$ on a straight line.   The position, velocity, and acceleration of a point P on the circumference of the wheel are to be calculated.
SOLUTION: As shown in Fig. 1.4-12 the x, y coordinate system, tied to the reference body K, is placed so that the x axis coincides with the straight path and the y axis intersects the center C of the wheel at time $t = 0$.   Point P is specified in terms of polar

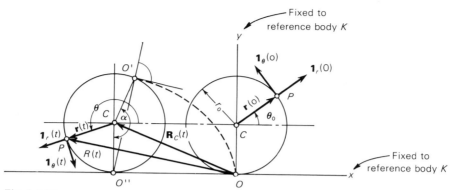

Fig. 1.4-12

coordinates r, θ, with the origin at the moving center C of the wheel, and θ is measured from the horizontal. If we denote the position of C by the vector $\mathbf{R}_C(t)$ and that of P by the vector $\mathbf{R}(t)$, we have (see Fig. 1.4-12)

$$\mathbf{R}(t) = \mathbf{R}_C(t) + \mathbf{r}(t) \tag{a}$$

We denote the point of contact of the wheel on the x axis at time $t = 0$ by O, and at time t by O''. Let O' be a point on the rim of the wheel such that O' and O coincide at time $t = 0$. If the wheel rolls without slipping, the distance $\overline{OO''}$ must equal the length of arc $\overline{O''O'}$. Hence

$$\overline{OO''} = r_0\alpha$$

where α denotes the angle through which the wheel is turned. The radial line fixing point P on the rim undergoes the same angular displacement. However, the latter angle is seen from Fig. 1.4-12 to be $\theta - \theta_0$; thus $\alpha = \theta - \theta_0$, and therefore

$$\overline{OO''} = r_0(\theta - \theta_0) \tag{b}$$

Inspection of Fig. 1.4-12 then yields

$$\mathbf{R}_C(t) = -r_0(\theta - \theta_0)\mathbf{i} + r_0\mathbf{j} \tag{c}$$

Differentiating Eq. (c), we obtain

$$\dot{\mathbf{R}}_C(t) = -r_0\dot{\theta}\mathbf{i} \tag{d}$$

and

$$\ddot{\mathbf{R}}_C(t) = -r_0\ddot{\theta}\mathbf{i} \tag{e}$$

Furthermore, we have

$$\mathbf{r}(t) = r_0\mathbf{1}_r \tag{f}$$

and remembering that

$$\begin{aligned}
\mathbf{1}_r &= \cos\theta\,\mathbf{i} + \sin\theta\,\mathbf{j} \\
\mathbf{1}_\theta &= -\sin\theta\,\mathbf{i} + \cos\theta\,\mathbf{j} \\
\dot{\mathbf{1}}_r &= \dot{\theta}\mathbf{1}_\theta
\end{aligned} \tag{g}$$

we obtain, with Eqs. (a), (c), (f), and (g),

$$\mathbf{R}(t) = r_0\{[-(\theta - \theta_0) + \cos\theta]\mathbf{i} + (1 + \sin\theta)\mathbf{j}\} \tag{h}$$

where $\theta = \theta_0 + \int_0^t \dot{\theta}\, dt$ serves as the parameter. Equation (h) is the parametric representation of the common cycloid, which is shown in Fig. 1.4-13.

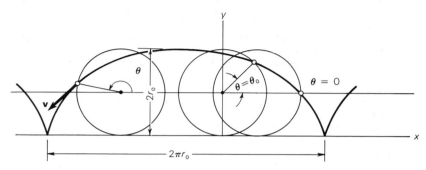

Fig. 1.4-13

For the velocity of point P, or $\dot{\mathbf{R}}(t) = \dot{\mathbf{R}}_C(t) + \dot{\mathbf{r}}(t)$, we obtain, by differentiation of Eq. (h),

$$\mathbf{v}(t) = r_0\dot{\theta}[-(1 + \sin\theta)\mathbf{i} + (\cos\theta)\mathbf{j}] \tag{i}$$

Note from Fig. 1.4-13 that the velocity vector is tangent to the cycloidal path and not to the rim of the wheel. Equation (i) also reveals that, when P coincides with O'', the velocity of P is zero, since for $\theta = (\tfrac{3}{2} + 2n)\pi$ $(n = 0, 1, 2, \ldots)$ we have

$$\mathbf{v} = r_0\dot{\theta}[-(1 - 1)\mathbf{i} + 0\mathbf{j}] = 0$$

For this reason the point of contact on the rim of the wheel in pure rolling motion (without slipping) is called the instantaneous center. For this instant the wheel point has zero velocity, and the observer on body K may describe the instantaneous wheel motion as a rotation about the point of contact. In Sec. 4.2 we devote more attention to this concept.

The acceleration of point P is found from

$$\mathbf{a}(t) = \ddot{\mathbf{R}}_C(t) + \ddot{\mathbf{r}}(t) \qquad \text{or} \qquad \mathbf{a}(t) = \dot{\mathbf{v}}$$

Thus, by differentiating Eq. (i), we find

$$\mathbf{a}(t) = r_0\ddot{\theta}[-(1 + \sin\theta)\mathbf{i} + (\cos\theta)\mathbf{j}] - r_0\dot{\theta}^2[(\cos\theta)\mathbf{i} + (\sin\theta)\mathbf{j}] \tag{j}$$

Equation (j) shows that for $\ddot{\theta} = 0$, that is, $\dot{\theta} = \text{const}$, the vector $\mathbf{a}(t)$ always points to the center of the wheel, because then Eq. (j) yields $\mathbf{a}(t) = -r_0\dot{\theta}^2\mathbf{1}_r$,—see Eq. (g).

If $\dot{\theta}$ is not constant, this holds only for the acceleration vector of the point of contact of the wheel with the path.

PROBLEMS

1.4-1   A particle moves in the xy plane with the velocity $v_x = 2$, $v_y = 4t - 2$. If it passes through the point $x = 2$, $y = 3$ at $t = 1$, determine the equation of the curve.

1.4-2   A particle moves in the xy plane according to the equation $x = t$ ft, $y = 2t^2 - 4$ ft. Determine the velocity and acceleration of the particle at $t = 2$ sec. Resolve the acceleration into tangential and normal components, and check the result by using the curvature equation.

1.4-3   A point moves along the curve $y^2 = 16x$ according to the equation $x = \frac{1}{2}t$. Determine the velocity and acceleration of the point at $t = 2$ sec.

1.4-4   A particle moves with a constant velocity of 2 ft/sec along a parabola $x = ky^2$ that passes through the point $x = 1$, $y = 1$, with the apex coinciding with the origin. Determine the acceleration of the particle as it passes through the origin.

1.4-5   For the parabola of Prob. 1.4-4 determine the radius of curvature at the point $x = \frac{1}{2}$.

1.4-6   A point moves along the curve $xy = 12$ ft^2 with a constant speed of 5 ft/sec. Determine v_x, v_y, a_x, and a_y when the point is at $x = 3$ ft and $y = 4$ ft and moving upward.

1.4-7   A point moves in a circle of radius 5 ft. When its projection on the horizontal diameter is 4 ft to the right of the center, the radial line has an angular velocity of 3 rad/sec counterclockwise and an angular acceleration of 2 rad/sec^2 clockwise. Determine the linear velocity and acceleration of the projection point on the horizontal diameter.

1.4-8   A fighter plane pulling out from a vertical dive undergoes an acceleration of $4g$ normal to its flight path at the bottom of the loop when its speed is 600 mph. Determine the radius of curvature of the flight path at this point.

1.4-9   A particle moves with a constant speed of 16 ft/sec along a parabola $y = x^2/25$ ft in a vertical plane with the origin at the lowest point. Determine the acceleration of the particle when $y = 4$ ft.

1.4-10   For a projectile with initial conditions of speed v_0 and elevation θ_0, derive the equation for the curve passing through the point x_1, y_1 by eliminating the time.

1.4-11   Show that a target at $x = R$, $y = 0$ can be hit by two values of the initial elevation θ_0 provided the initial velocity v_0 satisfies the condition $v_0 > \sqrt{Rg}$.

1.4-12   A gun has a muzzle velocity of 2,200 ft/sec. Determine the two angles of elevation required to hit a target 16 miles away at the same elevation, assuming no air resistance.

1.4-13   It is estimated that an athlete, in putting a shot, releases the shot at a height of 7 ft with a velocity of 34 ft/sec at an angle of 40° above the horizontal. Determine the range, the maximum height attained by the shot, and the time of flight.

1.4-14   A gun has a muzzle velocity v_0. Show that, when v_0 is sufficiently great, a target at (x,y) can be hit by two angles of elevation of the gun.

1.4-15   A rock thrown at an angle of 45° with the horizontal just clears a high-tension transmission line 24 ft high and 40 ft away along the horizontal. Determine the initial speed of the rock.

1.4-16   Find the greatest distance that a stone can be thrown inside a horizontal tunnel 10 ft high with an initial velocity of 80 ft/sec released at a height of 6 ft. Find also the corresponding time of flight.

1.4-17   After burnout a missile is in free flight under the influence of gravity only. Assuming that burnout is attained at height H, with velocity v_0, show that for maximum range beyond burnout, the inclination of the velocity vector should obey the equation

$$\frac{\cos 2\theta_0}{1 - \cos 2\theta_0} = \frac{Hg}{v_0{}^2}$$

1.4-18 A ball is thrown horizontally with velocity v_0 from a tower of height H. Determine the radius of curvature of the trajectory when its slope is 45° below the horizontal. HINT: The only acceleration is g downward, which can be resolved in the normal and tangential directions.

1.4-19 A particle is thrown with initial velocity v_0 in a direction normal to an inclined plane of angle α. With coordinates x, y parallel and normal to the inclined plane, develop equations for $\ddot{y}$, $\dot{y}$, y, $\ddot{x}$, $\dot{x}$, x. Determine the equation for the range measured along x.

1.4-20 A particle is thrown with initial velocity v_0. Determine the angle θ_0 that results in the shortest time for the particle to reach the plane AB of angle α shown in Fig. P 1.4-20.

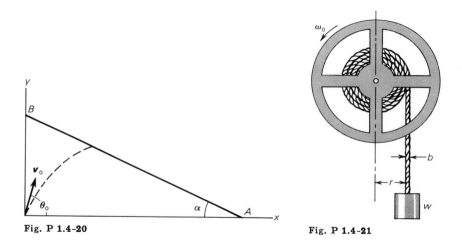

Fig. P **1.4-20**   Fig. P **1.4-21**

1.4-21 A weight w is being hoisted by a cable of diameter b wound on a slotted wheel, as shown in Fig. P 1.4-21. Determine the acceleration of w when the wheel is rotating at a constant speed ω_0.

1.4-22 An automobile race track is 1 mile in diameter. If a racing car traveling with constant speed completes one lap in 1 min, determine its acceleration.

1.4-23 A flywheel 1 ft in diameter rotates with constant angular acceleration. If a point on the rim changes in speed from 10 to 30 ft/sec in 10 revolutions, find the normal acceleration of a point on the rim after it has turned through another 5 revolutions.

1.4-24 Brakes applied to a flywheel rotating at 1,800 rpm cause it to decelerate at a rate of 10 rpm/sec. Find the number of revolutions made by the flywheel in coming to a stop.

1.4-25 Determine the angle θ between the resultant acceleration of a point on a wheel and the radial direction, and show that regardless of the radius this angle approaches zero as $t \to \infty$. Assume that the wheel starts from rest and increases in speed according to the equation $\omega = \alpha t$.

1.4-26   A centrifuge has a rotating arm 10 ft long.   Determine the constant angular speed that results in an acceleration of $20g$.

1.4-27   A point moves on a circle with a radius of 5 ft according to the equation

$$S = 2t^2 + \tfrac{1}{2}t^3$$

where S is measured in feet along the circumference and t is the time in seconds. Determine the acceleration of the point when $t = 2$ sec.

1.4-28   Pulleys A and B are connected by a belt.   The diameter of A is 6 in. and that of B is 12 in.   Pulley A starts from rest and accelerates at a rate of 60 rpm/sec. Determine the resultant acceleration of a point on the rim of pulley B when A has an angular velocity of 30 rpm.

1.4-29   Figure P 1.4-29 shows a mechanical integrator in which the small wheel of radius c rolls on a horizontal disk that rotates under it.   Show that, when the large disk rotates through an angle θ, the small wheel rotates through the angle ϕ:

$$\phi = \frac{1}{c} \int_0^\theta r(\theta)\, d\theta$$

thereby integrating the quantity $r(\theta)$.

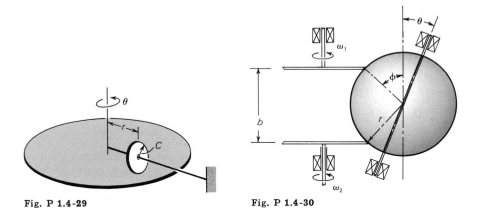

Fig. P 1.4-29   Fig. P 1.4-30

1.4-30   Figure P 1.4-30 shows a variable-speed drive consisting of a friction spherical rotor whose axis can be tilted by the angle θ.   Show that the speed ratio of the two shafts is

$$\frac{\omega_2}{\omega_1} = \frac{\sin(\phi - \theta)}{\sin(\phi + \theta)}$$

where $\cos \phi = b/2r$.   Plot the speed ratio as a function of θ when $\phi = 45°$.

1.4-31   A point A on a rotating wheel in the position shown in Fig. P 1.4-31 has a speed of 10 ft/sec and an acceleration of 12 ft/sec² in the y direction. Determine the angular acceleration of the wheel.

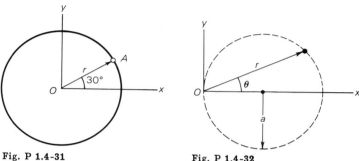

Fig. P 1.4-31   Fig. P 1.4-32

1.4-32   A particle moves on a circle of radius a. With the origin on the circumference, as shown in Fig. P 1.4-32, determine the velocity and acceleration in polar coordinates.

1.4-33   A point moves on a circle of radius R at constant angular speed ω_0. Determine its projection x on a diameter, and show that its acceleration satisfies the equation $\ddot{x} = -\omega^2 x$ for simple harmonic motion.

1.4-34   A particle undergoes simple harmonic motion with peak velocity of 5 ft/sec and peak acceleration of 15 ft/sec². Determine the period of the motion.

1.4-35   A point moves along the parabola shown in Fig. P 1.4-35 so that its projection along the y axis is harmonic. Show that its projection along the x axis is also harmonic with twice the period.

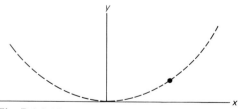

Fig. P 1.4-35

1.4-36   Figure P 1.4-36 shows a movable passenger loading tunnel used at large airports. The tunnel is hinged at O, and the other end, driven by wheels at A, moves out to meet the airplane. At a given instant OA is 100 ft and rotating at a constant angular velocity of 90°/min, while its length is increasing at a rate of 50 ft/min. Determine the acceleration of A.

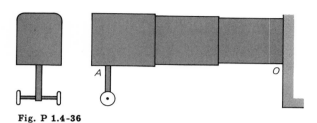

Fig. P 1.4-36

1.4-37   The end A of the bar AB moves with constant velocity v_A, as shown in Fig. P 1.4-37.   Determine the angular velocity $\dot{\theta}$ in terms of θ, h, and v_A.

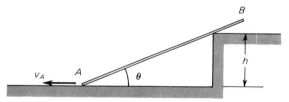

Fig. P 1.4-37

1.4-38   The arm $\overline{CP} = r$ of Fig. P 1.4-38 rotates counterclockwise with constant angular velocity ω_0.   The arm $\overline{OA}$ passes through a slider at P and rocks about point O. Determine the polar coordinates of the slider P and the angular velocity of $\overline{OA}$

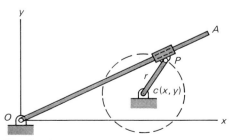

Fig. P 1.4-38

1.4-39 A particle moves along a spiral $r = r_0 e^{\alpha\theta}$. Show that the equation for its velocity is

$$\dot{\mathbf{r}} = (\alpha r \dot{\theta})\mathbf{1}_r + (r\dot{\theta})\mathbf{1}_\theta$$

1.4-40 A point moves along a logarithmic spiral $r = Ce^{\alpha\theta}$ such that $\omega = \dot{\theta} = $ constant. Determine x, $\dot{x}$, and $\ddot{x}$.

1.4-41 Show that the following linear equation exists among x, $\dot{x}$, and $\ddot{x}$, as found in Prob. 1.4-40:

$$\ddot{x} + b\dot{x} + cx = 0$$

Determine b and c in terms of α and $\dot{\theta}$.

1.4-42 A telephone pole is raised by backing a truck against it, as shown in Fig. P 1.4-42. If the angular velocity $\dot{\theta}$ of the pole is to be a constant, show that the required

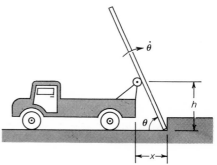

Fig. P 1.4-42

speed of the truck is

$$\dot{x} = \frac{h\dot{\theta}}{\sin^2 \theta}$$

1.4-43 The crank of the engine shown in Fig. P 1.4-43 is running at 3,600 rpm. Find the velocity and acceleration of the piston when $\omega t = 45°$.

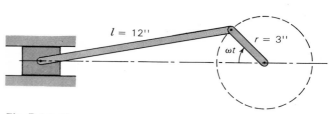

Fig. P 1.4-43

1.4-44   An engine similar to that shown in Fig. P 1.4-43, with an $l/r = 4$ and a stroke of 8 in., is running at a speed of 1,200 rpm.   Plot the piston velocity for every 30° of the crank.

1.4-45   In Prob. 1.4-44 plot the phase-plane diagram for the piston.

1.4-46   A solid flat piece of metal representing an arc of a cylinder of radius R and angle 120° has one end pushed down a vertical guide, as shown in Fig. P 1.4-46.   Determine the velocity $\dot{x}$ and the acceleration $\ddot{x}$ of the contact point C with the floor when A is given a constant velocity v_A downward.

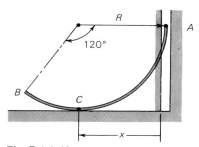

Fig. P 1.4-46

1.4-47   Determine the velocity and acceleration of a point a distance b from the center of a wheel of radius r_0 rolling with angular velocity and acceleration $\dot{\theta}$ and $\ddot{\theta}$ along the x axis.   Describe the path of the point compared with the cycloid of a point on the rim.

1.4-48   A particle m is attached to a string that is wound around a cylinder of radius R, as shown in Fig. P 1.4-48.   If the string unwinds at a constant rate $\dot{\phi} = \omega$, determine the equation for the position of m in polar coordinates r, θ.   What is the velocity and acceleration of m when $\phi = 60°$?   Assume that initially m rests against the cylinder on the x axis.

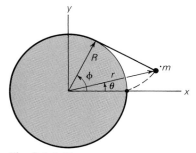

Fig. P 1.4-48

1.4-49   An antiaircraft missile is flying with constant speed v along a plane path.   The
time rate of change $\dot{\gamma}$ of the inclination angle γ to the horizontal is measured by
a turn indicator (see page 390).   Find the components of the missile's acceleration in the directions of $\mathbf{1}_n$ and $\mathbf{1}_r$ and the radius of curvature of the path.

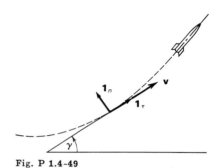

Fig. P 1.4-49

1.4-50   A particle moves along a parabola $y = 4 - 2x^2$ according to the equation
$x = 0.5t$.   Determine the velocity and acceleration at $t = 2$ sec, and find the
tangential and normal components of the acceleration.   The coordinates x and
y are given in feet, when t is given in seconds.

1.4-51   A particle moves along a spiral $r = r_0 e^{b\theta}$, where $\theta = \omega_0 t$.   Determine the equation for the velocity and acceleration in polar coordinates.   Find the equation
for the radius of curvature.

1.5   THREE - DIMENSIONAL MOTION

In Sec. 1.2 the fundamental concepts of position, velocity, and acceleration
were described for a particle in three-dimensional motion by means of cartesian coordinates.

The results found in Sec. 1.4c are also valid for three-dimensional motion.
Here we saw that the time rate of change of the position vector, that is, the
velocity vector, was always tangent to the path of motion.   The time rate
of change of the velocity vector, that is, the acceleration vector, was resolved
into two components: one parallel to the velocity vector, which accounts
for the rate of change of the magnitude of the velocity; and a second vector,
normal to the velocity vector, which was present only when the velocity
vector changed its direction.   The two components formed an instantaneous
plane called the osculating plane of the path in that particular point.

Although the vectorial viewpoint, as taken in Sec. 1.4c, was most helpful
in the basic understanding of the relationship between velocity and acceleration of a particle on the one hand and its path on the other, when dealing

with actual problems, we eventually have to describe the motion in specific coordinate systems, usually in cartesian coordinates. Besides, other coordinates may be quite useful, and thus, in this section, we also discuss the application of cylindrical coordinates, which can be viewed as an extension of polar coordinates with a third axis added to them. For spherical coordinates the reader is referred to Prob. 1.5-19.

CYLINDRICAL COORDINATES

We denote the instantaneous position of the point P in cylindrical coordinates by R, θ, z, which are, respectively, the radial, azimuthal, and longitudinal coordinates of point P, as shown in Fig. 1.5-1. For $R = $ const the

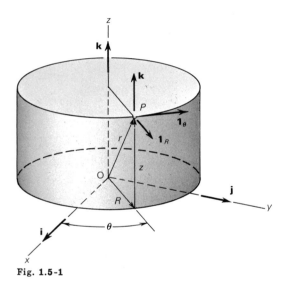

Fig. 1.5-1

point P moves on a cylindrical surface; hence the name *cylindrical coordinates*. We relate these cylindrical coordinates to the cartesian x, y, z coordinates, fixed in the reference body K, by noting that R is in the xy plane and θ is the angle included by R and the x axis. The positive sense of θ is determined by the rotation that moves a right-handed screw in the positive z direction. The unit vectors are defined so that $\mathbf{1}_R$ points in the radial direction, $\mathbf{1}_\theta$ in the azimuthal direction, and $\mathbf{k}$ along the positive z axis.

With respect to the reference body K the cartesian unit vector $\mathbf{k}$ is constant, because its direction does not change, whereas $\mathbf{1}_R$ and $\mathbf{1}_\theta$ change their direction with respect to body K. The triad $\mathbf{1}_R$, $\mathbf{1}_\theta$, $\mathbf{k}$ constitutes a right-handed coordinate system: $\mathbf{1}_R \times \mathbf{1}_\theta = \mathbf{k}$.

The position of the point P may be described in cartesian as well as in cylindrical coordinates:

$$\mathbf{r} = x\mathbf{i} + y\mathbf{j} + z\mathbf{k} = R\mathbf{1}_R + z\mathbf{k} \tag{1.5-1}$$

Successive differentiations yield the velocity and acceleration of point P:

$$\mathbf{v} = \frac{d\mathbf{r}}{dt} = \dot{R}\mathbf{1}_R + R\dot{\mathbf{1}}_R + \dot{z}\mathbf{k} \tag{1.5-2}$$

$$\mathbf{a} = \frac{d\mathbf{v}}{dt} = \ddot{R}\mathbf{1}_R + 2\dot{R}\dot{\mathbf{1}}_R + R\ddot{\mathbf{1}}_R + \ddot{z}\mathbf{k} \tag{1.5-3}$$

The derivatives of the unit vectors appearing in these equations can be taken from our discussion of polar coordinates in Sec. 1.4—see Eqs. (1.4-7) and (1.4-8):

$$\dot{\mathbf{1}}_R = \dot{\theta}\mathbf{1}_\theta \tag{1.5-4}$$
$$\dot{\mathbf{1}}_\theta = -\dot{\theta}\mathbf{1}_R \tag{1.5-5}$$

A second differentiation of $\mathbf{1}_R$ leads to

$$\ddot{\mathbf{1}}_R = \ddot{\theta}\mathbf{1}_\theta + \dot{\theta}\dot{\mathbf{1}}_\theta$$
$$= \ddot{\theta}\mathbf{1}_\theta - \dot{\theta}^2\mathbf{1}_R \tag{1.5-6}$$

where $\ddot{\theta}$ is called the angular acceleration. Hence, we obtain for the velocity and acceleration of point P with respect to body K, expressed in cylindrical coordinates,

$$\mathbf{v} = \dot{R}\mathbf{1}_R + R\dot{\theta}\mathbf{1}_\theta + \dot{z}\mathbf{k}$$
$$= v_R\mathbf{1}_R + v_\theta\mathbf{1}_\theta + v_z\mathbf{k} \tag{1.5-7}$$
and
$$\mathbf{a} = \ddot{R}\mathbf{1}_R + 2R\dot{\theta}\mathbf{1}_\theta + R\ddot{\theta}\mathbf{1}_\theta - R\dot{\theta}^2\mathbf{1}_R + \ddot{z}\mathbf{k}$$
$$= (\ddot{R} - R\dot{\theta}^2)\mathbf{1}_R + (R\ddot{\theta} + 2\dot{R}\dot{\theta})\mathbf{1}_\theta + \ddot{z}\mathbf{k}$$
$$= a_R\mathbf{1}_R + a_\theta\mathbf{1}_\theta + a_z\mathbf{k} \tag{1.5-8}$$

The acceleration of point P may be expressed in still another form by recognizing that

$$R\ddot{\theta} + 2\dot{R}\dot{\theta} = \frac{1}{R}\frac{d}{dt}(R^2\dot{\theta}) \tag{1.5-9}$$

Thus the alternative expression for the acceleration of point P becomes

$$\mathbf{a} = (\ddot{R} - R\dot{\theta}^2)\mathbf{1}_R + \frac{1}{R}\frac{d}{dt}(R^2\dot{\theta}) \cdot \mathbf{1}_\theta + \ddot{z}\mathbf{k} \tag{1.5-10}$$

For the special case $R = R_0 = $ const (point P moves on the surface of the circular cylinder of radius R_0) we have $\dot{R} = \ddot{R} = 0$, which leads to the special equations

$$\mathbf{v} = R_0\dot{\theta}\mathbf{1}_\theta + \dot{z}\mathbf{k} \tag{1.5-11}$$

$$\mathbf{a} = -R_0\dot{\theta}^2\mathbf{1}_R + R_0\ddot{\theta}\mathbf{1}_\theta + \ddot{z}\mathbf{k} \tag{1.5-12}$$

ILLUSTRATIVE EXAMPLE 1.5-1 (SEE ILLUSTRATIVE EXAMPLE 1.2-1)
The path of a point P is described by the position vector

$$\mathbf{r}(t) = x(t)\mathbf{i} + y(t)\mathbf{j} + z(t)\mathbf{k}$$

with $x(t) = 1t$ ft, $y(t) = 1t$ ft, and $z(t) = 2t^2$ ft ($[t] = $ sec). Determine the tangential and normal acceleration of point P as well as the radius of curvature of its path.
SOLUTION: The acceleration $\mathbf{a}$ of point P is easily found by twice differentiating $\mathbf{r}(t)$:

$$\mathbf{a} = \ddot{\mathbf{r}}(t) = 4\mathbf{k}$$

To obtain a_τ, consider that it is the projection of $\mathbf{a}$ on the tangent to the path and thus is found as the scalar product of $\mathbf{a}$ and the tangential unit vector $\mathbf{1}_\tau$:

$$a_\tau = \mathbf{a} \cdot \mathbf{1}_\tau$$

The tangential unit vector is determined as[1]

$$\mathbf{1}_\tau = \frac{\mathbf{v}}{v} = \frac{\dot{\mathbf{r}}}{v} = \frac{1\mathbf{i} + 1\mathbf{j} + 4t\mathbf{k}}{\sqrt{1^2 + 1^2 + (4t)^2}}$$

Hence we obtain

$$a_\tau = \mathbf{a} \cdot \mathbf{1}_\tau = \frac{4\mathbf{k} \cdot (1\mathbf{i} + 1\mathbf{j} + 4t\mathbf{k})}{\sqrt{2 + 16t^2}} = \frac{16t}{\sqrt{2 + 16t^2}} \quad \text{ft/sec}^2$$

Now we know that

$$|\mathbf{a}| = \sqrt{a_\tau{}^2 + a_n{}^2}$$

Thus we have

$$a_n{}^2 = a^2 - a_\tau{}^2 = 16 - \frac{(16t)^2}{2 + 16t^2} = \frac{32}{2 + 16t^2} \quad \text{ft/sec}^2$$

In view of $a_n = v^2/\rho$ the radius of curvature is found from

$$\rho = \frac{v^2}{a_n} = \frac{(2 + 16t^2)\sqrt{2 + 16t^2}}{\sqrt{32}} = \sqrt{\frac{(2 + 16t^2)^3}{32}} \quad \text{ft}$$

Therefore for $t = 0$, we have $\rho = 0.5$ ft, and for $t \to \infty$, ρ goes to infinity; that is, with $t \to \infty$ the path becomes a straight line asymptotically.

ILLUSTRATIVE EXAMPLE 1.5-2
Water enters a sprinkler through the vertical pipe and flows out through two tubes making an angle α with the vertical, as shown in Fig. 1.5-2. If the sprinkler's angular velocity and acceleration about the vertical axis are $\dot{\theta}$ and $\ddot{\theta}$, respectively, determine the velocity and acceleration of a water particle that is traveling through the tube with constant velocity v_0.
SOLUTION: Using cylindrical coordinates, with the z axis along the vertical and the origin at the junction of the two tubes, Eqs. (1.5-7) and (1.5-8) are applicable, with $R = \xi \sin \alpha$,

---

[1] Since $\mathbf{v}$ does not change in the x and y directions, v_x and v_y being constant, the path of point P is represented by a plane curve.

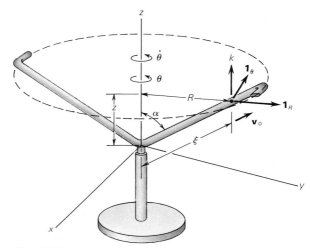

Fig. 1.5-2

$\dot{R} = \dot{\xi} \sin \alpha = v_0 \sin \alpha$, $\dot{z} = v_0 \cos \alpha$, and $\ddot{R} = \ddot{z} = 0$. The velocity and acceleration of the water particle are then [see Eqs. (1.5-7) and (1.5-8)]

$$\mathbf{v} = v_0 \sin \alpha \mathbf{1}_R + \dot{\theta} \xi \sin \alpha \mathbf{1}_\theta + v_0 \cos \alpha \mathbf{k}$$
$$\mathbf{a} = -\xi \dot{\theta}^2 \sin \alpha \mathbf{1}_R + (\xi \ddot{\theta} \sin \alpha + 2v_0 \dot{\theta} \sin \alpha) \mathbf{1}_\theta$$

PROBLEMS

1.5-1   A particle moves in 2 sec from position $(1,-2,1)$ to $(-3,5,4)$, stated in feet. What are the x, y, z components of the average velocity during the 2 sec? Find the unit vector indicating its direction.

1.5-2   The position of a particle at any time t is expressed by the equation

$$\mathbf{r} = 2t^2\mathbf{i} - 4t\mathbf{j} + t^3\mathbf{k} \qquad \text{ft}$$

Determine its velocity at $t = 2$ sec.

1.5-3   For Prob. 1.5-2, determine the unit vector along the velocity vector at any time t.

1.5-4   The velocity of a point in space is given by the equation $\mathbf{v} = 2\mathbf{i} + 3t\mathbf{j} + t^2\mathbf{k}$. Express this in the form $\mathbf{v} = v(t)\mathbf{1}_r$ by factoring out $\mathbf{1}_r$.

1.5-5   The velocity, stated in feet per second, of a particle moving in space is expressed by the equation

$$\mathbf{v} = 10[-(0.866 \sin 2t)\mathbf{i} + (0.50 \sin 2t)\mathbf{j} + (\cos 2t)\mathbf{k}]$$

Determine the unit vector $\mathbf{1}_r$, and compute its value at $t = \pi/4$.

1.5-6   Determine the acceleration of the particle referred to in Prob. 1.5-5.

1.5-7   The coordinates of a point in space are $x = t$ ft, $y = 2t^2$ ft, and $z = t^3$ ft. Write the general expression for its velocity and acceleration.

1.5-8   The position of a particle moving in space is given by the equation

$$\mathbf{r} = 2\mathbf{i} + 2t^2\mathbf{j} + t^2\mathbf{k} \text{ ft}$$

Determine its velocity and acceleration, and describe its motion.

1.5-9   The position of a particle in space is given by the equation $\mathbf{r} = 2t\mathbf{i} + 3\mathbf{j} + 2t^2\mathbf{k}$ ft. Determine the tangential and normal components of the acceleration.

1.5-10   In Prob. 1.5-9, determine the tangential and normal components of the acceleration at $t = \pi/4$ sec and the radius of curvature at this instant.

1.5-11   At a particular instant a particle has a velocity $3\mathbf{i} + 4\mathbf{j}$ and an acceleration $\mathbf{i} + \mathbf{j} - \mathbf{k}$. Determine its normal and tangential components of acceleration.

1.5-12   Determine the radius of curvature of the path taken by the particle in Prob. 1.5-11 at the specified instant, giving its direction.

1.5-13   A particle moves along a parabola $z = cR^2$ with constant speed v_0. The parabola itself is spinning with θ about the z axis. How does the normal acceleration vary with R?

1.5-14   The position of a particle at time t is

$$\mathbf{r} = (1 + t)\mathbf{i} + t^2\mathbf{j} + 2t\mathbf{k}$$

Determine $\mathbf{v}$, $\mathbf{a}$, a_τ, and a_n.

1.5-15   In Prob. 1.5-14 determine the radius of curvature ρ.

1.5-16   A weight w is hoisted by a flexible cable of diameter b wound around a frustum of a cone with radii R_1 and R_2 in the axial length l, as shown in Fig. P 1.5-16. Determine the velocity and acceleration of w when the cone is rotated with constant speed ω_0.

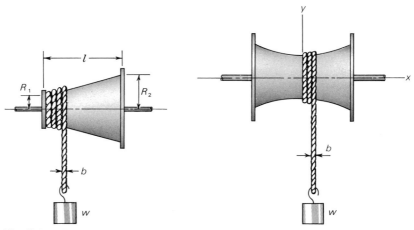

Fig. P 1.5-16   Fig. P 1.5-17

1.5-17   A weight w is raised by a hoist whose drum has a variable radius of $r = r_0 + Cx^2$, as shown in Fig. P 1.5-17. If the diameter of the flexible cable is b and the drum is rotated at a constant angular speed of ω rad/sec, determine the velocity and acceleration of the weight. Assume C to be so small that the variation in the horizontal component of the distance between the cable centers is negligible.

1.5-18   A turntable rotating with θ is also vibrating up and down, according to $z = z_0 \sin \omega t$ (see Fig. P 1.5-18). A particle is moving in a slot of the table such that $R = R_0 + r \sin \Omega t$. Determine the velocity and acceleration of the particle as functions of t.

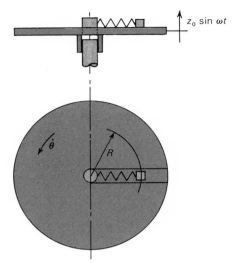

Fig. P 1.5-18

1.5-19 Any position in space can also be stated in terms of the spherical coordinates r, ψ, ϕ of Fig. P 1.5-19. The velocity and acceleration expressed in spherical

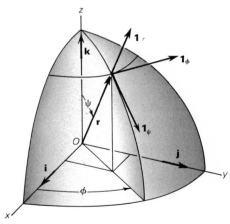

Fig. P 1.5-19

coordinates are

$$\mathbf{v} = \dot{r}\mathbf{1}_r + r\dot{\psi}\mathbf{1}_\psi + (r\dot{\phi}\sin\psi)\mathbf{1}_\phi$$
$$\mathbf{a} = (\ddot{r} - r\dot{\psi}^2 - r\dot{\phi}^2\sin^2\psi)\mathbf{1}_r + (r\ddot{\psi} - r\dot{\phi}^2\sin\psi\cos\psi + 2\dot{r}\dot{\psi})\mathbf{1}_\psi$$
$$+ (r\ddot{\phi}\sin\psi + 2r\dot{\phi}\dot{\psi}\cos\psi + 2\dot{r}\dot{\phi}\sin\psi)\mathbf{1}_\phi$$

Derive these expressions.

1.5-20   The half angle θ of a merry-go-round rotating with $\dot{\phi}$ is changing with time, according to $\theta = \theta_0 + \alpha \sin \omega t$ (see Fig. P 1.5-20). Determine the velocity and acceleration of the points at the end of the bars of length R as functions of t.

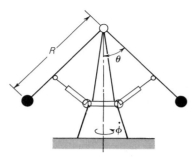

Fig. P 1.5-20

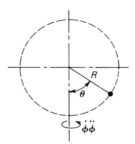

Fig. P 1.5-21

1.5-21   A point is moving with constant θ along a circle that is rotating with ϕ, $\ddot{\phi}$ about one diameter (see Fig. P 1.5-21). Determine the velocity and acceleration of the point as functions of θ. In particular, consider the results for $\theta = \pi/2$ and $\theta = \pi$.

1.5-22   A point on a machine moves along a helix according to the equation

$$\mathbf{r} = (10 \sin \pi t)\mathbf{i} + (10 \cos \pi t)\mathbf{j} + (2t)\mathbf{k}$$

Determine its acceleration at any time t, and show that it is always horizontal and normal to the path.

1.5-23   A package is sent down a helical chute of radius R_0 and pitch h (that is, h is the vertical distance traveled in one turn of the helix), as shown in Fig. P 1.5-23. The acceleration of the package in the direction of the path is given for $t \geq 0$ as $g \sin \alpha$. Determine (a) the velocity of the package after having fallen through the height H, and state how it depends on the pitch h; (b) the time the package took to fall through the height H.

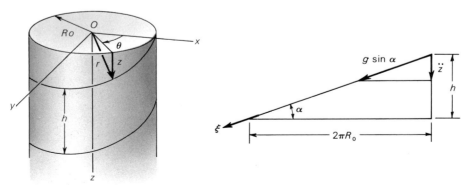

Fig. P 1.5-23

DYNAMICS
OF A
PARTICLE

So far we have dealt with the given motion of a point. If the point is a particle or belongs to an extended material body, the question arises of how its motion came about. It is the object of the present work to answer this question, that is, to study the relationships among the motion of material bodies, their material properties, and the actions necessary to "produce" their motions. Hence we have to add the concepts of force and mass to the kinematic quantities of position, velocity, and acceleration.

We first limit our consideration, as in Chap. 1, to one particle or point body with finite mass but infinitely small dimensions. Although such bodies do not exist, the results obtained for a particle are also applicable to extended bodies, since, as will be shown in Sec. 4.4, the center of mass of such bodies moves like a particle having the entire mass of the body. The theory developed in the present chapter is based on the axioms formulated by Newton (1642–1727).[1] Axioms are laws of nature gained from experience. They are extracted from the results of carefully planned experiments or from the observation and analysis of natural phenomena. They are always subject to tests in the light of our growing experience, which sometimes forces us to change or abolish axioms when they are incompatible with new experimental findings. For example, the classical theory of mechanics based on Newton's work had to be superseded by relativistic mechanics when it was found to lead to erroneous results in the study of light and of fast-moving electrons. Such speeds do not occur, however, in the field of engineering mechanics, and therefore Newton's axioms are still valid laws of nature for the kind of mechanics that we propose to discuss.

2.1 AXIOMATICS

THREE NEWTONIAN AXIOMS OF MECHANICS
In this section we state Newton's axioms and their mathematical formulation as given by Euler.[2] A thorough philosophical discussion of this very

---

[1] Isaac Newton's axioms are stated in his revolutionary treatise "Philosophiae naturalis principia mathematica" (1686).

[2] Euler (1707–1783) was the first to formulate Newton's axioms in cartesian coordinates: "Entdeckung eines neuen Prinzips der Mechanik" (1752). Euler showed in this work that it was possible to develop, on the basis of Newton's axioms, a theory that was valid for the whole field of mechanics. The reader should remember that in the eighteenth century, even after Euler's work was published, a large number of axioms were being used that were valid only for very narrow sections of mechanics [see the paper by C. A. Truesdell, A Program toward . . . (*Arch. Hist. Exac. Sci.*, vol. 1, p. 3, 1960)].

important topic, which requires a deeper understanding than can be expected from a beginner, is not attempted, since it is not essential for the practical application of the theory.   The question of which reference frame[1] Newton's laws are valid in is discussed in Sec. 5.3.   But let us already note here that reference frames in which Newton's laws are valid, at least with sufficient accuracy for the problem at hand, are customarily called newtonian or inertial reference frames, and otherwise nonnewtonian reference frames. However, it is also common usage to drop the words *newtonian* or *inertial* when the applicability of Newton's laws is self-evident.

Here are Newton's axioms:[2]

I   Every body continues in its state of rest, or of uniform motion in a right line, unless it is compelled to change that state by forces impressed upon it.

II   The change of motion is proportional to the motive force impressed, and is made in the direction of the right line in which that force is impressed.

III   To every action there is always an opposed and equal reaction; or the mutual actions of two bodies upon each other are always equal, and directed to contrary parts.

Axiom I had already been formulated by Galilei[3] as a result of his experiments of the falling body.   Although it is implicitly contained in axiom II, it is always stated separately, because it was a revolutionary discovery and the lever to overthrow the reigning sterile concepts of mechanics, as formulated by Aristotle and his followers, that had hampered the advance of physics for eighteen centuries.   Axiom III was already well known in the field of statics and was now extended by Newton to the field of dynamics.

We now turn to the mathematical formulation of axioms II and III. Let $\mathbf{F}$ be the force and $\mathbf{G}$ the quantity of motion, which is defined as the product of the mass m of the particle and its velocity $\mathbf{v}$.   Then Newton's second law states:

$$\mathbf{F} = \frac{d\mathbf{G}}{dt} = \frac{d(m\mathbf{v})}{dt} \qquad \blacktriangleleft \quad (2.1\text{-}1)$$

If we assume that $dm/dt = 0$, that is, that the mass of the particle does not

---

[1] The reader is again (see Sec. 1.1) reminded that the words *reference frame* are meant to convey the same meaning as *reference body*.
[2] The formulation is quoted from Sir Isaac Newton's "Principia" (1686), translated into English by Andrew Motte, 1729, and published by the University of California Press.
[3] Galileo Galilei (1564–1642) stated his law of inertia in his famous work "Discorsi e dimostrazioni matematiche" (1638).   Note the quasi-symbolic coincidence of Galilei's death and Newton's birth.

change with time, Eq. (2.1-1) can be written

$$F = m\frac{d\mathbf{v}}{dt} = m\mathbf{a} \qquad \blacktriangleleft \quad (2.1\text{-}2)$$

and since the mass m is a scalar quantity, the vector $\mathbf{a}$ has the same direction as $\mathbf{F}$. In the dynamics of one particle we use Newton's second law as formulated by Eq. (2.1-2): force equals mass times acceleration. In view of the fact that in engineering mechanics[1] it is advantageous to use force as the primary physical quantity, Eq. (2.1-2) serves to determine the dimension of mass as [lb sec²/ft]. It could also serve as a means to measure mass. However, this is done more conveniently with the use of the third axiom and Newton's law of gravitational attraction.

Newton's second law is often written like an equation of equilibrium:[2]

$$\mathbf{F} + (-m\mathbf{a}) = \mathbf{0} \qquad \blacktriangleleft \quad (2.1\text{-}3)$$

Then the term $(-m\mathbf{a})$ is called the inertia force. We shall understand this definition more thoroughly when we deal with the motion of a particle in a moving reference frame (see Chap. 5).

The mathematical statement of Newton's third law can be formulated with reference to Fig. 2.1-1, which shows two particles interacting with each

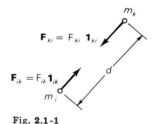

Fig. 2.1-1

other. If $\mathbf{F}_{ik}$ is the force exerted in some arbitrary way by particle k on particle i, and $\mathbf{F}_{ki}$ is the force exerted by particle i on particle k, axiom III states that

$$\mathbf{F}_{ik} + \mathbf{F}_{ki} = \mathbf{0}$$

or

$$F_{ik}\mathbf{1}_{ik} + F_{ki}\mathbf{1}_{ki} = 0 \qquad \text{with } \mathbf{1}_{ik} = -\mathbf{1}_{ki} \qquad \blacktriangleleft \quad (2.1\text{-}4)$$

Hence $F_{ik} = F_{ki}$.

[1] To deal with statics and the strength of materials without the use of force as a primary physical concept would be very inconvenient. Even C. F. Gauss (1777–1855), the most eminent mathematician of his age, suggested the use of force as a primary physical quantity, because this seemed to him to be more useful for his studies in the field of electromagnetism. The attempt by H. Hertz (1857–1894) to free the science of mechanics from the concept of force was not encouraging (see H. Hertz, "Collected Works," vol. III, "Principles of Mechanics").

[2] This so-called kinetostatic approach to problems of dynamics was first employed by D'Alembert (1717–1783) to deal with the dynamics of extended bodies and systems of bodies (D'Alembert's principle).

APPLICABILITY OF PARTICLE DYNAMICS TO EXTENDED BODIES

As soon as one wishes to apply Newton's laws and subsequent theorems to practical engineering problems, there arises the question of the conditions under which the theory developed for the dynamics of a particle of zero spatial dimensions also suffices for the dynamical treatment of extended rigid[1] bodies. We show below that this is always possible when two non-parallel lines fixed in the moving body do not change their direction during the motion or, in other words, when the body is in pure *translation*. For example, the book shown in Fig. 2.1-2 is in translatory motion on a circular path. It is immediately evident that every point of the body then has, at any instant, the same velocity and the same acceleration (see Fig. 2.1-3).

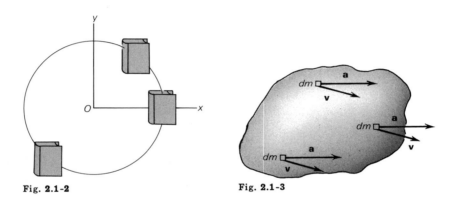

Fig. 2.1-2   Fig. 2.1-3

Now imagine that an extended rigid body is made up of an infinite number of infinitesimal mass elements dm and that the force is distributed throughout the body so that every mass element dm is subjected to an infinitesimal force $d\mathbf{F}$ that "produces" its acceleration $\mathbf{a}$:

$$d\mathbf{F} = \mathbf{a}\, dm \qquad (2.1\text{-}5)$$

The resultant force $\mathbf{F}$ is then found by integration over the whole body of mass m. Considering that $\mathbf{a}$ is the same for every mass element, we obtain

$$\mathbf{F} = \mathbf{a} \int_m dm = \mathbf{a}m \qquad (2.1\text{-}6)$$

Thus we find the same equation as given by Newton's second law for the particle of mass m—see Eq. (2.1-2). However, we must remember that Eq. (2.1-6) was derived for a distributed body force, and we must ask what single force $\mathbf{F}$ is truly equivalent to the distributed body force that produces the same acceleration $\mathbf{a}$ for all mass elements of the body. From Eq. (2.1-6)

[1] A body is considered rigid when any two points in the body never change their mutual distance.

we already know the magnitude and direction of such force. But where do we have to place its line of action relative to the body?

From the study of statics we are familiar with the concept of the equivalence of forces: in order that a single force alone be equivalent to any system of several forces or to distributed forces, it is, in the first place, necessary that the latter "add up" to that single force. This is certainly the case here, where all distributed forces $d\mathbf{F} = \mathbf{a}\,dm$ point in the same direction. Next, we have to require that the magnitude and direction of the single force are equal to the magnitude and direction of the resultant of the distributed forces. This requirement is, according to Eq. (2.1-6), fulfilled if the single force $\mathbf{F}$ equals $m\mathbf{a}$. Finally, the line of action of the single force $\mathbf{F}$ must be the same as that of the resultant of the distributed forces. The line of action is found by equating the moment of the resultant about an arbitrary point A of the body to that of the distributed body forces about the same

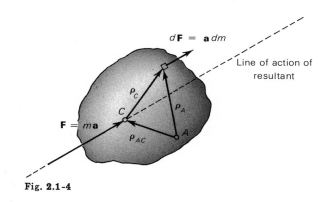

Fig. 2.1-4

point (see Fig. 2.1-4):

$$\varrho_{AC} \times \mathbf{F} = \varrho_{AC} \times \mathbf{a}m = \int_m \varrho_A \times \mathbf{a}\,dm$$

or

$$m\mathbf{a} \times \varrho_{AC} = \mathbf{a} \times \int_m \varrho_A\,dm \qquad (2.1\text{-}7)$$

Equation (2.1-7) is satisfied when

$$\varrho_{AC} = \frac{\int_m \varrho_A\,dm}{m} \qquad \blacktriangleleft \quad (2.1\text{-}8a)$$

In $\xi,\ \eta,\ \zeta$ coordinates fixed in the body with their origin at point A, Eq.

(2.1-8a) is

$$\xi_C = \frac{\int_m \xi \, dm}{m} \qquad \eta_C = \frac{\int_m \eta \, dm}{m} \qquad \zeta_C = \frac{\int_m \zeta \, dm}{m} \qquad \blacktriangleleft \quad (2.1\text{-}8b)$$

Substituting in Eq. (2.1-8a)

$$\varrho_A = \varrho_{AC} + \varrho_C \qquad \text{(see Fig. 2.1-4)}$$

we obtain

$$\varrho_{AC} = \frac{\varrho_{AC} \int_m dm + \int_m \varrho_C \, dm}{m}$$

Thus,

$$\int_m \varrho_C \, dm = \mathbf{0} \qquad \blacktriangleleft \quad (2.1\text{-}9)$$

The point C, which is fixed in the body, according to Eq. (2.1-8a), is called the center of mass. It is a property of the body depending solely on its mass distribution.   We may therefore assert that a body remains in transla-tory motion when it is subjected to forces such that the line of action of their resultant contains the center of mass C of the body.

Now what if several external forces, perhaps including distributed forces also, act on the body?   The answer is obvious in view of the discussion above. The resultant of all external forces, whether given surface and body forces or reactions, must be a single force with a line of action that passes through the center of mass of the body if the body is to remain in translatory motion.

FREE-BODY TECHNIQUE

In the application of Newton's laws it is necessary to define the body to which they are to be applied.   For this purpose we isolate the body or the part of the body under consideration from its surroundings.   A sketch of this isolated body is called the free-body diagram, and the forces that act on the "free body" are established by recognizing that besides the body forces, such as gravitational attraction, magnetic force, and the like, any contacting body and constraints exert forces on it.   It must be emphasized that it is the force acting on the isolated body and not the force exerted by the isolated body on its surroundings that constitutes the left side of the equation $\Sigma \mathbf{F} = m\mathbf{a}$.

Often these forces, mainly the constraint forces, are not known in magni-tude and direction, in which case the free-body diagram should show their components in the coordinates adopted for the problem.

LAW OF GRAVITATION

Aside from the three axioms, one of Newton's greatest contributions to the field of mechanics is his law of gravitation.   Referring again to Fig. 2.1-1, if the forces are brought about through the mutual attraction of the two particles, the masses of which are m_i and m_k, Newton's law of gravitation in unison with his third law states that

$$F_{ik} = F_{ki} = \Gamma \frac{m_i m_k}{d^2} \qquad \blacktriangleleft \qquad (2.1\text{-}10)$$

where d† denotes the distance between the two particles and Γ‡ is the universal constant of gravity. Since the weight w of a mass, which can be measured, for example, by means of a spring scale in pounds, is overwhelmingly due to the gravitational attraction of the earth, we recognize from Eq. (2.1-10) that the weight of a body is proportional to its mass. The factor of proportionality can be found by measuring the acceleration[1] g of a freely falling body that is solely acted upon by its weight, since from Eq. (2.1-2) we can write

$$\mathbf{w} = m\mathbf{g} \qquad \text{or} \qquad w = mg \qquad (2.1\text{-}11)$$

In engineering, a constant value $g = 32.2$ ft/sec^2 is used at sea level as well as for small elevations,[2] but in the United States[3] its standard value is $g = 32.174$ ft/sec^2. We keep in mind that on account of Eq. (2.1-11) the weight of a body permits the determination of its mass with sufficient accuracy for engineering purposes by using

$$m \text{ [lb sec}^2/\text{ft]} = \frac{w \text{ [lb]}}{32.2 \text{ ft/sec}^2} \qquad (2.1\text{-}12)$$

The international standard unit of mass is one kilogram (kg); its weight (force) is equal to 2.2046 lb. In the United States, Congress has defined, as the mass unit, the pound mass avoirdupois equal to 1/2.2046 kg. Its weight, based on $g = 32.174$ ft/sec^2, is one pound force and is taken as the unit of force in engineering. Since in engineering force is considered a primary quantity and mass is "degraded" to a derived quantity, the engineering unit of mass is the one that experiences, under the action of one pound force, the acceleration of one foot per second per second. It is called a slug and is equal to 32.174 lb mass, because its weight gives it an acceleration 32.174 times larger than one foot per second per second.

ILLUSTRATIVE EXAMPLE 2.1-1
Determine the maximum acceleration that may be imparted to the homogeneous block in Fig. 2.1-5 by a horizontal force applied to point A if tilting of the block is to be avoided

---

† As far as extended bodies are concerned, for homogeneous spheres only, we have d simply as the distance between their centers of mass.
‡ If d is measured in centimeters and the masses m_i and m_k are given in grams [g], then the gravitational constant is $\Gamma = 6.658 \times 10^{-8}$ cm^3/g sec^2.
[1] Chiefly because of the earth's rotation and because of the fact that the earth is not a perfect homogeneous sphere (the distance of the body on the earth's surface from its center changes with the body's location), g and hence w vary from place to place.
[2] For an elevation of $h = 1{,}000$ ft, the variation is less than 0.1 percent.
[3] By Act of Congress.

so that the body remains in translatory motion. The mass of the two small rollers can be neglected in comparison with the mass m of the block. Friction is also disregarded.

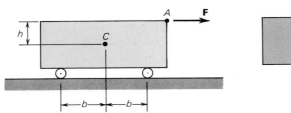

Fig. 2.1-5

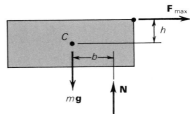

Fig. 2.1-6

SOLUTION: Consider that at the instant when the block is in danger of tilting, the left roller no longer supports the block, so that the free-body diagram is as shown in Fig. 2.1-6. In order that the block be accelerated solely in the horizontal direction, the forces shown in Fig. 2.1-6 must be in equilibrium as far as the vertical direction and their moments with respect to the center of mass C are concerned. Only then is the resultant of the forces indicated in Fig. 2.1-6 a horizontal force with its line of action through the center of mass, thereby ensuring the block's translatory motion. Hence,

$$N = mg$$

and with the center of mass C as reference point

$$-Nb + F_{max}h = 0 \quad \text{or} \quad F_{max} = mg\,\frac{b}{h}$$

Thus we have, from Newton's second law,

$$a_{max} = \frac{F_{max}}{m} = \frac{b}{h}\,g$$

ILLUSTRATIVE EXAMPLE 2.1-2
From Newton's law of gravitational attraction, determine the weight w of an object of mass m_0 at distances R, $2R$, $3R$, etc., from the center of the earth (mass m_e), where R is the radius of the earth, and plot the results in terms of w/w_0, where w_0 is the weight of the object at the earth's surface.
SOLUTION: From Newton's law of gravitational attraction—Eq. (2.1-10)—we have

$$w = \frac{\Gamma m_e m_0}{d^2}$$

At the surface of the earth $d = R$, so that $w_0 = \Gamma m_e m_0 / R^2$. At any other distance d we then have

$$w = \frac{\Gamma m_e m_0}{R^2}\left(\frac{R}{d}\right)^2 = w_0\left(\frac{R}{d}\right)^2$$

Thus

$$\frac{w}{w_0} = \left(\frac{R}{d}\right)^2$$

The result is plotted in Fig. 2.1-7.

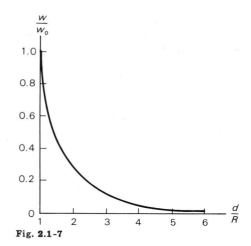

Fig. **2.1-7**

ILLUSTRATIVE EXAMPLE 2.1-3

Show that the attraction of a particle of mass m_0 at a distance $r_0 < R$ from the center of a solid homogeneous sphere of radius R is not due to the material outside the radius r_0.

SOLUTION: Let C be the center of a concentric spherical shell of infinitesimal thickness dr and radius $r > r_0$, as shown in Fig. 2.1-8.   Forming a cone about m_0, the elementary

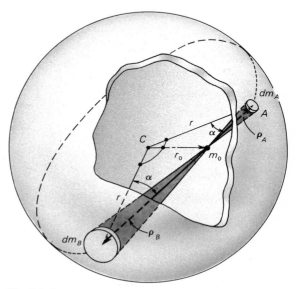

Fig. **2.1-8**

mass dm_A cut out of the shell at A is proportional to $\rho_A{}^2/\cos\alpha$, and the mass element dm_B at B is proportional to $\rho_B{}^2/\cos\alpha$. Since the attractive force on m_0 is proportional to the masses and inversely proportional to the square of the distances ρ_A and ρ_B, respectively, the attraction by the mass elements at A and B cancel each other. Every point on the spherical shell can be treated similarly, and by varying r from r_0 to R, it is evident that the part of the sphere $r > r_0$ has no influence on m_0.

ILLUSTRATIVE EXAMPLE 2.1-4
The mass m of a spherical pendulum of length l describes a horizontal circle, as shown in Fig. 2.1-9. Determine the velocity in terms of the parameter θ.

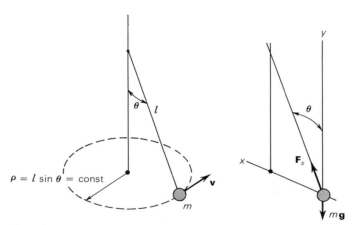

Fig. 2.1-9

SOLUTION: Drawing the free-body diagram and summing the forces in the vertical and horizontal directions, we find, from the fundamental equation $\mathbf{F} = m\mathbf{a}$,

$$\Sigma F_y = F_s \cos\theta - mg = 0$$
$$\Sigma F_x = F_s \sin\theta = m\frac{v^2}{\rho} = m\frac{v^2}{l\sin\theta}$$

Eliminating the string force F_s, the equation for the velocity of m is obtained in terms of θ:

$$v = \sqrt{lg\frac{\sin^2\theta}{\cos\theta}}$$

Note that the velocity v goes to infinity if θ approaches $90°$.

ILLUSTRATIVE EXAMPLE 2.1-5
A mass particle m is suspended by a linear spring of stiffness k [lb/in.], as shown in Fig. 2.1-10. If m is displaced from the equilibrium position by a distance x_0 and released, determine the differential equation of motion and its solution.

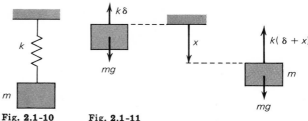

Fig. 2.1-10   Fig. 2.1-11

SOLUTION: In the equilibrium position the weight mg is balanced by the spring force $k\delta$, where δ is the statical deflection of the spring. When displaced from the equilibrium position by x, Newton's equation applied to the mass gives (see Fig. 2.1-11)

$$mg - k(\delta + x) = -kx = m\ddot{x}$$

Thus the differential equation[1] of motion of m is

$$\ddot{x} + \frac{k}{m}x = 0$$

The general solution of this equation is

$$x = C_1 \sin pt + C_2 \cos pt$$

where $p = \sqrt{k/m}$ [1/sec]. Thus for the initial conditions $x(t = 0) = x_0$ and $\dot{x}(t = 0) = 0$, the equation above becomes

$$x = x_0 \cos pt$$

Since the motion is repeated when $p\tau = 2\pi$, the period of oscillation is

$$\tau = \frac{2\pi}{p} = 2\pi \sqrt{\frac{m}{k}} \quad \text{[sec]}$$

This relationship between the period τ and p is responsible for p being called the circular frequency.

PROBLEMS

2.1-1   A particle of mass m weighing 6.44 lb moves along the x axis under a force $F = (3 + 2x)$ lb. If its speed at $x = 0$ is 4 ft/sec, determine the speed at $x = 5$ ft.

2.1-2   A particle weighing 3.22 lb is acted upon by a force $\mathbf{F} = (3t^2\mathbf{i} - 2\mathbf{k})$ lb. When $t = 0$, the velocity is $10\mathbf{j}$ ft/sec. What is it when $t = 2$ sec?

2.1-3   A mass moves on a straight line under the action of a force $F = k/x^2$ lb. If its velocity at x_0 is v_0, what is it at $x = 3x_0$?

2.1-4   A 20-lb box resting on a bathroom scale in an elevator reads 25 lb when the elevator starts up. Draw the free-body diagram of the box and determine the acceleration of the elevator.

[1] If $[k]$ = lb/in. and $[x]$ = in., then m must be stated in lb sec²/in.

2.1-5   A sled sliding down a 30° inclined plane attains a velocity expressed by the equation $v = 0.3gt$. Determine the coefficient of friction between the sled and the inclined plane.

2.1-6   In the equation for the gravitational force of attraction, $F = \Gamma m_1 m_2/d^2$, the force is measured in dynes when m is measured in grams and d in centimeters. Give the definition of a dyne, and determine how many dynes there are in a pound.

2.1-7   The universal constant of gravity Γ is 6.658×10^{-8} cm^3/g sec^2. Show that its value in feet, pounds, and seconds is 3.44×10^{-8} ft^4/lb sec^4.

2.1-8   At the earth's surface a body falls toward the center of the earth with an acceleration of 32.2 ft/sec^2. Using 3,960 miles for the radius of earth, determine the quantity Γm_e, where m_e is the mass of the earth.

2.1-9   Determine the numerical value of the earth's gravitational acceleration g in miles per hour per hour.

2.1-10   Find the gravitational force of attraction between two steel spheres of radius 12 in. if they are just touching each other. Compare this with the attraction of the earth on one of the spheres.

2.1-11   Determine the distance from the earth's center to the neutral point where the attraction of the earth on a space probe is equal to that of the moon. The mass ratio of the moon to the earth is 1:81, and the distance between them is 239,000 miles.

2.1-12   Astronomers claim that the sun is traveling at 630,000 mph in a circular orbit around the center of the galaxy, which is approximately 25,000 light-years away. Determine the quantity Γm of the galaxy, assuming it to exert a central force.

2.1-13   The element m of an accelerometer consists of a bar hinged to a frictionless bearing, with the other end tied to a string of known tensile strength (see Fig. P 2.1-13). If F_t is the tensile strength of the string, determine the acceleration a that will break it.

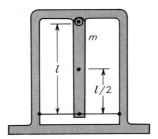

Fig. P 2.1-13

2.2   FIRST AND SECOND PROBLEMS OF MECHANICS

The so-called first problem of mechanics is quite simple. Given complete kinematic information about the motion of a body or a system of bodies, we seek the associated forces. In the case of one particle, the kinematic information may be given in the form

$$\mathbf{r} = \mathbf{r}(t) \qquad \text{or} \qquad x = f_1(t) \qquad y = f_2(t) \qquad z = f_3(t)$$

in which case the associated resultant force is

$$m\ddot{\mathbf{r}} = \mathbf{F} \quad \text{or} \quad m\ddot{x} = m\frac{d^2f_1}{dt^2} = F_x \quad \text{etc.}$$

Furthermore it may be pointed out that the quasi-static (or kinetostatic) point of view, as displayed in Eq. (2.1-3),

$$\mathbf{F} + (-m\mathbf{a}) = \mathbf{0}$$

is generally advantageous in the treatment of first problems, since we may then apply the well-known rules of statics for the determination of the unknown forces.

ILLUSTRATIVE EXAMPLE 2.2-1
What are the forces **A** and **B** exerted by the bearings on the rigid shaft shown in Fig. 2.2-1, when the unbalance of mass m rotates with constant angular velocity ω [rad/sec]?

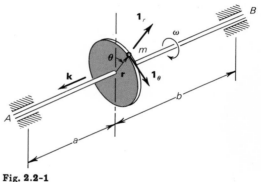

Fig. 2.2-1

SOLUTION: For the sake of convenience, we treat the problem in polar coordinates (see Fig. 2.2-1). Because of the type of bearings indicated in Fig. 2.2-1 we know that the bearing forces **A** and **B** have no components in the shaft direction. Thus Newton's second axiom yields the two equations

$$A_\theta + B_\theta = ma_\theta \quad \text{and} \quad A_r + B_r = ma_r$$

Since the angular velocity of the shaft ω is constant, we have $a_\theta = 0$ and $a_r = -r\omega^2$, and thus we may write

$$A_\theta + B_\theta = 0 \tag{a}$$
$$A_r + B_r = -mr\omega^2 \tag{b}$$

For the four unknowns A_θ, B_θ, A_r, and B_r we need two more equations.
   As a first step we take a quasi-static point of view by rewriting Eq. (b) as follows— see Eq. (2.1-3)—

$$A_r + B_r - (-mr\omega^2) = A_r + B_r + mr\omega^2 = 0 \tag{c}$$

The inertia force $mr\omega^2$, thus introduced, is usually called the centrifugal force.

Hence we consider Eqs. (a) and (c) static-equilibrium equations for the bearing forces and the inertia force $mr\omega^2$. Equilibrium of this force group also requires that the force moments about an arbitrary reference point vanish. Choosing the bearing A as reference point, we may thus write the following two moment equations:

About the θ direction through A:

$$mr\omega^2 a + B_r(a + b) = 0 \tag{d}$$

About the r direction through A:

$$-B_\theta(a + b) = 0 \tag{e}$$

Equations (a) and (e) reveal that both A_θ and B_θ are zero, and Eqs. (c) and (d) yield

$$A_r = -mr\omega^2 \frac{b}{a + b} \qquad B_r = -mr\omega^2 \frac{a}{a + b}$$

Thus we see that the forces exerted by the bearings on the shaft are always directed opposite to the positive r direction. Since the unit vector $\mathbf{1}_r$ rotates with angular velocity ω, the bearing forces also rotate with the same angular speed.

In the second problem of mechanics the forces are given, and the motion of a body or a system of bodies due to these forces is sought. This is far more difficult, because it requires the solution of one or more differential equations. The degree of difficulty depends essentially on the functions describing the forces, as listed below in the order of increasing difficulty:

1 Forces constant in magnitude and direction (for example, weight in motions not covering too great distances)

2 Forces that are given functions of time (for example, harmonic forces: $\mathbf{F} = \mathbf{F}_0 \sin \Omega t$)

3 Forces that depend on the position of the particle relative to the other body (for example, spring force or gravitational attraction)

4 Forces that are functions of the velocity of the body (for example, viscous friction or more complicated laws of resistance)

5 Forces that are functions of acceleration (for example, inertia of water mass set in motion by a moving ship, effective air mass in flutter of airplane wings, and the like)

In the most general case we have, for a single particle of mass m, the following three differential equations of second order:

$$\begin{aligned}
m\ddot{x} &= F_x(t; x, y, z; \dot{x}, \dot{y}, \dot{z}; \ddot{x}, \ddot{y}, \ddot{z}) \\
m\ddot{y} &= F_y(t; x, y, z; \dot{x}, \dot{y}, \dot{z}; \ddot{x}, \ddot{y}, \ddot{z}) \\
m\ddot{z} &= F_z(t; x, y, z; \dot{x}, \dot{y}, \dot{z}; \ddot{x}, \ddot{y}, \ddot{z})
\end{aligned} \tag{2.2-1}$$

stated in cartesian coordinates. The reader is invited to state these equations in other types of coordinates also.

Although it is often impossible to obtain a closed solution of such differential equations, we may sometimes find expressions for the velocity (first integrals) rather simply by means of the momentum and the energy theorems, discussed later.

Finally it should be remarked that many problems in mechanics are of a mixed type. Consider, for example, the gyrocompass (see Sec. 6.5), where gravity and the rotation of the earth jointly determine its behavior. Furthermore, we very frequently encounter cases in which some forces are given and others, mostly constraint forces, are unknown. Then we are also faced with a problem of the mixed type.

ILLUSTRATIVE EXAMPLE 2.2-2
Establish and solve the differential equation for the motion of the simple pendulum shown in Fig. 2.2-2.

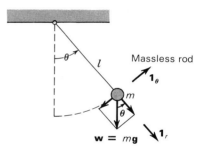

Fig. 2.2-2

SOLUTION: Considering the component of the weight in the tangential direction of the particle's path, the equation of motion becomes, in view of Fig. 2.2-2,

$$F_\theta = ma_\theta$$

or—see Eq. (1.3-11), with $r = l$ and $\dot{r} = 0$—

$$-mg \sin \theta = ml\ddot{\theta} \qquad (a)$$

where we find the force to be a nonlinear function of the angle θ. If we restrict the amplitude of the oscillation to small angles, we can replace $\sin \theta$ by the first term of the series

$$\sin \theta = \theta - \frac{\theta^3}{3!} + \cdots \qquad (b)$$

and thus linearize the equation of motion:

$$\ddot{\theta} + \frac{g}{l}\theta = 0 \qquad (c)$$

The solution of this equation is well known and is equal to

$$\theta = C_1 \sin pt + C_2 \cos pt \qquad (d)$$

where $p = \sqrt{g/l} = 2\pi/\tau$ is the circular frequency of oscillation, with τ equal to the duration of one period.

The constants C_1 and C_2 depend on the initial conditions, that is, on the angular displacement θ_0 and the angular velocity $\dot{\theta}_0$ at time $t = 0$. Then we have, from Eq. (d), for $t = 0$, $\theta_0 = C_2$, and differentiating Eq. (d) with respect to time, we find for $t = 0$, $\dot{\theta}_0 = \sqrt{g/l}\, C_1$. Hence the complete solution of Eq. (c) is given by

$$\theta = \theta_0 \cos pt + \frac{\dot{\theta}_0}{p} \sin pt \qquad (e)$$

ILLUSTRATIVE EXAMPLE 2.2-3
This example demonstrates how the dynamic equations as well as the equations describing the kinematic conditions of the problem are established. With a given muzzle speed v_1 determine the angle of elevation β in order to hit an object on a tower, as shown in Fig. 2.2-3. Neglect air resistance.

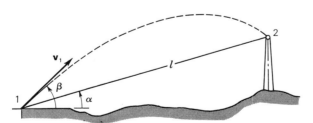

Fig. 2.2-3

SOLUTION: The equations for the motion of the particle of mass m are established using cartesian coordinates, as shown in Fig. 2.2-4. Since, during flight, the particle is subjected solely to the gravity force (its weight) $-mg\mathbf{j}$, we have

$$m\ddot{x} = 0 \qquad (a)$$
$$m\ddot{y} = -mg \qquad (b)$$

Besides, we may set up the equations satisfying the kinematic conditions (flight time

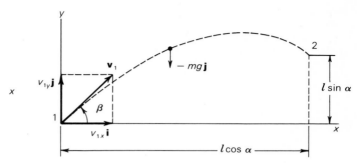

Fig. 2.2-4

$t_2 - t_1$):

$$\int_{t_1}^{t_2} \dot{x}\, dt = l \cos \alpha \tag{c}$$

$$\int_{t_1}^{t_2} \dot{y}\, dt = l \sin \alpha \tag{d}$$

$$v_{1x} = v_1 \cos \beta \tag{e}$$

$$v_{1y} = v_1 \sin \beta \tag{f}$$

These six equations suffice to solve our problem.

From Eq. (a) we know immediately that (see also Fig. 2.2-4)

$$\dot{x} = \text{const} = v_{1x} \tag{g}$$

Integration of Eq. (b) yields

$$\dot{y} = \dot{y}(t_1) - g(t - t_1) = v_{1y} - g(t - t_1) \tag{h}$$

From the substitution of Eqs. (g) and (h) in Eqs. (c) and (d), respectively, we then obtain

$$v_{1x}(t_2 - t_1) = l \cos \alpha \tag{i}$$

and

$$v_{1y}(t_2 - t_1) - g\left(\frac{t_2{}^2 - t_1{}^2}{2} - t_1 t_2 + t_1{}^2\right) = l \sin \alpha$$

or

$$v_{1y}(t_2 - t_1) - g\,\frac{(t_2 - t_1)^2}{2} = l \sin \alpha \tag{j}$$

Equations (i) and (e) yield, for the flight time,

$$t_2 - t_1 = \frac{l \cos \alpha}{v_1 \cos \beta} \tag{k}$$

Substituting Eqs. (k) and (f) in Eq. (j), we find

$$l \cos \alpha \tan \beta - \frac{g}{2}\,\frac{l^2 \cos^2 \alpha}{v_1{}^2 \cos^2 \beta} = l \sin \alpha \tag{l}$$

or

$$l \cos \alpha\,\frac{\sin 2\beta}{2} - \frac{g}{2}\,\frac{l^2 \cos^2 \alpha}{v_1{}^2} = \frac{l \sin \alpha}{2}\,(1 + \cos 2\beta)$$

or

$$\sin (2\beta - \alpha) = \sin \alpha + \frac{gl}{v_1{}^2}\cos^2 \alpha \tag{m}$$

Equation (m) represents the relationship defining the angle β for a given muzzle speed v_1. It deserves a little more discussion. For example, for $\beta = \alpha$ or $\beta = 90°$ we see that v_1 must be infinite. Furthermore we know that the sum of the two terms on the right side of Eq. (m) cannot be larger than unity. Hence the minimum muzzle velocity, just sufficient to hit the object at point 2, is

$$v_{1,min} = \cos \alpha \sqrt{\frac{gl}{1 - \sin \alpha}}$$

In this case the angle β is found from $2\beta - \alpha = 90°$ to be

$$\beta = \frac{90° - \alpha}{2}$$

This confirms, for $\alpha = 0$, the well-known result that $\beta = 45°$.

Finally, Eq. (m) tells us that for a given α and for $v_{1,min} < v_1 < \infty$ two different angles β are always obtained such that

$$2\beta_1 - \alpha + 2\beta_2 - \alpha = 180°$$
or
$$\beta_1 + \beta_2 = 90° + \alpha$$

PROBLEMS

2.2-1   A balloon is descending with acceleration a. How much ballast must be thrown out to rise again with the same acceleration? Assume the buoyant force of the balloon to be the same in each case.

2.2-2   A ballistic missile reaches its highest point after burnout at an altitude of 800 miles. If its speed at this instant is 15,000 mph, determine the radius of curvature of the flight path at this point.

2.2-3   A particle of mass $\frac{1}{2}$ slug traveling at a speed of 25 ft/sec is acted upon by forces whose resultant at a specified instant is 60 lb in a direction 30° from its tangential vector $\mathbf{1}_\tau$. Find its radius of curvature and the tangential acceleration at this instant.

2.2-4   A particle of mass m moves along a smooth catenary curve

$$y = \frac{C}{2} (e^{x/c} + e^{-x/c}) = C \cosh \frac{x}{c}$$

with constant speed (see Fig. P 2.2-4). Determine the reaction of the curve on m.

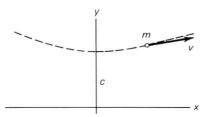

Fig. P 2.2-4

2.2-5   Referring to Illustrative Example 2.2-2, what is the maximum amplitude of the oscillation if the initial values θ_0 and $\theta_0 \sqrt{l/g}$ are very small compared with unity?

2.2-6   An 18,000-lb airplane is catapulted from a carrier ship at a speed of 100 mph relative to the deck. The length of the catapult run is 70 ft, and the force acting on the airplane is assumed to start with a value of F_0 and decrease to zero in a cosine variation with the distance. Determine the value of F_0. The velocity of the carrier ship is constant.

2.2-7   A steam turbine rotating at 2,400 rpm has blades extending from 24 to 34 in. Determine the maximum stress in the blades, which are uniform in cross section and made of steel.

2.2-8   Determine the stiffness k lb/in. of the spring in a centrifugal device (see Fig. P 2.2-8) that allows a plunger to move out $\frac{1}{2}$ in. at 120 rpm, thereby tripping a speed-control circuit. The plunger weighs 1.6 lb, and its center of gravity is 30 in. from the center of rotation. At $\omega = 0$ the spring force in the position shown is zero. Neglect the mass of the spring.

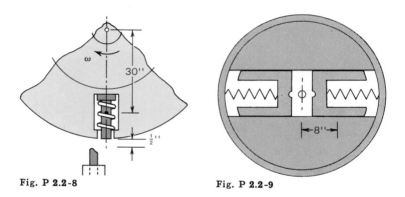

Fig. P 2.2-8   Fig. P 2.2-9

2.2-9   A centrifugal device (see Fig. P 2.2-9) has sliding plungers that weigh 6 lb each, and its center of mass is 8 in. from the center of the wheel at zero speed when the springs are unstrained. If the stiffness of the spring is 20 lb/in., determine the position of the plungers at a speed of 86 rpm. Neglect friction and the mass of the springs.

2.2-10   A wheel with a frictionless outer rim is rotating at constant angular speed ω, as shown in Fig. P 2.2-10. A small weight w is placed on the wheel next to the rim

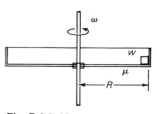

Fig. P 2.2-10

with zero speed.   If the coefficient of friction between w and the wheel is μ, find the time for w to attain the same speed as the wheel.

2.2-11   A gasoline-powered model airplane weighing 0.64 lb travels in a horizontal circle at the end of a light 100-ft cord that is elevated 30° above the horizontal.   If it takes 3 sec to complete each revolution around the circle, determine the tension in the cord and the lift of the wings.

2.2-12   A highway curve of radius of curvature R is banked at an angle θ with the horizontal.   What is the maximum speed that a car can round the curve without skidding if the coefficient of friction is μ?

2.2-13   In approaching an airfield, an airplane makes a horizontal turn of a radius of 3,000 ft at a speed of 135 mph.   Determine the angle of bank of the airplane.

2.2-14   A 10-lb block is supported by an elastic cord and rests in a groove on a smooth rotating cone of 30° slope, as shown in Fig. P 2.2-14.   The elastic cord has an unstretched length of 1 ft and requires 8 lb to stretch it 1 ft.   Determine the position x of the block and its speed of rotation that just cause it to leave the cone.

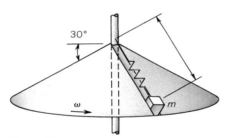

Fig. P **2.2-14**

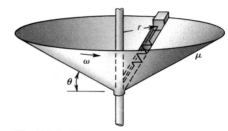

Fig. P **2.2-15**

2.2-15   A weight w rests in a groove on an inverted conical turntable at a radial distance r from the axis of rotation, as shown in Fig. P 2.2-15.   The coefficient of friction between the weight and the surface is μ.   (a) Find the constant angular velocity ω of the turntable for which the motion of the weight impends up the incline; (b) given $\theta = 30°$, $r = 10$ in., and $\mu = 0.20$, find ω.

2.2-16   A small ball of mass m is made to roll inside a hemispherical bowl of radius R. Determine the relationship between the speed v and the angle θ from the vertical for it to roll in a horizontal circle.

2.2-17   A spherical pendulum of length l rotating about a vertical axis with angular speed ω is describing a cone.   Show that the half angle of the cone is equal to

$$\theta_0 = \cos^{-1} \frac{g}{l\omega^2}$$

2.2-18   The flyball governor shown in Fig. P 2.2-18 has equal arms that support weights w_1 and w_2.   Determine the relationship between the angular speed and the angle θ when rotating at constant speed ω_0.

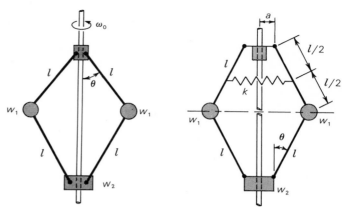

Fig. P 2.2-18   Fig. P 2.2-19

2.2-19   In the flyball governor shown in Fig. P 2.2-19 the weight w_2 is raised, and the spring of stiffness k is stretched as w_1 moves out.   The unstretched length of the spring is $2a$.   Determine the relationship between the angular velocity ω and the quantities given.

2.2-20   A spring of stiffness k with unstretched length of $2l$ is placed in a flyball governor, as shown in Fig. P 2.2-20.   For steady rotation determine the relationship between the angular velocity and the quantities given.

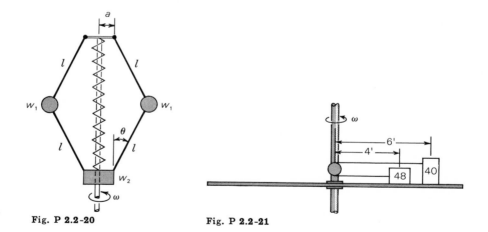

Fig. P 2.2-20   Fig. P 2.2-21

2.2-21   Two weights of 48 and 40 lb lie on a horizontal turntable for which $\mu = 0.25$ and are connected by a cord passing over a pulley (see Fig. P 2.2-21).   What is the angular speed for which the weights remain in the positions shown?   If the speed is greater than this, which way do the weights move?

2.2-22   A small particle of mass m is made to move inside a smooth circular cylinder of radius r with vertical axis.   Find the force between the cylinder and m if at $t = 0$ the velocity $v = v_0$ at an angle α with the horizontal.

2.2-23   A particle starting from rest slides down a 30° inclined plane with $\mu = 0.10$. What is the speed after traveling 4 ft?   How much time has elapsed?

2.2-24   A force F acting at an angle θ above the horizontal moves a block with coefficient of friction μ (see Fig. P 2.2-24).   Determine the angle θ that results in the largest horizontal acceleration of the block.   Where is the resultant normal reaction $(F \sin \theta < w)$?

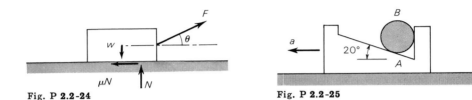

Fig. P **2.2-24**   Fig. P **2.2-25**

2.2-25   If A is given an acceleration a to the left (see Fig. P 2.2-25), determine the forces on B.   Assume all surfaces are smooth.

2.2-26   Blocks A and B weigh 32.2 and 16.1 lb respectively (see Fig. P 2.2-26).   With $\mu = 0.20$ between A and B, and $\mu = 0$ between A and the floor, determine the maximum force F that can be applied without B sliding off A.

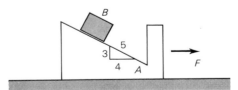

Fig. P **2.2-26**

2.2-27   Weights $w_1 > w_2$ are released in the position shown in Fig. P 2.2-27.   If the weight of the smooth table is w_3, show that the total upward reaction of the floor on the table is equal to

$$w_1 + w_2 + w_3 - \frac{w_1{}^2}{w_1 + w_2}$$

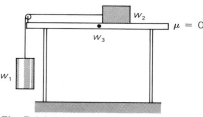

Fig. P **2.2-27**

2.2-28   The girder shown in Fig. P 2.2-28 weighs ½ ton, and the motor weighs 300 lb.
It is hoisting a 1-ton load with an acceleration of 5 ft/sec². Determine the reactions at *A* and *B*.

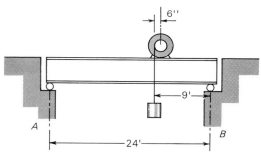

Fig. P **2.2-28**

2.2-29   A weight *w* suspended from a pulley is hoisted by the motor *M*, which rotates
at constant speed ω_0 (see Fig. P 2.2-29). Determine the vertical acceleration of
w and the tension in the rope as a function of *y*.

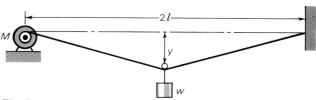

Fig. P **2.2-29**

2.2-30   For the system shown in Fig. P 2.2-30, (a) assume $\mu = 0$, and determine the angle θ_0 for which equal weights $w_1 = w_2$ remain in equilibrium; (b) if $\theta = \theta_0/2$, determine the acceleration of w_2 for $\mu = 0$; (c) for $\theta = \theta_0/2$ determine μ_{min} for which the system remains in equilibrium.

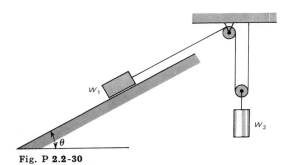

Fig. P 2.2-30

2.2-31   Two small cars weighing $w_1 = 200$ lb and $w_2 = 100$ lb are connected by a flexible cable around a pulley C and are free to roll on an inclined plane.   If the cars are released from rest in the position shown in Fig. P 2.2-31, find the time t required for them to exchange positions.   Neglect rolling resistance and the friction of the pulley.

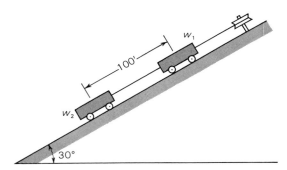

Fig. P 2.2-31

2.2-32   A 400-lb skip is rolling with negligible friction down an inclined track and unwinds an attached cable from a drum, as shown in Fig. P 2.2-32.   When the skip reaches a velocity of 10 ft/sec down the plane, a constant retarding moment of 40 ft lb is applied to the drum.   Determine the velocity of the skip 2 sec later.

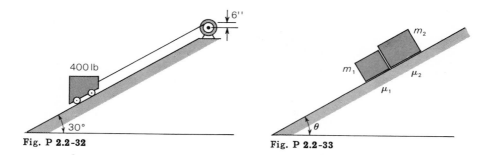

Fig. P 2.2-32   Fig. P 2.2-33

2.2-33   Two blocks m_1 and m_2 slide down an inclined plane of angle θ (see Fig. P 2.2-33). The coefficients of friction between the blocks and the plane are μ_1 and μ_2, with $\mu_1 > \mu_2$.   Determine the force between the two masses.

2.2-34   Two rectangular blocks are placed on an inclined plane, as shown in Fig. P 2.2-34. The friction force between w_1 and w_2 is f_1, and that between w_2 and the inclined plane is f_2.   (a) Show that, if $f_1 = f_2 = 0$, $\ddot{x}_1 = \ddot{x}_2$ and the two blocks slide together.   For finite values of f_1 and f_2, under what condition is it possible to have (b) $\ddot{x}_2 < \ddot{x}_1$, (c) $\ddot{x}_2 > \ddot{x}_1$?   Verify your answers by means of free-body diagrams.

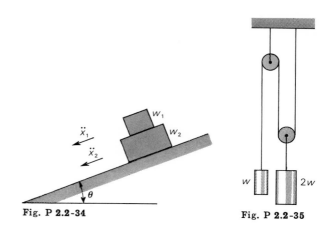

Fig. P 2.2-34   Fig. P 2.2-35

2.2-35   For the pulley system shown in Fig. P 2.2-35, what additional weight added to w gives it a downward acceleration of $0.20g$?   Neglect the mass of the pulleys.

2.2-36   If the additional weight of Prob. 2.2-36 is added to the larger weight, determine the upward acceleration of w.

2.2-37   For the pulley system shown in Fig. P 2.2-37 determine the acceleration of w_1 and w_2 when released.   Neglect the mass of the pulleys.

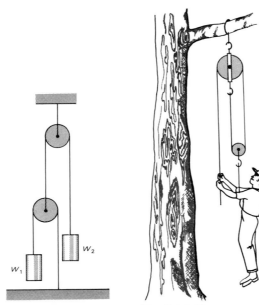

Fig. P 2.2-37   Fig. P 2.2-38

2.2-38   A 165-lb tree trimmer lowers himself on a pulley system by allowing the rope to slip through his gloves (see Fig. P 2.2-38). If the friction force between gloves and rope is 40 lb, what is his acceleration?   Neglect the mass of the pulleys.

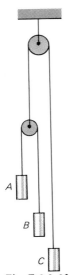

Fig. P **2.2-39**

2.2-39   In the pulley system shown in Fig. P 2.2-39, the weights are $A = w$, $B = 1.5w$, and $C = 2.5w$, and the pulleys have negligible mass.   All three weights are released from the same level.   Determine the acceleration of each weight and its relative position after 2 sec.

2.2-40   A uniform flexible chain of length L and weight w slides off a table through a curved guide (see Fig. P 2.2-40).   Assuming the guide to be frictionless but the coefficient of friction between the chain and table top to be μ, determine the equation for the acceleration of the chain.   If the chain is to start with zero initial velocity, determine the amount of the overhang and the final velocity of the chain as it leaves the table top.

Fig. P **2.2-40**

2.2-41   If the chain of Prob. 2.2-40 is started with zero velocity with an overhang ξ_0 exceeding x_0, the minimum overhang necessary to start the motion of the chain, determine its final velocity as a function of ξ_0/L.

2.2-42   Plate A is half the length of plate B and weighs half as much (see Fig. P 2.2-42). The coefficient of friction between A and B is μ and between B and D is zero. When released from the position shown, find the distance B has traveled when only half of A is still on B.

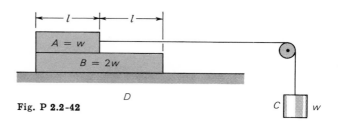

Fig. P **2.2-42**

2.2-43   A block of timber of weight w starts to slide when a truck bed is raised to 35° with the truck standing still, as shown in Fig. P 2.2-43.   Determine the acceleration of the truck that just causes the timber to slide down when the truck bed is fixed at 15°.

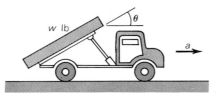

Fig. P 2.2-43

2.2-44   A sled of mass m is given an initial velocity v_0 along a horizontal plane. If the resistance opposing the motion is kmv, where k is a constant, determine the time required for the sled velocity to become $\frac{1}{10}v_0$. What distance is covered during this time?

2.2-45   It is estimated that the terminal velocity of a raindrop is approximately 20 ft/sec. (a) Assuming the drag to be given by the equation $F_d = kv$, determine k; (b) determine the equation for the velocity versus time.

2.2-46   With its engines shut off, a jet plane with initial speed v_0 is put into a straight glide, making an angle α with the horizontal. Assuming the drag to be proportional to the square of the velocity, determine the equation for the speed of the plane, and find its terminal speed.

2.2-47   A rocket sled weighing 3,220 lb reaches a constant speed of 700 ft/sec under a thrust of 8,000 lb. Assuming the resistance to be kv^2, determine the distance covered in slowing to a speed of 70 ft/sec after the engine is shut off.

2.2-48   A small sphere of mass m is allowed to fall through a viscous fluid. Assuming the resistance to be kv, where k depends on the radius of the sphere and the viscosity of the fluid, determine the equation for the distance fallen by the sphere as a function of time.

2.2-49   A parachutist jumps and immediately opens his chute. Assuming that he starts with zero vertical velocity and that the resistance to his motion is kv^2, where $k = 0.00124w$ (w = weight of man), determine (a) his speed after t sec, (b) his terminal speed. How high a jump is this equivalent to without a parachute?

2.2-50   A bullet is shot vertically upward with a muzzle speed of v_0. Assuming air resistance to be kv^2, determine the height to which it goes and the velocity with which it returns to earth.

2.2-51   A glider weighing 800 lb is being towed by an airplane weighing 2,000 lb, as shown in Fig. P 2.2-51. When the airplane attains a speed of 100 mph traveling horizontally, the tow cable at an angle of 15° has a tension of 100 lb. If the cable is suddenly released from this condition, determine the initial acceleration relative between them. Neglect weight of cable.

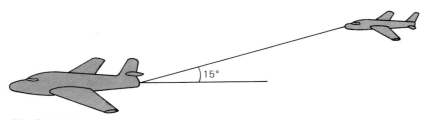

Fig. P 2.2-51

2.2-52   Write the equation of plane motion for the system shown in Fig. P 2.2-52.

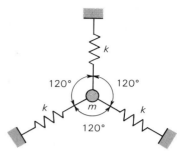

Fig. P 2.2-52

2.2-53   The natural frequency for the systems shown in Fig. P 2.2-53 can be written as $\omega = \sqrt{k_{eq}/m}$.   Determine k_{eq} for each system.

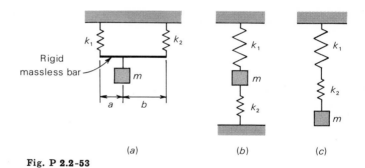

(a)   (b)   (c)

Fig. P 2.2-53

2.2-54   A circular cylinder of cross-sectional area A is weighted to float in a stable vertical position (see Fig. P 2.2-54). If depressed slightly and released, determine the period of oscillation.

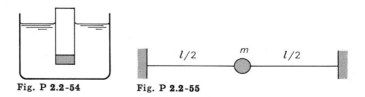

Fig. P 2.2-54   **Fig. P 2.2-55**

2.2-55   A weight w is attached to the middle point of a string of length l that is subjected to a tension F_t (see Fig. P 2.2-55). Find the natural frequency for lateral deflections of the weight, assuming that deflections are small and that the tension in the string remains constant.

2.2-56   An airplane main landing-gear assembly consists of a cylinder, plunger, and spring mounted vertically between the wheel and engine nacelle of the airplane (see Fig. P 2.2-56).   The landing gear is to be designed to withstand loads equivalent to dropping the airplane vertically through a distance of 5 ft.   The relationship between main landing gear, nose wheel, and center of gravity of the airplane is such that 90 percent of the landing load is carried by the two main wheels and the landing-gear assemblies.   The airplane weighs 12,000 lb.   The equivalent spring constant for the tire is 10,000 lb/in.   Determine the necessary spring constant and travel of the shock strut so that the tire deflection does not exceed $4\frac{1}{2}$ in.

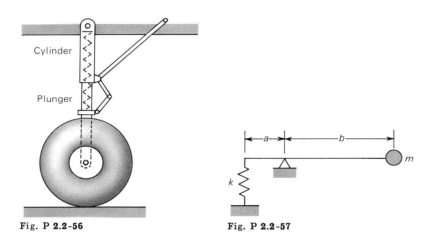

Fig. P 2.2-56   Fig. P 2.2-57

2.2-57   Set up the differential equation of motion for the system shown in Fig. P 2.2-57, and determine the natural frequency.   The bar is stiff and assumed weightless.

2.2-58   Assuming small displacements, compute the natural frequency of the pendulum shown in Fig. P 2.2-58.   The rod is massless, infinitely stiff, and is hinged at point O.   The mass is restrained by a spring of stiffness k.

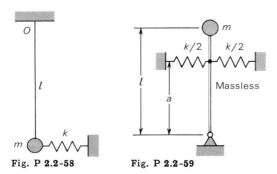

Fig. P 2.2-58   Fig. P 2.2-59

2.2-59   An inverted pendulum is supported by springs of stiffness k, as shown in Fig. P 2.2-59.   Determine the natural frequency of small oscillation and the condition under which the system becomes unstable.

2.2-60   The balance shown in Fig. P 2.2-60 consists of a rigid massless rod of length $2l$ which is pivoted at its center and which supports two equal masses m at either end.   An additional mass m is placed on the right-hand extremity and then released.   Assuming small deflections, calculate the natural frequency of the new system and the variation with time of the angle that the rod makes with the horizontal.

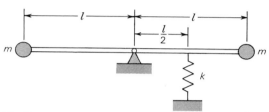

Fig. P 2.2-60

2.2-61   A uniform rod of length l is supported by two grooved wheels that rotate in opposite directions with constant angular speed ω (see Fig. P 2.2-61).   The coefficient of friction between the rod and wheels is μ.   Write the equation of motion of the rod, using x for the displacement of its center from the midpoint between the wheels, and determine its behavior.   What happens if the direction of rotation of the wheels is reversed?

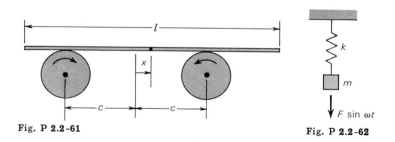

Fig. P 2.2-61   **Fig. P 2.2-62**

2.2-62   A simple spring-mass system of mass m and spring stiffness k is subjected to a force $F \sin \omega t$ for the period $0 < t < 2\pi/\omega$ (see Fig. P 2.2-62).   Find the resulting motion of the mass if its initial displacement and velocity are zero.

2.2-63   A linear spring-mass system with undamped natural frequency ω is placed on a horizontal plane for which the coefficient of static and kinetic friction is μ. Determine its dead zone.

2.2-64   A mass m attached to a nonlinear spring with a force $F_s = -kx^2$ sgn x
moves on a rough horizontal plane for which the frictional force is a constant C.
Determine the dead zone.

2.2-65   A 32.2-lb cylindrical plunger of 100 in.^{2} cross section is accurately machined so
that a thin film of light oil effects nearly perfect air seal and at the same time
offers negligible frictional resistance to motion in the vertical cylinder with sealed
lower end (see Fig. P 2.2-65).   If the plunger is released from rest from the position
shown, where the air pressure inside the tube is equal to the atmospheric pressure
of 14.7 lb/in.^{2}, find the maximum velocity v attained by the plunger.   The
absolute pressure in the cylinder varies inversely as the volume, and the pressure
of the atmosphere on the top of the plunger is essentially constant.

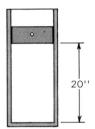

20''

Fig. P **2.2-65**

2.2-66   If in Prob. 2.2-65 the cylinder, with the plunger in the equilibrium position, is
dropped through a height of 9 ft, what is the maximum relative displacement of
the plunger?

2.2-67   A 20,000-lb aircraft is launched from an aircraft carrier by a catapult that
exerts a force shown in Fig. P 2.2-67.   The carrier is traveling at a constant
speed of 30 mph.   Determine the force F_0 if the airspeed of the aircraft is to be
100 mph.

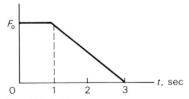

Fig. P **2.2-67**

2.3   THEOREM OF MOMENTUM

In Secs. 2.3 to 2.6 we study various aspects of Newton's second law that
arise through certain mathematical manipulations of the basic equation
(2.1-1).

Let us multiply Eq. (2.1-1) by the time increment dt:

$$\mathbf{F}(t)\, dt = d(m\mathbf{v}) = d\mathbf{G}$$

and then integrate over the time interval $\langle t_1, t_2 \rangle$:

$$\int_{t_1}^{t_2} \mathbf{F}(t)\, dt = \mathbf{G}(t_2) - \mathbf{G}(t_1) = m[\mathbf{v}(t_2) - \mathbf{v}(t_1)] \quad \blacktriangleleft \quad (2.3\text{-}1)$$

Referring to Eq. (2.3-1) we may formulate the theorem of momentum as follows: *The time integral of the total force acting on a mass m equals the change of its momentum.* This theorem is especially useful when we wish to determine the velocity of a particle at a given time. For very short time intervals $(t_2 - t_1 \rightarrow 0)$, as in impact problems, the time integral of the force is customarily called an impulse, denoted by the symbol $\hat{\mathbf{F}}$.

ILLUSTRATIVE EXAMPLE 2.3-1
A 50-lb block resting on a rough horizontal floor (see Fig. 2.3-1) is acted upon by a horizontal force that acts through the center of mass and varies with time, as shown in Fig. 2.3-2. If the coefficient of friction between the block and the floor is $\mu = 0.60$, determine its velocity after 6 sec.

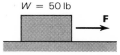

Fig. **2.3-1**

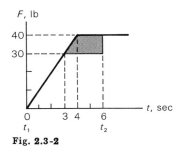

Fig. **2.3-2**

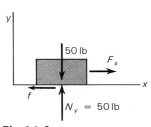

Fig. **2.3-3**

SOLUTION: We first draw the free-body diagram of the block in Fig. 2.3-3. As F_x increases, the friction force f also increases until it reaches $\mu N = 0.6 \times 50 = 30$ lb, and the block remains at rest until F_x exceeds 30 lb at $t = 3$ sec. Thus the resulting force is $F_z = 0$ for the interval $0 \leq t \leq 3$ sec:

$$F_x = (10t - 30) \text{ lb} \quad \text{for the interval 3 sec} \leq t \leq 4 \text{ sec}$$
and
$$F_z = (40 - 30) \text{ lb} \quad \text{for } t \geq 4 \text{ sec}$$

Thus the left side of the momentum equation (2.3-1) is (see the shaded area in Fig. 2.3-2)

$$\int_3^4 (10t - 30)\,dt + \int_4^6 (40 - 30)\,dt = (5t^2 - 30t)\Big|_3^4 + 20 = 25 \text{ lb sec}$$

Equating this time integral of the force to the change in momentum, that is,

$$m\dot{x}_2 - m\dot{x}_1 = m\dot{x}_2 = 25 \text{ lb sec}$$

we obtain the velocity at $t_2 = 6$ sec:

$$\dot{x}_2 = \frac{25 \times 32.2}{50} = 16.1 \text{ ft/sec}$$

ILLUSTRATIVE EXAMPLE 2.3-2

When the brakes are applied, a car of weight 3,500 lb decelerates from 60 to 20 mph in 4 sec. Determine the average retarding force F_{av} of the pavement on the car. Would this car skid if the coefficient of friction between the pavement and the tire were 0.50?
SOLUTION: From the theorem of momentum we have

$$F_{av}t = m(v_2 - v_1)$$
$$F_{av} = \frac{3,500}{32.2}\left(\frac{60 - 20}{4}\right)\frac{88}{60} = 1,595 \text{ lb}$$

To develop this force, the coefficient of friction must equal

$$\mu = \frac{1,595}{3,500} = 0.455$$

Thus with $\mu = 0.50$ the car would not skid.

PROBLEMS

2.3-1   A particle weighing 3.22 lb is acted upon by a force $\mathbf{F} = (2t^2\mathbf{i} - 3\mathbf{j})$ lb. When $t = 0$, the velocity is $6\mathbf{k}$ ft/sec. What is the velocity when $t = 2$ sec?

2.3-2   A small-caliber bullet weighing 0.022 lb has a muzzle velocity of 2,800 ft/sec. Assuming the time variation of the pressure in the barrel to be a half-sine variation over a time interval of 0.002 sec, determine the peak force on the bullet.

2.3-3   A man weighing 161 lb jumps with negligible initial velocity from a 2-ft-high platform. Assuming that the reaction of the ground on his feet increases linearly to a maximum in 0.075 sec and decreases linearly to his normal weight in another 0.075 sec, determine the maximum force acting on the man's feet during the landing.

2.3-4   A toboggan and passengers with total weight of 322 lb slide down a 30° snowbank, attaining a speed of 50 mph in 5.5 sec. Determine the frictional drag on the toboggan, assuming that it is a constant.

2.3-5   A ball weighing 1 lb is thrown vertically upward. Neglecting air resistance, find the velocity at $t = 1$ sec if the velocity at $t = 0$ is 30 ft/sec.

2.3-6   A machine gun fires six hundred 4-oz bullets per minute into a stationary target in which the bullets come to rest. Each bullet on impact has a velocity of 1,200 ft/sec. Find the average force exerted on the target.

2.3-7   A particle A with a mass of 1 slug has an initial velocity of $\mathbf{v}_0 = 10\mathbf{i} + 6\mathbf{j}$. After the particle strikes a particle B, the velocity becomes $\mathbf{v} = 16\mathbf{i} - 3\mathbf{j} + 4\mathbf{k}$. If the time of encounter is 10 msec, what average force is exerted on particle A? What is the change of momentum of particle B?

2.3-8   A particle weighing 100 lb is moving on a horizontal smooth plane with a velocity of 1,200 ft/sec. At $t = 0$ a constant horizontal force F is acting on the particle, so that it comes to rest in 0.01 sec. Determine the magnitude of F.

2.3-9   A particle weighing 5 lb bounces against a surface, as shown in Fig. P 2.3-9. If the approach velocity is 20 ft/sec and the velocity of departure is 15 ft/sec, find the magnitude and direction of the impulse to which the mass is subjected.

Fig. P 2.3-9

2.3-10   A particle of mass 1 slug is at rest. A force having a known variation with time acts on the particle. That is,

$$\mathbf{F}(t) = t^2\mathbf{i} + (6t + 10)\mathbf{j} + 1.6t^3\mathbf{k}$$

After 10 sec what is the magnitude of the velocity of the body?

2.3-11   A body is dropped from rest. Neglecting drag, determine (a) the time required for it to acquire a velocity of 50 ft/sec, (b) the time needed to increase its velocity from 50 to 70 ft/sec.

2.3-12   A hockey puck moves at 30 ft/sec from goal A to B (see Fig. P 2.3-12). It is intercepted by a player who whisks it at 80 ft/sec toward goal A, as shown. The puck is also rising from the ice at a rate of 10 ft/sec. What is the impulse on the puck, whose weight is 5 oz?

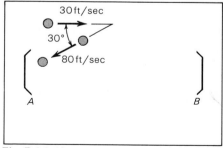

Fig. P 2.3-12

2.3-13   A body weighing 100 lb climbs up an incline of 30° with a velocity of 50 ft/sec at time $t = 0$. The coefficient of friction is $\mu = 0.3$. At what time t_e is the body at rest?

2.3-14   If the body of Prob. 2.3-13 slides down the incline from rest, what is its velocity after the same time t_e?

2.3-15   A tennis ball of mass m strikes a plane with velocity

$$\mathbf{v}_1 = -30\mathbf{i} - 20\mathbf{j} - 50\mathbf{k} \qquad \text{ft/sec}$$

and rebounds with velocity $\mathbf{v}_2 = -18\mathbf{i} - 12\mathbf{j} + 48\mathbf{k}$ ft/sec, where x and y are in the plane of the wall and z is normal to the wall.   Determine the impulse exerted by the wall in the tangential and normal direction to the wall.

2.4   THEOREM OF MOMENT OF MOMENTUM

The particle of mass m shown in Fig. 2.4-1 has, in a newtonian reference frame K, the momentum

$$\mathbf{G} = m\mathbf{v}$$

Analogous to the definition of the force moment $\mathbf{M} = \mathbf{r} \times \mathbf{F}$ we define the

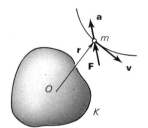

Fig. 2.4-1

moment of momentum with respect to point O in the newtonian reference body:

$$\mathbf{H}_O = \mathbf{r} \times \mathbf{G} = m\mathbf{r} \times \mathbf{v} \qquad \blacktriangleleft \qquad (2.4\text{-}1)$$

Differentiating Eq. (2.4-1) with respect to time, we obtain

$$\frac{d\mathbf{H}_O}{dt} = m(\dot{\mathbf{r}} \times \mathbf{v} + \mathbf{r} \times \dot{\mathbf{v}})$$

Since $\dot{\mathbf{r}} = \mathbf{v}$, we have $\dot{\mathbf{r}} \times \mathbf{v} = \mathbf{0}$, and thus

$$\dot{\mathbf{H}}_O = m\mathbf{r} \times \dot{\mathbf{v}} = \mathbf{r} \times (m\dot{\mathbf{v}}) = \mathbf{r} \times (m\mathbf{a}) \qquad (2.4\text{-}2)$$

According to Eq. (2.1-2), $\mathbf{F} = m\mathbf{a} = m\dot{\mathbf{v}}$ (see Fig. 2.4-1), and so Eq. (2.4-2) becomes

$$\dot{\mathbf{H}}_O = \mathbf{r} \times \mathbf{F}$$

or

$$\mathbf{M}_O = \dot{\mathbf{H}}_O \qquad \blacktriangleleft \qquad (2.4\text{-}3)$$

The last equation states that *the time rate of change of the moment of momen-*

tum of a particle about a fixed point is equal to the force moment about the same point. This is quite analogous to Newton's law

$$\mathbf{F} = \dot{\mathbf{G}} \qquad (2.1\text{-}1)$$

Following the procedure of Sec. 2.3, we integrate Eq. (2.4-3) with respect to time over the time interval $\langle t_1, t_2 \rangle$ and obtain

$$\int_{t_1}^{t_2} \mathbf{M}_O \, dt = \mathbf{H}_O(t_2) - \mathbf{H}_O(t_1) \qquad \blacktriangleleft \quad (2.4\text{-}4)$$

Equation (2.4-4) is the theorem of moment of momentum, which states that *the time integral of the moment about a fixed point of the total force acting on a mass m equals the change of its moment of momentum about this same point.* For extremely short time intervals, as occur in impact problems, the time integral $\int_{t_1}^{t_2} \mathbf{M}_O \, dt$ is usually called an impulse moment, denoted by the symbol $\hat{\mathbf{M}}_O$.

Let us now consider the important special case in which during the motion of the particle the force acting on it always points to the fixed origin O; that is, the point O is always on the line of action of the force. Then we have

$$\mathbf{M}_O = \mathbf{r} \times \mathbf{F} = 0 \qquad (2.4\text{-}5)$$

A force $\mathbf{F}$ that for all positions $\mathbf{r}(t)$ satisfies Eq. (2.4-5) is called a *central force*. For example, a particle moving near the earth experiences a central force, its weight, on account of the gravitational attraction toward the earth's center. The gravitational field is therefore called a central-force field. If Eq. (2.4-5) holds, then in view of Eq. (2.4-3)

$$\mathbf{H}_O = \mathbf{r} \times m\mathbf{v} = \text{const} \qquad (2.4\text{-}6)$$

which is true only if $\mathbf{r}$ and $\mathbf{v}$ lie always in the same plane. Therefore, as the first result we extract from Eq. (2.4-6) the statement that *the motion of a particle in a central-force field is plane motion of constant moment of momentum.*

Second, it is easy to deduce, from Eq. (2.4-6), Kepler's second law for planetary motion, which, neglecting the interference from other planets, stars, and satellites, takes place in the central-force field of the sun. Inspection of Fig. 2.4-2 shows that $|\mathbf{r} \times d\mathbf{r}|$ equals twice the shaded area, which is

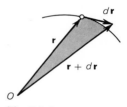

Fig. **2.4-2**

swept over by the position vector **r** during the infinitesimal time increment dt. Thus $\frac{1}{2}|\mathbf{r} \times d\mathbf{r}/dt| = \frac{1}{2}|\mathbf{r} \times \mathbf{v}|$ may be termed the magnitude of the areal velocity of the position vector. In view of Eq. (2.4-6) the areal velocity is constant for a particle moving under the action of a central force. This is exactly what Kepler's[1] second law states: The area swept out by the radius from the sun to the planet is traversed at a constant rate.

ILLUSTRATIVE EXAMPLE 2.4-1
Considering the earth to have a central-force field, the speed of a satellite in an elliptic orbit is given at perigee (the point closest to the earth center) to be v_p (see Fig. 2.4-3). Determine the speed v_a of the satellite at apogee (the point farthest from the earth center).

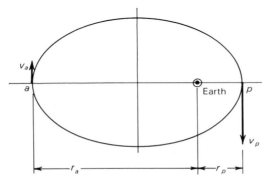

Fig. 2.4-3

SOLUTION: With the r_p and r_a as the perigee and apogee distances, respectively, we have, from Eq. (2.4-6), considering that $\mathbf{v}_p$ and $\mathbf{v}_a$ are normal to $\mathbf{r}_p$ and $\mathbf{r}_a$,

$$v_p r_p = v_a r_a$$

Thus the apogee velocity is

$$v_a = v_p \frac{r_p}{r_a}$$

ILLUSTRATIVE EXAMPLE 2.4-2
A particle of mass m is given an angular velocity $\dot{\theta}_0$ about the vertical axis of a conical funnel at a radial distance R_0 (see Fig. 2.4-4). Determine the equation of motion, and establish the radius of the stable orbit.
SOLUTION: Using cylindrical coordinates R, θ, z, that is, a combination of polar coordinates parallel to the xy plane and the z coordinate, and assuming the walls of the cone to

---

[1] It is interesting to note that Kepler (born 1571 in Weil, Germany; died 1630 in Regensburg, Germany) was in error as far as his explanation of the cause of the motion was concerned.   He believed that the force was always acting tangentially to the planet's path.   Of his three laws the first two were published in 1609, the third in 1619.

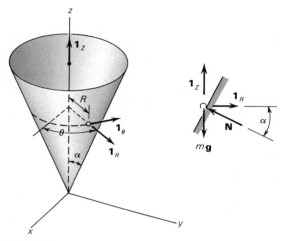

Fig. 2.4-4

be smooth, the force acting on the mass m is (see Fig. 2.4-4)

$$\mathbf{F} = -N \cos \alpha \; \mathbf{1}_R + 0 \cdot \mathbf{1}_\theta + (N \sin \alpha - mg)\mathbf{1}_z \qquad (a)$$

The acceleration in cylindrical coordinates is [see Eq. (1.5-9)]

$$\mathbf{a} = (\ddot{R} - R\dot{\theta}^2)\mathbf{1}_R + (2\dot{R}\dot{\theta} + R\ddot{\theta})\mathbf{1}_\theta + \ddot{z}\mathbf{1}_z \qquad (b)$$

Since $R/z = \tan \alpha$, $\ddot{z} = \ddot{R}/\tan \alpha$. Also $2\dot{R}\dot{\theta} + R\ddot{\theta} = \dfrac{1}{R}\dfrac{d}{dt}(R^2\dot{\theta})$, so that $\mathbf{a}$ can be rewritten as

$$\mathbf{a} = (\ddot{R} - R\dot{\theta}^2)\mathbf{1}_R + \frac{1}{R}\frac{d}{dt}(R^2\dot{\theta})\mathbf{1}_\theta + \frac{\ddot{R}}{\tan \alpha}\mathbf{1}_z \qquad (c)$$

Substituting into Newton's equation $\mathbf{F} = m\mathbf{a}$ and examining the components along $\mathbf{1}_R$, $\mathbf{1}_\theta$, and $\mathbf{1}_z$, we obtain the three scalar equations

$$-N \cos \alpha = m(\ddot{R} - R\dot{\theta}^2) \qquad (d)$$

$$0 = \frac{m}{R}\frac{d}{dt}(R^2\dot{\theta}) \qquad (e)$$

$$N \sin \alpha - mg = m\frac{\ddot{R}}{\tan \alpha} \qquad (f)$$

Equation (e) indicates that the moment of momentum $m(R^2\dot{\theta}) = H_z = mR_0^2\dot{\theta}_0$ is a constant. Replacing $R\dot{\theta}^2$ in Eq. (d) by H_z^2/R^3m^2 and eliminating N between Eqs. (d) and (f), we obtain

$$-\left(\ddot{R} - \frac{H_z^2}{R^3m^2}\right)\tan \alpha - g = \frac{\ddot{R}}{\tan \alpha} \qquad (g)$$

Rearranging and noting that $(1 + \tan^2 \alpha)/\tan \alpha = \sec^2 \alpha/\tan \alpha = 1/(\sin \alpha \cos \alpha)$, the equation above reduces to

$$\ddot{R} - \frac{H_z^2}{R^3m^2}\sin^2 \alpha = -g \sin \alpha \cos \alpha \qquad (h)$$

Its steady-state solution is easily determined by letting $\ddot{R} = 0$, the result being

$$R^3 = \frac{H_z^2}{gm^2}\tan\alpha = \frac{(R_0^2\dot{\theta}_0)^2}{g}\tan\alpha \qquad (i)$$

Looking at Eq. (h) for $\ddot{R}$, if $\dot{\theta}_0$ is made larger than the value required to satisfy Eq. (i) for the initial radius R_0, then $\ddot{R}$ is positive and the sphere rolls up to a larger radius. If $\dot{\theta}_0$ is smaller than the required value for steady rotation, the sphere rolls down to a smaller radius. A steady rotation at a constant radius is possible only if the initial conditions satisfy Eq. (i), that is, $1/R_0 = (\dot{\theta}_0^2/g)\tan\alpha$.

PROBLEMS

2.4-1   The velocity of a particle of weight w is $\mathbf{v} = 4\mathbf{i} + 3\mathbf{j} + 6\mathbf{k}$ when in the position $\mathbf{r} = -\mathbf{i} + 2\mathbf{j} + 3\mathbf{k}$. Find the moment of momentum about the origin.

2.4-2   The linear momentum of a particle of mass $m = 2$ slugs is

$$m\mathbf{v} = 6\mathbf{i} - (2t + 4)\mathbf{j} + 2t\mathbf{k}$$

No force is acting on the particle, and its position at $t = 0$ is $(-6,4,-1)$. Determine the moment of momentum about the origin at $t = 2$ sec.

2.4-3   A smooth horizontal rod of negligible weight is rotating about a vertical axis through its center. There are two sliders, each of mass m on the rod, a distance r_1 from the axis of rotation and held in position by strings (see Fig. P 2.4-3). If the strings are released, the sliders move out to r_2. Determine the new angular velocity of the rod.

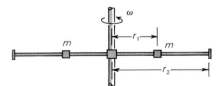

Fig. P 2.4-3

2.4-4   If in Prob. 2.4-3 the masses are allowed to move out at constant speed v by restraining the strings, determine the angular acceleration of the rod.

2.4-5   In Prob. 2.4-3 what rotational impulse must be applied to the vertical shaft in order to maintain constant angular speed ω?

2.4-6   In Prob. 2.4-3 a torque of $M = 10t$ ft lb is applied, starting at the instant when the masses are at r_1 with angular velocity ω_1. Determine the angular velocity at any time t.

2.4-7   A mass m on the end of a string is traveling in a circle of radius R with velocity v_0 on a horizontal table, as shown in Fig. P 2.4-7. If the string is pulled through the hole with constant velocity V, determine the polar coordinates r and θ of the mass, starting at the instant when the string is pulled in. Determine the tension in the string.

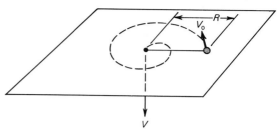

Fig. P 2.4-7

2.4-8   A particle of mass m on the end of a string passing through a hole at O rotates on a horizontal table, as shown in Fig. P 2.4-8.   With $r = 4$ ft, the particle is given a velocity of 6 ft/sec.   The string is now pulled in with constant speed, so that at the time it hits the peg P, which is 2 ft from O, $r = 3$ ft.   Determine the angular velocity of the string after it strikes the peg.

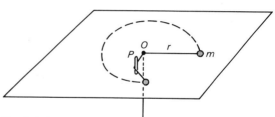

Fig. P 2.4-8

2.4-9   Mass m on the end of a string passing through the top of a tower rotates with angular velocity of 120 rpm in position 1 at a radial distance R (see Fig. P 2.4-9).

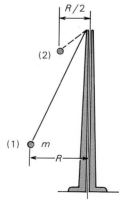

Fig. P 2.4-9

The string is slowly pulled down, so that the mass in position 2 has a radial distance of $R/2$. Determine the angular velocity in the new position.

2.4-10   A simple pendulum 3 ft long is held in a horizontal position and released (see Fig. P 2.4-10). Two feet directly below the point of support A is a peg P, which the string strikes. Find the velocity of the mass m and the tension in the string when m is in position B.

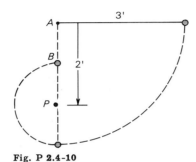

Fig. P 2.4-10

2.5 POWER, WORK, AND KINETIC ENERGY

We define the concept of mechanical power exerted by the force $\mathbf{F}$ on a particle moving with respect to a newtonian reference body K with the velocity

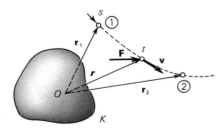

Fig. 2.5-1

$\mathbf{v}$ (see Fig. 2.5-1) by the scalar product

$$P = \mathbf{F} \cdot \mathbf{v} \qquad\qquad \blacktriangleleft \quad (2.5\text{-}1)$$

Hence, the power P is a scalar quantity and presents itself as the time rate of change of the work W done by the force $\mathbf{F}$. Integrating Eq. (2.5-1) with respect to t over the time interval $\langle t_1, t_2 \rangle$, we obtain the work $W_{1,2}$ done during the time interval $\langle t_1, t_2 \rangle$, while the particle moved from the position $\mathbf{r}_1$

to the position $\mathbf{r}_2$ or traveled through the path $s_2 - s_1$:

$$W_{1,2} = \int_{t_1}^{t_2} P \, dt = \int_{t_1}^{t_2} \mathbf{F} \cdot \mathbf{v} \, dt = \int_{t_1}^{t_2} \mathbf{F} \cdot \frac{d\mathbf{r}}{dt} \, dt \quad \blacktriangleleft \quad (2.5\text{-}2)$$

From Eq. (2.5-2) we take the differential of work to be

$$dW = \mathbf{F} \cdot d\mathbf{r} \qquad (2.5\text{-}3)$$

Using the tangential unit vector $\mathbf{1}_r$, we can write

$$d\mathbf{r} = ds\mathbf{1}_r$$

and thus

$$dW = (\mathbf{F} \cdot \mathbf{1}_r) \, ds$$

Hence, we obtain the work done as the line integral:

$$W_{1,2} = \int_{s_1}^{s_2} (\mathbf{F} \cdot \mathbf{1}_r) \, ds \quad \blacktriangleleft \quad (2.5\text{-}4)$$

The dot product $\mathbf{F} \cdot \mathbf{1}_r$ is the scalar force component acting tangentially to the path. In order to evaluate Eq. (2.5-4), $\mathbf{F}$ should be known for every point on the path s between s_1 and s_2. Hence, in the general case, when the force relationship is as stated in Eqs. (2.2-1), the motion of the particle must be known in order to compute $W_{1,2}$.

If there are several forces $\mathbf{F}_i$ acting on the particle, we obtain their power as well as their work by algebraic addition of the contribution of each force, since both power and work are scalar quantities:

$$P = \sum_{i=1}^{n} \mathbf{F}_i \cdot \mathbf{v} = \sum_{i=1}^{n} P_i$$

$$W = \sum_{i=1}^{n} W_i$$

The concept of work is closely related to the concept of kinetic energy. Considering that according to Newton's second law—see Eq. (2.1-2)—

$$\mathbf{F} = m \frac{d\mathbf{v}}{dt}$$

the differential of work—see Eq. (2.5-3)—is

$$dW = \mathbf{F} \cdot d\mathbf{r} = m \frac{d\mathbf{v}}{dt} \cdot d\mathbf{r}$$

or considering $1/dt$ as a scalar multiplier,

$$dW = m \, d\mathbf{v} \cdot \frac{d\mathbf{r}}{dt} = m \, d\mathbf{v} \cdot \mathbf{v} = \tfrac{1}{2} m \, d(\mathbf{v} \cdot \mathbf{v}) = \tfrac{1}{2} m \, d(v^2)$$

or

$$dW = d(\tfrac{1}{2} m v^2) \qquad (2.5\text{-}5)$$

We denote the expression $\frac{1}{2}mv^2$ as the kinetic energy T.   Therefore

$$dW = dT = d(\tfrac{1}{2}mv^2) \tag{2.5-6}$$

The integration of Eq. (2.5-6) between stations 1 and 2 yields

$$W_{1,2} = \int_{T_1}^{T_2} dT = T_2 - T_1 = \tfrac{1}{2}m(v_2^2 - v_1^2) \quad \blacktriangleleft \quad (2.5\text{-}7)$$

where $W_{1,2}$ may be taken from Eq. (2.5-4).

Hence, we can formulate the following work theorem: *The work done by the total force acting on a particle along its path beginning at point 1 and ending at point 2 equals the change of the kinetic energy of the particle.*

CONCLUDING REMARKS

In the preceding sections we obtained the theorems of work and of momentum through integration of the fundamental equation

$$\mathbf{F} = m\mathbf{a} = m\ddot{\mathbf{r}} \tag{2.1-2}$$

The momentum theorem—Eq. (2.3-1)—was the result of the first integral of Eq. (2.1-2) with respect to time, and the work theorem—Eq. (2.5-7)—resulted from the integration of Eq. (2.1-2) with respect to the path along which the particle moved.

It is from the fact that, in using the momentum theorem as well as the work theorem, one integration of Eq. (2.1-2) has already been carried out that we derive so much benefit from their application to the solution of problems of dynamics.   Since the momentum theorem was obtained by forming the time integral of the total force acting on the particle, it is always applied with advantage if the problem is essentially the calculation of the change in velocity after a force has been exerted on the particle for some time.   On the other hand, if the force is independent of the motion of the particle and is known for every point in the space through which the particle moves, and the question is how the velocity changes between two points on a given path, then the use of the work theorem is indicated.   Frequently the data are given in terms of time and space, and in such cases the combined application of both theorems represents the most economical and elegant means of solution.

ILLUSTRATIVE EXAMPLE 2.5-1

A four-engine jet plane is cruising at a constant speed of $v = 500$ mph.   At this speed each of its engines develops a thrust of 6,000 lb.   Determine the total power developed.

SOLUTION: From Eq. (2.5-1) the power developed by the four engines is

$$P = 4 \times 6,000 \times 500 \times \tfrac{88}{60} = 1.76 \times 10^7 \text{ ft lb/sec}$$
$$= \frac{1.76 \times 10^7}{550} = 32,000 \text{ hp}$$

ILLUSTRATIVE EXAMPLE 2.5-2

A package of mass m is to be dropped through a height h onto a honeycomb pad that has a constant crushing stress σ_c [lb/in.²], as shown in Fig. 2.5-2.   Determine the cross-sectional

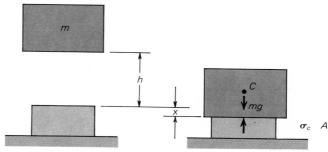

Fig. 2.5-2

area of the pad necessary to limit the deceleration of the mass to n times g, and compute the distance x_{max} through which the pad is crushed.

SOLUTION: We choose two positions of zero velocity, the starting position and the final position of the package.   Since the kinetic energy for both positions is zero, its change also remains zero, and the work done by the forces acting on m must equal zero.

The work done by the gravity force on m between the starting and final positions is $mg(h + x_{max})$.   The work done by the resistive force of the honeycomb pad is $-\sigma_c A x_{max}$. Thus from Eq. (2.5-7)

$$mg(h + x_{max}) - \sigma_c A x_{max} = 0 \tag{a}$$

or

$$x_{max} = \frac{mgh}{\sigma_c A - mg} \tag{b}$$

The area necessary to restrict the deceleration to $-ng$ is established from Newton's second law:

$$mg - \sigma_c A = -m(ng)$$

Thus

$$A = \frac{mg(1 + n)}{\sigma_c} \tag{c}$$

Substituting Eq. (c) into (b), we obtain

$$x_{max} = \frac{h}{n} \tag{d}$$

The student should verify these results by dividing the path of the package into two parts, the height h (free fall of the package) and the crushing distance x_{max}.

ILLUSTRATIVE EXAMPLE 2.5-3

A jet plane weighing 120,000 lb comes in for a landing at $v_1 = 120$ mph and immediately applies a reverse thrust of 20,000 lb until the speed is reduced to $v_2 = 40$ mph.   How far does it travel during this time, assuming that the brakes are not applied and that the drag is negligible?

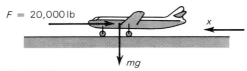

Fig. 2.5-3

SOLUTION: Figure 2.5-3 shows the airplane with the reverse thrust as the only force in the x direction.   Its work during the reduction of the plane's speed is

$$W_{1,2} = -20,000(x_2 - x_1) \qquad \text{lb ft}$$

and the change in kinetic energy is

$$T_1 - T_2 = \frac{1}{2}\frac{120,000}{32.2}(120^2 - 40^2)(88\!\!/\!60)^2$$

Thus we have, from Eq. (2.5-7),

$$x_2 - x_1 = \frac{1}{2 \times 32.2}\frac{120,000}{20,000}(120^2 - 40^2)(88\!\!/\!60)^2 = 2,560 \text{ ft}$$

PROBLEMS
2.5-1   A gasoline engine runs at 1,200 rpm and delivers 8 hp.   What is its torque?

2.5-2   A body moves without friction through a straight tunnel from one point of the earth's surface to another (see Fig. P 2.5-2).   The gravitational attraction is

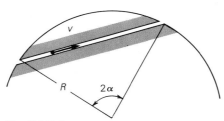

Fig. P 2.5-2

proportional to the distance of the body from the earth's center, and this force points toward the center.   Consider the earth at rest.   The body starts its motion with an initial velocity of zero.   Determine (a) the traveling time, (b) the maximum speed reached during motion.   NOTE: Both questions have to be solved with the work theorem, and the answers given in closed form in terms of the given values R, α, g.

2.5-3   Ships' propellers must operate at low speed, but the turbines that drive them rotate at high speed.   A turbine running at 4,000 rpm is geared down to a propeller shaft that is running at 100 rpm.   If 12,000 hp is being developed, determine the torque transmitted by the 4,000- and 100-rpm shafts.

2.5-4   A windmill of 20 ft diameter drives an electric generator. How many kilowatts of power versus wind speed v can the generator produce if 10 percent of the energy of the air passing through the windmill can be extracted (weight of air = 0.0802 lb/ft³ and 1 kw = 737 ft lb/sec)?

2.5-5   The motorman of an electric streetcar increases the power of the motor by gradually cutting out the resistance. If he wishes to increase the velocity of the streetcar linearly, in what manner must the power increase?

2.5-6   A train weighing 500 tons is pulled along a horizontal track by an engine whose drawbar pull varies with the velocity in such a way that its power remains constant and equal to 220 hp. How long does it take to travel 1,000 ft, starting from rest (neglect rolling friction)?

2.5-7   A particle of mass m weighing 6.44 lb moves along the x axis under a force of $F = (3 + 2x)$ lb. If its speed at $x = 0$ is 4 ft/sec, what is it at $x = 5$ ft?

2.5-8   A mass moves on a straight line under the action of a force of $F = k/x^2$. If its velocity at x_0 is v_0, what is the power at $x = 3x_0$?

2.5-9   A block weighing w lb is dragged along a smooth horizontal floor by a horizontal force that varies so that the power developed by it is equal to kt^2 ft lb/sec, where t is in seconds. Determine (a) the velocity of w at time t, (b) the distance traveled in time t, and (c) the numerical values for (a) and (b) if $w = 100$ lb, $k = 15$ ft lb/sec³, and $t = 10$ sec. What is the average power during the first 10 sec?

2.5-10   Torque is transmitted from one shaft to another through the springs connected to opposite flanges of the coupling (see Fig. P 2.5-10). If each spring has a stiffness k and an unstretched length l, determine the angle θ as a function of the speed and horsepower transmitted.

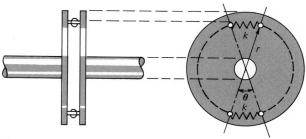

Fig. P **2.5-10**

2.5-11   For any airplane the induced drag varies inversely as the square of the velocity, and the parasite (skin) drag varies as v^2. Expressing the total drag as

$$D = \frac{K_1}{v^2} + K_2 v^2$$

determine the most efficient operating speed of the airplane.

2.5-12   A block of weight w is pulled up the rough incline of angle θ by a motor whose output torque is constant and equal to M_0 (see Fig. P 2.5-12). What is the velocity of the block after it moves a short distance s along the incline, starting from rest?

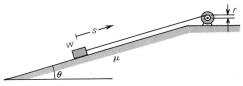

Fig. P 2.5-12

2.5-13   A block weighing 300 lb is pulled up the inclined plane by a force F that varies with time, its magnitude in pounds being $F = 240 + 20t$, where t is the time in seconds after the force is first applied (see Fig. P 2.5-13).   The coefficient of friction between the block and the plane is 0.2.   Assuming the block to be initially at rest, determine (a) the velocity of the block 3 sec after F starts to act, (b) the power being developed by F at this instant.

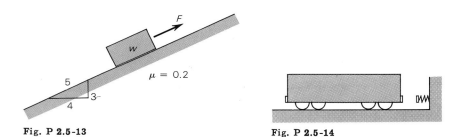

Fig. P 2.5-13   **Fig. P 2.5-14**

2.5-14   With brakes applied, a freight car weighing 64,400 lb strikes a spring bumper with a velocity of 2 mph, coming to a stop after compressing the springs 3.0 in. (see Fig. P 2.5-14).   If the horizontal retarding force of the brakes is 10,000 lb, determine the stiffness of the bumper springs in pounds per foot.   How far back does the car move on the rebound (neglect the kinetic energy of rotation of the wheels)?

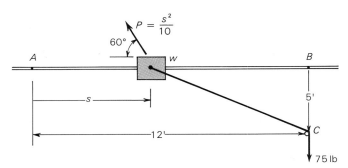

Fig. P 2.5-15

2.5-15 A block w weighs 100 lb and moves along a straight line AB (see Fig. P 2.5-15). The force of friction is constant at 15 lb. A cord passes over a smooth peg at C and has a constant force of 75 lb applied to it. The force P is always inclined at 60° to the horizontal as shown but varies in magnitude such that $P = \frac{1}{10}s^2$ (units being lb and ft) and s is the distance of the block from point A. If the block has a velocity of 6 ft/sec to the right as it passes point A, what will be its velocity at point B?

2.5-16 A smooth track AB in the form of a quadrant of a circle lies in the vertical plane, has a radius of 4 ft, and is tangent to the horizontal and vertical at A and B, respectively (see Fig. P 2.5-16). A small body C weighing 5 lb is made to move along the track from A to B by forces P, Q, and F. Force P always acts through B and is always 10 lb; force Q always acts horizontally and is always 15 lb; force F always acts tangentially to the path, and its value in pounds is $F = 10 - 5s$, when s is given in feet. If the body starts from A with zero velocity, determine the velocity when it reaches B.

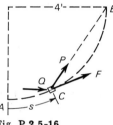

Fig. P 2.5-16

2.5-17 A motor hoisting a weight w is rotating at constant speed (see Fig. P 2.5-17). Determine the acceleration of w as a function of h. What power is required of the motor as a function of h?

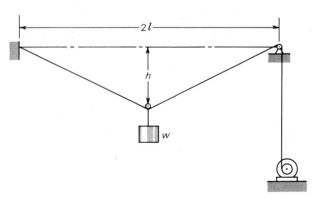

Fig. P 2.5-17

2.5-18   A cylindrical drum of radius r is made to rotate at constant angular velocity ω about its horizontal axis (see Fig. P 2.5-18). Inside is a mass m that slides up to an angle θ that depends on the coefficient of friction μ between it and the drum. Determine the power necessary to maintain this rotation, in terms of μ, r, ω, and mg.

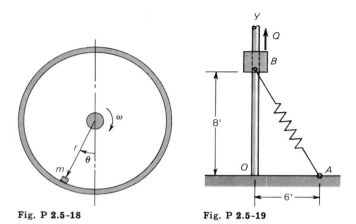

Fig. P **2.5-18**   Fig. P **2.5-19**

2.5-19 B represents a block weighing 20 lb that slides without friction along a vertical rod OY (see Fig. P 2.5-19). A spring is attached to B and to a fixed point A on the floor; the natural length of the spring is 3 ft, and it stretches 1 ft for each 20 lb of pull. A vertical force Q, whose magnitude in pounds is $Q = 40 + 20s$, where s is the distance in feet from the floor to the bottom of the block, acts on the block while it moves from the floor to the position shown. Determine (a) the work done on the block during this displacement by each of the forces that acts on it, (b) the velocity of the block when it reaches the position shown, assuming it to have started from rest.

2.5-20   In a certain performance test an automobile weighing w lb starts from rest and accelerates under constant power P to a speed of v mph. Determine the distance traveled during the test.

2.5-21   A car of weight w is traveling at a speed of 40 mph downhill ($\alpha = 10°$). In order not to hit a roadblock, the brakes are applied 60 ft before it, so that the

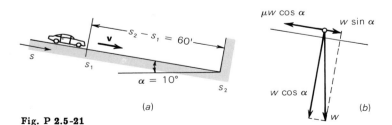

Fig. P **2.5-21**

wheels are blocked and the car skids (see Fig. P 2.5-21).   Assuming dry friction
with a coefficient of $\mu = 0.8$, at what speed does the car hit the roadblock?

2.5-22   A shotput of weight w is thrown on a steep downward slope (see Fig. P 2.5-22).
The distance between the start of the free motion and its end on the ground was
measured to be 50 ft.   The "flight" time was clocked as $t_2 - t_1 = 2$ sec.   Neglecting air resistance, calculate the initial velocity $\mathbf{v}_1$ and the final velocity $\mathbf{v}_2$.

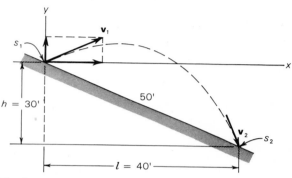

Fig. P 2.5-22

2.6 POTENTIAL, POTENTIAL FORCES, AND ENERGY THEOREM

We now investigate the question: Under what conditions can the work
integral—Eq. (2.5-4)—be evaluated when only the end points 1 and 2 of the
body's path are known and no further relationships between time, velocity,
and path are provided?   Then, obviously, a unique value of $W_{1,2}$ can be
found only if the work depends on the end points 1 and 2 of the path, irrespective of the configuration of the path between them:

$$W_{1,2} = \int_{r_1}^{r_2} \mathbf{F} \cdot d\mathbf{r} = W(\mathbf{r}_2, \mathbf{r}_1) \qquad (2.6\text{-}1)$$

Before establishing the necessary conditions in general terms, we treat two
practically important examples where they are satisfied.

We consider the linear spring shown in Fig. 2.6-1, and we calculate the

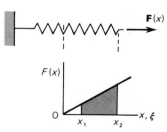

Fig. 2.6-1

work done by a force $F(x)$ to extend it from its unloaded position $x = 0$ to position x.

Since $F(x) = kx$, we obtain

$$\int_0^x kx\,dx = \tfrac{1}{2}kx^2$$

This work is stored as potential energy in the spring; that is, it can be fully "extracted" from the spring when it contracts to its unloaded position. However, it is necessary to point out that the potential energy is defined only with reference to a given energy level.   For example, with respect to a position $x_1 < x_2$, the potential energy of the spring extended to position x_2 is

$$\tfrac{1}{2}k(x_2^2 - x_1^2)$$

as indicated by the shaded area in the force-displacement curve in Fig. 2.6-1.   This expression shows that the work done on the spring, that is, the potential energy stored in the spring, depends only on the end points x_1 and x_2 of the path.   It is immaterial if, for example, the spring was first extended from x_1 beyond x_2 and then contracted to the end point x_2.

If we denote the function $kx^2/2$ by $U(x)$, then the change in potential energy due to the extension of the spring from x_1 to x_2 could be written

$$U(x_2) - U(x_1) = \tfrac{1}{2}kx_2^2 - \tfrac{1}{2}kx_1^2 \qquad (2.6\text{-}2)$$

The function $U(x) = kx^2/2$ is called the potential of the linear spring.

It is now interesting to recognize that the force which is exerted by an extended spring and which is always opposite to the spring's displacement from the unloaded position is

$$-kx = -\frac{dU}{dx} \qquad (2.6\text{-}3)$$

Thus the force exerted by a spring on a body can be expressed as $-dU/dx$.

We now define the potential of the gravitational field "generated" by the masses m_1 and m_2 in an inertial reference frame as

$$U = -\frac{\Gamma m_1 m_2}{r} \qquad (2.6\text{-}4)$$

It is then easily verified that—see Eq. (2.6-3) and Fig. 2.6-2—

$$\mathbf{F}_{12} = -\frac{dU}{dr}\,\mathbf{1}_r = -\Gamma\frac{m_1 m_2}{r^2}\,\mathbf{1}_r \qquad (2.6\text{-}5)$$

If we form the dot product between $\mathbf{F}_{12}$ and $d\mathbf{r} = dr\mathbf{1}_r$, thereby defining the infinitesimal work dW of the gravitational force, we obtain

$$dW = \mathbf{F}_{12} \cdot d\mathbf{r} = -dU \qquad (2.6\text{-}6)$$

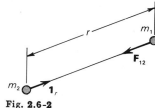

Fig. 2.6-2

Thus the work W done on m_1 by the gravitational field in bringing m_1 from $r = \infty$ to r is

$$W = -\int_{\infty}^{r} \frac{\Gamma m_1 m_2}{r^2}\, dr = \frac{\Gamma m_1 m_2}{r} = -U(r) \qquad (2.6\text{-}7)$$

since U is zero at $r = \infty$. Hence, the potential U is the negative of the work W done by the gravitational force in moving particle m_1 from infinity to a position whose distance from m_2 is r.

We now generalize these ideas by pursuing the last example further. Placing a cartesian coordinate system with its origin in mass m_2, we may substitute $r = (x^2 + y^2 + z^2)^{\frac{1}{2}}$ in Eq. (2.6-4), and so we can easily verify that

$$-\frac{\partial U}{\partial x} = \Gamma m_1 m_2 \frac{\partial}{\partial x}(x^2 + y^2 + z^2)^{-\frac{1}{2}}$$

$$-\frac{\partial U}{\partial x} = -\Gamma \frac{m_1 m_2}{r^2}\frac{x}{r} = -F_{12}\frac{x}{r}$$

Similarly,

$$-\frac{\partial U}{\partial y} = -\Gamma \frac{m_1 m_2}{r^2}\frac{y}{r} = -F_{12}\frac{y}{r} \qquad \blacktriangleleft \quad (2.6\text{-}8)$$

$$-\frac{\partial U}{\partial z} = -\Gamma \frac{m_1 m_2}{r^2}\frac{z}{r} = -F_{12}\frac{z}{r}$$

Hence, we realize that these negative partial derivations of the potential are the cartesian components of the gravitational force that are derived from the potential of the gravity field—Eq. (2.6-4). Whenever forces can be derived from a scalar function $U(\mathbf{r})$ or $U(x,y,z)$ in the manner described by Eqs. (2.6-5) and (2.6-8), they are referred to as potential forces, and the function U is called the potential of the force field. Equations (2.6-8) show that the cartesian components of a vector can be found by the partial differentiation of a scalar function. We shall see later (Sec. 3.7) that it is possible to set up the equations of motion for complicated conservative systems by partial differentiation of the scalar quantities T (kinetic energy) and U (potential energy).

From Eq. (2.6-6) we may, furthermore, derive the following theorems:

a   The work done by a potential force along a path between two fixed points is independent of the path (see Fig. 2.6-3):

$$W_{1,2} = \int_1^2 dW = - \int_1^2 dU = U_1 - U_2 \qquad \blacktriangleleft \quad (2.6\text{-}9)$$

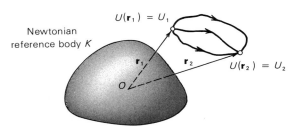

Fig. 2.6-3

b   The work done by a potential force along an arbitrary closed path is zero:

$$\oint dW = \oint \mathbf{F} \cdot d\mathbf{r} = 0 \qquad \blacktriangleleft \quad (2.6\text{-}10)$$

Equation (2.6-10) is a necessary and sufficient condition for the existence of a potential $U(\mathbf{r})$, since $\mathbf{F}$ must be a potential force, as defined by Eqs. (2.6-5), to satisfy Eq. (2.6-10).

Another check is the three conditions

$$\frac{\partial F_y}{\partial x} - \frac{\partial F_x}{\partial y} = 0 \qquad \text{etc.} \qquad \blacktriangleleft \quad (2.6\text{-}11)$$

which are easily verified, considering that $F_x = -\partial U/\partial x$ and $F_y = -\partial U/\partial y$.

Referring to Eqs. (2.5-6) and (2.6-6), we have, in the case in which all the forces doing work on a particle are potential forces,

$$dU + dT = 0$$

or

$$U + T = E = \text{const} \qquad \blacktriangleleft \quad (2.6\text{-}12)$$

which expresses the law of conservation of total mechanical energy E in the sole presence of potential forces, which, therefore, are also called conservative forces.

Equation (2.6-12) may serve to set up the differential equation for the motion of a particle subjected to conservative forces by stating that

$$\frac{dE}{dt} = 0$$

ILLUSTRATIVE EXAMPLE 2.6-1

Using the energy concept, establish the equation of motion for the spring-mass system in Fig. 2.6-4, with spring constant k and mass m.

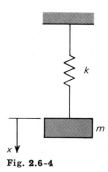

Fig. 2.6-4

SOLUTION: With $U = kx^2/2$ and $T = m\dot{x}^2/2$ we have

$$E = \frac{kx^2}{2} + \frac{m\dot{x}^2}{2}$$

Thus
$$\frac{dE}{dt} = kx\dot{x} + m\ddot{x}\dot{x} = 0$$

or
$$m\ddot{x} + kx = 0$$

On the other hand, when $U(\mathbf{r})$, as well as the speed v_1 of the particle at a certain point 1, is known and we wish to know the speed v_2 at another point 2, then Eq. (2.6-12) is best used in the form

$$U_1 + T_1 = U_2 + T_2 \qquad \blacktriangleleft \quad (2.6\text{-}13)$$

The total mechanical (potential plus kinetic) energy of a material body at point 1 is equal to its total energy at point 2.

ILLUSTRATIVE EXAMPLE 2.6-2

A spring of constant k [lb/ft] is compressed by δ [ft]. When released, it expels a mass m [lb sec^2/ft] so that it falls on the ground h ft below (see Fig. 2.6-5). Neglecting friction and air resistance, calculate the speed v_2 in feet per second.

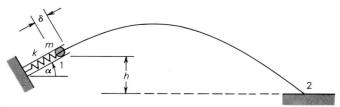

Fig. 2.6-5

SOLUTION: The potential energy of the spring is $k\delta^2/2$, and that of the mass in the gravity field with respect to the ground level at point 2 is mgh. Furthermore the kinetic energy at point 1 is zero. Hence the total initial energy is

$$U_1 + T_1 = \frac{k\delta^2}{2} + mgh$$

At point 2 the potential energy is zero, and the kinetic energy is $mv_2^2/2$. Thus we have, from Eq. (2.6-13),

$$\frac{k\delta^2}{2} + mgh = m\frac{v_2^2}{2}$$

or

$$v_2 = \left(\frac{k\delta^2 + 2mgh}{m}\right)^{\frac{1}{2}}$$

ILLUSTRATIVE EXAMPLE 2.6-3

A rocket fired vertically acquires a velocity v_1 at burnout, which takes place at a height h_1 above the earth's surface. Determine the distance $h_2 - h_1$ through which it coasts in attaining its maximum altitude h_2. After burnout the rocket moves in the gravitational field of the earth without resistance of the atmosphere.

SOLUTION: We use Eq. (2.6-13), since only potential forces are involved. With R as the radius of the earth Eq. (2.6-13) yields, in view of Eq. (2.6-4),

$$-\frac{\Gamma m_1 m_2}{R + h_1} + \frac{m_1 v_1^2}{2} = -\frac{\Gamma m_1 m_2}{R + h_2} + 0 \tag{a}$$

where m_1 is the mass of the rocket at burnout and m_2 that of the earth. Equation (a) leads to

$$m_1 g R^2 \frac{h_2 - h_1}{(R + h_1)(R + h_2)} = \frac{m_1 v_1^2}{2} \tag{b}$$

considering that $\Gamma m_1 m_2 / R^2 = m_1 g$—see Eq. (2.1-5).
  Hence we find, from Eq. (b),

$$h_2 - h_1 = \frac{v_1^2}{2g} \frac{(R + h_1)^2}{R^2 - (R + h_1)v_1^2/2g} \tag{c}$$

Equation (c) indicates that, for $v_1 = R\sqrt{2g/(R + h_1)}$, h_2 becomes infinite. For example, for $h_1 = 0$ and $v_1 \geq \sqrt{2gR} = 25{,}023$ mph, the rocket never returns.

ILLUSTRATIVE EXAMPLE 2.6-4

If a particle m_0 is dropped into a hole that passes through the center of the earth, how long does it take to reach the other side, assuming the earth to be homogeneous and neglecting frictional resistance as well as the earth's rotation?

SOLUTION: It was shown in Illustrative Example 2.1-3 that m_0 is attracted only by the mass within the sphere of radius r measured from the center of the earth. Since the volume is $\frac{4}{3}\pi r^3$, the force acting on m_0 is

$$F(r) = -\frac{\Gamma(\mu\frac{4}{3}\pi r^3)m_0}{r^2} = -Km_0 r$$

where μ is the mass density of the earth.

The constant K can be evaluated at the earth's surface $(r = R)$, where

$$F(R) = -m_0 g = -Km_0 R$$

Thus

$$K = \frac{g}{R}$$

Hence

$$F(r) = -m_0 g \frac{r}{R}$$

Applying Newton's second law, the equation of motion is

$$-m_0 g \frac{r}{R} = m_0 \ddot{r}$$

or

$$\ddot{r} + \frac{g}{R} r = 0$$

Its solution for the initial conditions $r(0) = R$ and $\dot{r}(0) = 0$ is

$$r = R \cos \sqrt{\frac{g}{R}} t$$

When $r = -R$, we have $\sqrt{g/R}\, t = \pi$. Thus the time required for m_0 to reach the other side of the earth is

$$t = \pi \sqrt{\frac{R}{g}} = 42 \text{ min}$$

It should be noticed that this is the same time required if m_0 is sent around the earth as a satellite (assuming zero air friction) at zero altitude.

When the body is subjected to conservative as well as nonconservative forces, of which the latter do the work $W_{1,2}^*$ along the path between points 1 and 2, we use, instead of Eq. (2.6-13), the relation

$$U_1 + T_1 + W_{1,2}^* = U_2 + T_2 \qquad \blacktriangleleft \qquad (2.6\text{-}14)$$

Among the most important nonconservative forces are those due to friction. We deal with a general type of friction, where the friction force exerted on a material body is written

$$\mathbf{F}_{fr} = -f(v) \frac{\mathbf{v}}{v} \qquad f(v) > 0 \qquad (2.6\text{-}15)$$

so that it is always opposed to the velocity of the body.

Substituting this force in Eq. (2.6-10) we obtain, with $d\mathbf{r} = \mathbf{v}\, dt$,

$$\oint \mathbf{F} \cdot d\mathbf{r} = -\oint f(v) \frac{\mathbf{v}}{v} \cdot \mathbf{v}\, dt = -\oint f(v) v\, dt < 0 \qquad (2.6\text{-}16)$$

Thus, since the integrand is always positive—see the definition of $f(v)$ in Eq. (2.6-15) and consider that v is the magnitude of the velocity—the criterion for the existence of a potential is not satisfied. Hence, frictional forces are nonconservative. Because they dissipate mechanical energy, they are also called dissipative. Since they do not have a potential, the work $W_{1,2}^*$ can, in general, be evaluated only when the motion of the body is known.

ILLUSTRATIVE EXAMPLE 2.6-5

Determine the work done by a dry-friction force (coulomb friction) on a body sliding on a rough surface in a straight line from x_1 to x_2 and back.

SOLUTION: In this simple case $f(v)$ is constant and equal to the weight of the body times the coefficient of sliding friction; that is, $f(v) = \mu w$. Hence with the use of Eq. (2.6-16) we find

$$W = -\mu w(|x_2 - x_1| + |x_1 - x_2|) = -2\mu w|x_2 - x_1|$$

PROBLEMS

2.6-1   Set up the differential equation of motion for the system shown in Fig. P 2.2-57 by the energy method.

2.6-2   Solve Prob. 2.2-58 by the energy method.

2.6-3   Solve Prob. 2.2-59 by the energy method.

2.6-4   Solve Prob. 2.2-60 by the energy method.

2.6-5   A smooth tube forming a quadrant of a vertical circle acts as a guide for a chain AB of the same length (see Fig. P 2.6-5). If released with A on the vertical axis, determine its velocity at any position θ.

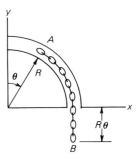

Fig. P 2.6-5

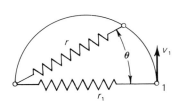

Fig. P 2.6-6

2.6-6   A particle of mass m is made to move in a horizontal plane along a smooth circular wire of diameter r_1 by means of an elastic linear spring of unstretched length r_0 and force $F = k(r - r_0)$ attached to the rim, as shown in Fig. P 2.6-6. If the motion is started at 1 with velocity v_1, determine the velocity when m is in position θ. If $r_0 = \frac{1}{2}r_1$, determine the velocity when $\theta = 60°$.

2.6-7   Two slider weights are connected by a light rigid link and move with negligible friction in their guides. The upper slider is pushed against a spring, compressing it 1 ft, and released from the position shown in Fig. P 2.6-7. Determine the velocity of the upper weight as it crosses the center line of the vertical slot.

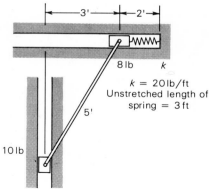

Fig. P 2.6-7

2.6-8   A slider of mass m is attached to a spring of stiffness k and unstretched length l and is free to slide along a smooth vertical post (see Fig. P 2.6-8). If released from position y_1 with zero velocity, determine position y_2, where the velocity is again zero.

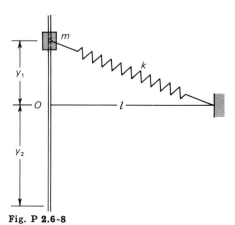

Fig. P 2.6-8

2.6-9   In Prob. 2.6-8 the friction force between the slider and post is constant and equal to F; determine position y_2 corresponding to zero velocity. What velocity does it have as it passes through O?

2.6-10 A simple pendulum of weight w and length l is released from rest at $\theta = 60°$, swings downward under the influence of gravity, and strikes a spring of stiffness k at $\theta = 0$, as shown in Fig. P 2.6-10. Neglecting the mass of the spring, determine the compression that it undergoes.

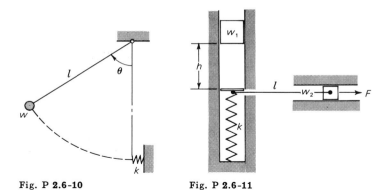

Fig. P **2.6-10**   Fig. P **2.6-11**

2.6-11   Weight w_1 drops through height h, strikes a spring of stiffness k that is connected to w_2 with constant resisting force F (see Fig. P 2.6-11).   Determine the maximum compression of the spring.   The massless, inextensible cord connecting k and w_2 is horizontal at the initial instant.

2.6-12   The car shown in Fig. P 2.6-12 has a velocity down the plane of 10 ft/sec in position 1.   In position 2, 10 ft farther down the track, the elastic cable becomes taut.   The scale of the elastic cable is 870 lb/ft.   The rolling resistance of the car is 150 lb.   Find the maximum tension in the cable produced in stopping the car.

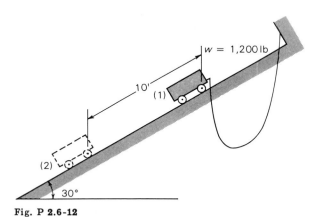

Fig. P **2.6-12**

2.6-13   A pilot in a vertical dive turns off his engine at 300 mph and goes into a vertical loop of 800 ft radius (see Fig. P 2.6-13).   Neglecting air resistance, determine his speed at the top of the loop, which is assumed to be circular.   What is the diameter of the largest loop that he can make without losing all his speed?

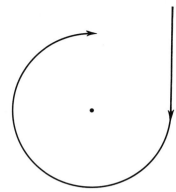

Fig. P 2.6-13

2.6-14   A small car starts at rest from A and rolls without friction along loop $ABCBD$
(see Fig. P 2.6-14).   Determine the least height h at which the car can start
without falling off the track.   What velocity does the car have at the end of
loop BD?

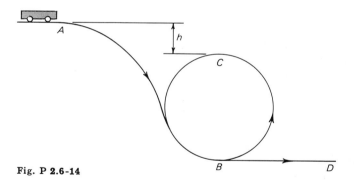

Fig. P **2.6-14**

2.6-15   A particle is given a horizontal velocity of $v_0 \leq \sqrt{gR}$ at the highest point of a
smooth horizontal cylinder of radius R, as shown in Fig. P 2.6-15.   Determine the
angle ϕ at which the particle leaves the cylinder.

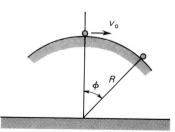

Fig. P **2.6-15**

2.6-16   A simple pendulum of length l strikes a peg at A, where $OA = a < l$ (see Fig. P 2.6-16).   What is the minimum value of θ that causes m to make a complete circle about A?

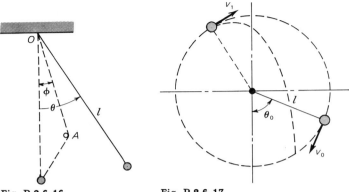

Fig. P 2.6-16   Fig. P 2.6-17

2.6-17   A simple pendulum is started with initial velocity v_0 at position θ_0 (see Fig. P 2.6-17).   Determine the position at which the tension in the massless and inextensible cord becomes zero and its velocity v_1 at this instant.   The motion after this instant is that of ballistic flight.   Determine the position at which the tension again becomes greater than zero.

2.6-18   For a given height h, determine the stretch x_0 from the equilibrium position necessary so that, when both masses are released at the same time, they come together with equal velocity (see Fig. P 2.6-18).

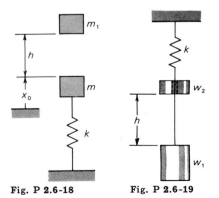

Fig. P 2.6-18   Fig. P 2.6-19

2.6-19   A weight w_1 is attached to a spring of stiffness k and hangs vertically in the equilibrium position (see Fig. P 2.6-19).   Another weight w_2 falls from rest through a height h and collides with weight w_1 without rebound. Deduce the subsequent motion of the weights.

2.6-20 A section of a hollow cylinder of weight w drops on the stop at the bottom of a thin rod of cross-sectional area A, length l, and modulus of elasticity E (see Fig. P 2.6-20). Show that the spring constant of the rod is $k = EA/l$ and that the maximum displacement of the stop is

$$x_{max} = \frac{w}{k} + \sqrt{\left(\frac{w}{k}\right)^2 + 2\frac{w}{k}h}$$

where h is the drop distance of w.

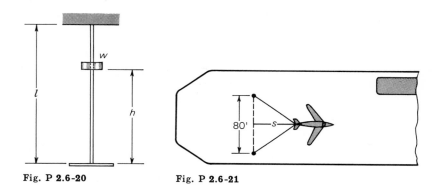

Fig. P **2.6-20**   Fig. P **2.6-21**

2.6-21 Planes landing on the deck of a carrier vessel are stopped by the engagement of a hook on the tail of the plane with a cable stretched across the landing deck (see Fig. P 2.6-21). The cable runs down over sheaves through holes in the deck and engages a spring snubbing gear below. The snubbing gear is arranged to give a tension in the cable directly proportional to the amount of cable pulled out. Find the distance s required to stop the plane when the following data are given:

Initial cable tension	1,000 lb
Velocity of vessel	30 mph into wind
Velocity of plane	90 mph into wind
Spring scale (each snubber)	350 lb/ft
Weight of plane	6,000 lb

2.6-22 Determine the gravitational potential due to a thin rod of length l and mass m at a point r from its center, where r makes an angle θ with the rod (see Fig. P 2.6-22).

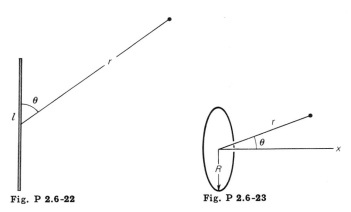

Fig. P 2.6-22   Fig. P 2.6-23

2.6-23   Determine the equation for the gravitational potential of a ring of radius R and mass m at a point r from its center, where r makes an angle θ with the normal to the plane of the ring (see Fig. P 2.6-23).

2.6-24   Using the potential established in Prob. 2.6-23, determine the x, y, z components of the force of attraction for the special case $\theta = 0$.

2.6-25   Assuming the earth to be a perfect sphere of radius R and mass M but with a ring of mass m around the equator to simulate its oblateness, determine the equation for its potential at a point p defined by Fig. P 2.6-25, where n is a normal to the plane of p and the x axis.

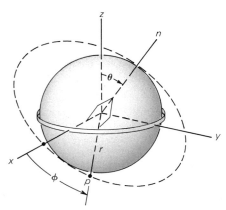

Fig. P 2.6-25

2.6-26   A mass particle m lies on the axis of symmetry of a thin uniform cylindrical tube of mass M, as shown in Fig. P 2.6-26.   Determine the force of gravitational attraction.

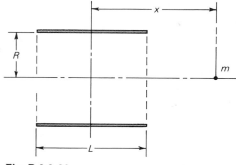

Fig. P 2.6-26

2.6-27 Show that the gravitational force of a thin uniform sphere of mass m_s and radius
R on a particle of mass m_0 a distance $x > R$ from its center is found as if m_s were
concentrated at its center as a particle.

2.7 SATELLITE AND PLANETARY MOTION

The motion of artificial satellites in earth-bound orbits is governed primarily
by the central-force gravitational field of the earth.   We found previously
that the motion in a central-force field is characterized by the invariance of
the moment-of-momentum vector taken about the force center O:

$$\mathbf{r} \times m\mathbf{v} = \text{const} \qquad (2.7\text{-}1)$$

and that the motion remains in a plane normal to this vector.   It is therefore
advantageous to adopt the polar coordinates of Sec. 1.4b for such problems,
with the origin at the center of the earth, as shown in Fig. 2.7-1.

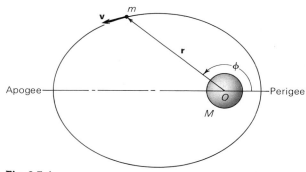

Fig. 2.7-1

The attractive force of the earth is given by Newton's law of gravity [that is, Eq. (2.1-10)]:

$$\mathbf{F} = -\Gamma \frac{Mm}{r^2} \mathbf{1}_r + 0 \, \mathbf{1}_\phi \qquad (2.7\text{-}2)$$

where M and m are the masses of the earth and the satellite, respectively. The motion of the satellite is then governed by the equation

$$-\Gamma \frac{Mm}{r^2} \mathbf{1}_r + 0 \, \mathbf{1}_\phi = m[(\ddot{r} - r\dot{\phi}^2)\mathbf{1}_r + (2\dot{r}\dot{\phi} + r\ddot{\phi})\mathbf{1}_\phi] \qquad (2.7\text{-}3)$$

which leads to the two scalar equations

$$\ddot{r} - r\dot{\phi}^2 = -\frac{\Gamma M}{r^2} \qquad (2.7\text{-}4)$$

$$2\dot{r}\dot{\phi} + r\ddot{\phi} = \frac{1}{r}\frac{d}{dt}(r^2\dot{\phi}) = 0 \qquad (2.7\text{-}5)$$

Equation (2.7-5) is, of course, the statement of the conservation of moment of momentum per unit mass taken about the center of the earth:

$$H = |\mathbf{r} \times \mathbf{v}| = r^2\dot{\phi} = \text{const} \qquad (2.7\text{-}6)$$

Since our interest is centered about the geometric shape of the orbit, we eliminate the independent variable t in terms of ϕ:

$$\dot{r} = \frac{dr}{d\phi}\dot{\phi} = \frac{dr}{d\phi}\frac{H}{r^2} = -H\frac{d}{d\phi}\frac{1}{r} \qquad (2.7\text{-}7)$$

Thus, by letting $1/r = u$, the following terms are expressed in terms of the new variables:

$$\dot{r} = -H\frac{du}{d\phi} \qquad (2.7\text{-}8)$$

$$\ddot{r} = -H\frac{d^2u}{d\phi^2}\dot{\phi} = -H^2u^2\frac{d^2u}{d\phi^2} \qquad (2.7\text{-}9)$$

considering that $\dot{\phi} = H/r^2 = Hu^2$.

Substituting these quantities into Eq. (2.7-4), the differential equation for the geometry of the orbit becomes

$$\frac{d^2u}{d\phi^2} + u = \frac{\Gamma M}{H^2} \qquad (2.7\text{-}10)$$

The general solution to Eq. (2.7-10) has the form

$$u = \frac{1}{r} = \frac{\Gamma M}{H^2} + C\cos(\phi - \phi_0) \qquad (2.7\text{-}11)$$

where C and ϕ_0 are arbitrary constants. The constant ϕ_0 is made zero, if (see Fig. 2.7-1) the reference line (fixed in an inertial frame) for ϕ connects point O and a point on the orbit, where $\dot{r} = 0$. The student should demonstrate this for himself by differentiating Eq. (2.7-11) with respect to time t. The other constant C can be evaluated from the fact that we have a conservative system that demands that the total energy be a constant.

The potential energy per unit mass is

$$U(r) = -\Gamma M \int_r^\infty \mathbf{1}_r \cdot \frac{d\mathbf{r}}{r^2} = -\frac{\Gamma M}{r} \tag{2.7-12}$$

where the reference of zero energy is chosen at $r = \infty$. Adding to this the kinetic energy per unit mass, the total energy becomes

$$E = \frac{v^2}{2} - \frac{\Gamma M}{r} \tag{2.7-13}$$

We now express this equation in terms of u and ϕ:

$$v^2 = \dot{r}^2 + (r\dot{\phi})^2 = H^2 \left[\left(\frac{du}{d\phi} \right)^2 + u^2 \right]$$

$$= H^2 \left[C \sin^2 \phi + \left(\frac{\Gamma M}{H^2} + C \cos \phi \right)^2 \right] \tag{2.7-14}$$

where Eq. (2.7-11) has been substituted for u and $du/d\phi$. With $u = 1/r$ and Eq. (2.7-14) inserted into Eq. (2.7-13) we can solve for the constant C, which becomes

$$C = \frac{\Gamma M}{H^2} \sqrt{1 + \frac{2EH^2}{(\Gamma M)^2}} \tag{2.7-15}$$

Equation (2.7-11) can now be expressed in the final form ($\phi_0 = 0$)

$$u = \frac{1}{r} = \frac{\Gamma M}{H^2} (1 + e \cos \phi) \tag{2.7-16}$$

where
$$e = \sqrt{1 + \frac{2EH^2}{(\Gamma M)^2}} \tag{2.7-17}$$

is the eccentricity of the orbit.

Equation (2.7-16) is a general expression valid for any central-force field that varies inversely as the square of the distance from the attracting center, which is called the focus. The equation represents a conic section, the classification of which depends on the eccentricity e as follows. The curve is

1   A hyperbola if $e > 1$

2   A parabola if $e = 1$

3 An ellipse with perigee corresponding to $\phi = 0$ if $0 < e < 1$

4 A circle if $e = 0$

5 An ellipse with apogee (point corresponding to maximum r) at $\phi = 0$ if $-1 < e < 0$

From the results obtained above, we now derive, for an elliptic orbit (case 3 above), the following useful relationships among the eccentricity e, the major semiaxis a, the moment of momentum H per unit mass of the orbiting body, the total energy E per unit mass of the orbiting body, the orbit period τ, and the attraction constant $\Gamma M = K$:

$$H = \sqrt{Ka(1 - e^2)}$$

$$e = \frac{r_p v_p{}^2}{K} - 1$$

$$E = \frac{-K}{2a}$$

$$\tau^2 = \frac{(2\pi)^2}{K} a^3$$

Three basic concepts are necessary for this problem:

1 GEOMETRY OF THE ELLIPSE

The geometry of the elliptic orbit, shown in Fig. 2.7-2, defines the various quantities of interest. From the definition of the conic section, the ratio

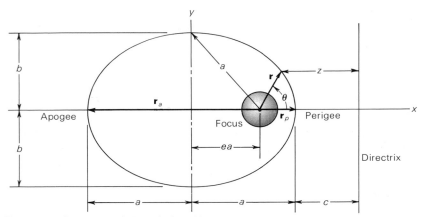

Fig. 2.7-2 Geometry of the elliptic orbit.

r/z for any point on the curve is equal to the eccentricity e. By considering three points on the curve, that is, perigee, apogee, and the point on the y axis, we have

$$e = \frac{r_p}{c} = \frac{r_a}{2a + c} = \frac{a}{a + c}$$

Thus we obtain

$$c = \frac{a(1 - e)}{e}$$
$$r_a = a(1 + e)$$
$$r_p = a(1 - e)$$

(2.7-18)

2 CONSERVATION OF MOMENT OF MOMENTUM
In a central-force field the moment of momentum about the focus is a constant. At perigee and apogee the velocity and the radial line are normal, thereby leading to the simple relationship

$$H = r_p v_p = r_a v_a \qquad (2.7\text{-}19)$$

3 CONSERVATION OF ENERGY
The satellite moving in a vacuum represents a conservative system, and the sum of the kinetic and potential energies remains constant. Thus for perigee and apogee, as well as for a point in general, we have—see Eq. (2.7-13)—

$$E = \tfrac{1}{2}v_p^2 - \frac{K}{r_p} = \tfrac{1}{2}v_a^2 - \frac{K}{r_a} = \tfrac{1}{2}v^2 - \frac{K}{r} \qquad (2.7\text{-}20)$$

We now look for useful relationships between the constants. Eliminating v_p and v_a in Eqs. (2.7-20) in terms of H from Eqs. (2.7-19), we obtain

$$E = \frac{H^2}{2r_p^2} - \frac{K}{r_p} = \frac{H^2}{2r_a^2} - \frac{K}{r_a} \qquad (2.7\text{-}21)$$

or

$$\frac{H^2}{2K}\left(\frac{1}{r_p} - \frac{1}{r_a}\right)\left(\frac{1}{r_p} + \frac{1}{r_a}\right) = \left(\frac{1}{r_p} - \frac{1}{r_a}\right)$$

or

$$\frac{H^2}{2K}\left(\frac{1}{r_p} + \frac{1}{r_a}\right) = 1$$

Substituting for r_p and r_a in terms of e and a from Eqs. (2.7-18), we obtain the first relationship

$$H = \sqrt{Ka(1 - e^2)} \qquad \blacktriangleleft \quad (2.7\text{-}22)$$

For a satellite orbiting the earth we have $K = \Gamma M = gR^2$.
If next Eq. (2.7-22) is substituted into Eq. (2.7-21), we obtain another

relationship

$$E = \frac{-K}{2a}$$ ◀ (2.7-23)

Using Eq. (2.7-23), Eq. (2.7-20) for the general point can now be written

$$\frac{rv^2}{K} = 2 - \frac{r}{a}$$ (2.7-24)

At perigee $r_p = a(1 - e)$, so that Eq. (2.7-24) leads to a simple relationship for the eccentricity:

$$e = \frac{r_p v_p{}^2}{K} - 1$$ ◀ (2.7-25)

Finally the period of the orbit can be simply obtained as

$$\tau = \frac{\text{area}}{\text{areal rate}} = \frac{\pi ab}{H/2} = \frac{2\pi a(a\sqrt{1 - e^2})}{\sqrt{Ka(1 - e^2)}}$$
$$= \frac{2\pi a^{3/2}}{\sqrt{K}}$$

or $$\tau^2 = \frac{(2\pi)^2}{K} a^3$$ ◀ (2.7-26)

which represents Kepler's third law, stating that the square of the orbit period is proportional to the cube of the major semiaxis a.

ILLUSTRATIVE EXAMPLE 2.7-1
A satellite is injected into orbit with velocity

$$\mathbf{v} = 0\,\mathbf{1}_r + v_p \mathbf{1}_\phi$$

at height $h_p = r_p - R$, where R is the radius of the earth. Determine the apogee height h_a and the velocity v_a.
SOLUTION: We use the relationships compiled above. Here Eqs. (2.7-18) indicate that

$$r_a = h_a + R = r_p \frac{1 + e}{1 - e} = (h_p + R)\frac{1 + e}{1 - e}$$

The eccentricity e is found from Eq. (2.7-25):

$$e = \frac{r_p v_p{}^2}{K} - 1 = \frac{(h_p + R)v_p{}^2}{gR^2} - 1$$

Furthermore the velocity of the satellite at apogee is found from Eqs. (2.7-19):

$$v_a = v_p \frac{r_p}{r_a}$$

PROBLEMS

2.7-1   For a satellite moving in a central-force field, show that the component of the velocity normal to the radial vector $\mathbf{r}$ from the focus is inversely proportional to r.

2.7-2   Determine the velocity of escape from the earth as a function of the distance from its center, and plot the result. Repeat for the moon. Neglect the rotation of the earth and the moon.

2.7-3   Determine the mass m_s of the sun by noting that the earth travels around it in a nearly circular orbit of radius 93×10^6 miles in $365\frac{1}{4}$ days. What is the ratio of the mass of the earth to that of the sun?

2.7-4   A satellite is in a circular orbit around the earth at an altitude of 300 miles above the surface. Using the value of $\Gamma m_e = K$, determine the time for one revolution of the satellite around the earth.

2.7-5   Determine the radius of an equatorial circular orbit around the earth for which the satellite remains stationary relative to the surface, that is, has a period of 24 hr.

2.7-6   Plot the circular orbit speed and its period for a satellite traveling around earth as a function of h/R_0, where h is the altitude above the surface and $R_0 = 3,960$ miles is the mean radius of the earth.

2.7-7   The mass of the moon is $\frac{1}{81}$ that of earth, and its radius is 1,080 miles. Prior to landing on the moon, a rocket ship has to go into a circular orbit 50 miles above its surface. What speed is required to accomplish this?

2.7-8   Show that the period of any elliptic orbit equals

$$\tau = \frac{\pi a b}{\frac{1}{2} r_1 v_{1\perp}} = \frac{2\pi}{\sqrt{K}} a^{3\!/\!2} = \frac{\text{area of ellipse}}{\text{area swept over per unit time}}$$

where a and b are the semimajor and semiminor axes of the orbit, and r_1 the radial distance at any time, and $v_{1\perp}$ the corresponding component of the velocity normal to r_1.

2.7-9   A satellite is injected into orbit at $r = 1.10R$ (R = radius of earth) in a direction parallel to the earth's surface and with a velocity 1.20 times that of a circular orbit of the same height. Determine (a) the eccentricity of the orbit, (b) the length of the semimajor axis a, and (c) the apogee distance from the center of the earth.

2.7-10   A satellite reaches perigee (lowest point) at an altitude of 200 miles with a speed of 18,500 mph. A retro-rocket is to be fired at this instant so that 180° later its altitude is reduced to 100 miles. Determine the change in velocity required by the retro-rocket and the time of the complete orbit.

2.7-11   On May 15, 1963, the spacecraft bearing Astronaut Cooper was put into orbit with the following altitudes: perigee, 100.0 miles; apogee, 166.1 miles. Determine the eccentricity of the orbit.

2.7-12   A satellite moves in a circular orbit at a velocity of $v_c = 20,000$ ft/sec. (a) What is the altitude of the orbit above the surface of the earth? (b) If the satellite is given a velocity increment of $v = 4,500$ ft/sec in essentially zero time, what is the eccentricity of the resulting orbit? (c) At what distance from the center of the earth is the satellite again moving at 20,000 ft/sec? Assume that

$$R_e = 3,960 \text{ miles} = 2.091 \times 10^7 \text{ ft}$$
$$g = 32.2 \text{ ft/sec}^2$$
$$K = gR_e{}^2 = 1.41 \times 10^{16} \text{ ft}^3/\text{sec}^2$$

2.7-13   The quantity Γm_s for the sun equals 4.68×10^{21} ft^3/sec^2. If a comet is observed at a distance of 5×10^6 miles traveling toward the sun with a velocity of 80 miles/

sec at an angle of 20° with the radial line between it and the sun, determine its orbit and calculate how close it comes to the sun.

2.7-14   A slender rod of length l is put into an orbit of radius R around the earth. If the rod is always oriented with its length pointing to the center of the earth, show that the centrifugal force always acts through the center of mass and that the resultant of the gravitational attraction that balances it acts at a point

$$R \sqrt{1 - \frac{1}{4}\left(\frac{l}{R}\right)^2} \approx R - \frac{1}{8} R \left(\frac{l}{R}\right)^2$$

that is closer to the earth by the second term $(R/8)(l/R)^2$.

2.7-15   A slender rod of length l is in orbit of radius R around the earth with its longitudinal axis always tangent to the path. Determine the center of force, and show that it is at a greater distance than R.

2.7-16   The total energy of a satellite per unit mass equals

$$E = \frac{v^2}{2} - \frac{K}{r}$$

Show that another form of this equation is

$$v^2 = K\left(\frac{2}{r} - \frac{1}{a}\right)$$

where a is the semimajor axis of the orbit.

2.7-17   A space probe of mass m is traveling from the earth to the moon. Simplifying the actual situation, we assume that the earth-moon line is fixed in space and that the space probe is moving along it. (a) What is the minimum speed that the space probe must have after burnout at 100 miles above the earth's surface in order not to fall back toward the earth? The moon/earth mass ratio is $\frac{1}{81}$. (b) What is the minimum speed when the space probe is not using the gravitational attraction of another celestial body?

DYNAMICS
OF SYSTEMS
OF PARTICLES

3.1 GENERAL REMARKS

Following the historical development of mechanics we now extend our discussion to the kinetic behavior of a system of particles. This topic is particularly important, because the theorems that we establish here are generally valid, and thus for the whole field of rigid-body mechanics also. In this sense Chaps. 4 and 6 may be considered special applications of the theory to be developed in this chapter.

Let the number of particles in a closed system be n, where the term *closed system* implies that it consists of the same n particles at all times. One might imagine a boundary surface (see Fig. 3.1-1) traveling with the system,

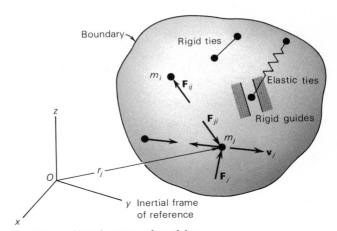

Fig. 3.1-1 Closed system of particles.

surrounding all the particles as an infinitely flexible, massless, closed bag. From the "outside" the system is subjected to external forces that are assumed to act directly as concentrated forces on the mass particles in the system. They may be of diverse nature, such as gravity, electromagnetic action, and the like, forces of reactions caused by external constraints, and may be surface as well as body forces. Inside the system there are "internal" forces that act among the various masses. They may be caused by mutual gravitational attraction, "massless" elastic or rigid ties, and the like. These internal forces obey Newton's third law. Hence to every force $\mathbf{F}_{jl}$† exerted by particle l on particle j there is a force $\mathbf{F}_{lj}$ exerted by particle j on particle l such that—see Eq. (2.1-4)—

$$\mathbf{F}_{lj} + \mathbf{F}_{jl} = 0 \qquad \blacktriangleleft \qquad (3.1\text{-}1)$$

and their lines of action coincide (see Fig. 3.1-1).

The problem of the dynamics of systems of particles has played a major role in the development of the science of mechanics, particularly celestial mechanics. Although it was possible to set up a number of general theorems, only the case of two bodies attracting each other has been solved completely in the sense that the orbits with respect to each other and also with respect to the center of mass can be determined in a closed form.[1] We therefore establish general theorems for a system of an arbitrary number of particles only to such extent as they are applicable to practical problems.

3.2 THEOREM OF MOMENTUM

We describe the dynamic behavior of a closed system of particles with respect to an inertial frame of reference. First we single out particle j of mass m_j (see Fig. 3.1-1). Its position as a function of time is denoted by the position vector $\mathbf{r}_j(t)$ and its velocity by $\mathbf{v}_j(t)$. It is acted on by the internal forces $\mathbf{F}_{jl}$ ($l = 1, 2, \ldots, n; l \neq j$) and the resultant external force $\mathbf{F}_j$.

According to Eq. (2.1-1) the momentum of particle j is

$$\mathbf{G}_j = m_j \mathbf{v}_j = \frac{d}{dt}(m_j \mathbf{r}_j) \qquad (3.2\text{-}1)$$

where $dm_j/dt = 0$ is assumed for every particle. The momentum of the system of particles is then defined by the vector sum

$$\mathbf{G} = \sum_{j=1}^{n} \mathbf{G}_j = \frac{d}{dt} \sum_{j=1}^{n} m_j \mathbf{r}_j \qquad \blacktriangleleft \qquad (3.2\text{-}2)$$

The position of the center of mass of the system of particles—see Eqs. (2.1-8) —is defined by

$$\mathbf{r}_C = \frac{\displaystyle\sum_{j=1}^{n} m_j \mathbf{r}_j}{\displaystyle\sum_{j=1}^{n} m_j} = \frac{\displaystyle\sum_{j=1}^{n} m_j \mathbf{r}_j}{m} \qquad \blacktriangleleft \qquad (3.2\text{-}3)$$

---

† Note that all internal forces carry two subscripts: the first to identify the particle that is subjected to the internal force, the second to identify the particle whose presence brings about the internal force.

[1] The first more or less complete analytical solution of the two-body problem is due to Euler: "Theoria motuum planetarum et cometarum" (Berlin, 1744). The problem of three bodies moving solely under the influence of their mutual gravitational attraction has occupied the minds of the greatest mathematicians. One can show that a closed solution cannot be found in full generality. Among the special cases of the three-body problem that were solved with mathematical rigor, the most famous is that treated by Lagrange (1736–1813), where the motion of the three bodies is such that the ratios of their mutual distances are constants.

where m denotes the total mass of the system. Since from Eq. (3.2-3) we have $\sum_{j=1}^{n} m_j \mathbf{r}_j = m\mathbf{r}_C$, we may rewrite Eq. (3.2-2) as

$$\mathbf{G} = \frac{d}{dt}(m\mathbf{r}_C) = m\mathbf{v}_C \qquad \blacktriangleleft \qquad (3.2\text{-}4)$$

which expresses the important result that *the linear momentum of a closed system of particles equals the product of its total mass with the velocity of the center of mass.* The reader is reminded that, generally, the center of mass does not coincide with any of the masses of the system and that it changes its position not only with respect to the inertial frame of reference, but also relative to the particles of the system.

If Newton's second law is applied to particle j, we obtain

$$\mathbf{F}_j + \sum_{l=1}^{n} \mathbf{F}_{jl} = \frac{d\mathbf{G}_j}{dt} \qquad l \neq j \qquad (3.2\text{-}5)$$

Hence, for the system of particles

$$\sum_{j=1}^{n} \mathbf{F}_j + \sum_{j=1}^{n} \left(\sum_{l=1}^{n} \mathbf{F}_{jl} \right) = \frac{d}{dt} \sum_{j=1}^{n} \mathbf{G}_j = \frac{d\mathbf{G}}{dt} \qquad l \neq j \qquad (3.2\text{-}6)$$

We then denote the resultant of all external forces by

$$\mathbf{F} = \sum_{j=1}^{n} \mathbf{F}_j$$

and remember that because of Eq. (3.1-1)

$$\sum_{j=1}^{n} \sum_{l=1}^{n} \mathbf{F}_{jl} = 0 \qquad l \neq j$$

Then, in view of Eq. (3.2-4),

$$\mathbf{F} = \frac{d\mathbf{G}}{dt} = \frac{d}{dt}(m\mathbf{v}_C) \qquad \blacktriangleleft \qquad (3.2\text{-}7)$$

which is identical to Eq. (2.1-1) for a single particle. So the center of mass of a system of particles moves like a single particle of mass m that is subjected to the resultant force of all external forces. The internal forces have no influence at all on the motion of the center of mass, although, as we can see from Eq. (3.2-5), they act in unison with the external force $\mathbf{F}_j$ to govern the motion of each particle j of the system.

Integrating Eq. (3.2-7) with respect to time, we obtain the theorem of linear momentum of a system of particles:

$$\int_{t_1}^{t_2} \mathbf{F} \, dt = m[\mathbf{v}_C(t_2) - \mathbf{v}_C(t_1)] = \sum_{j=1}^{n} m_j[\mathbf{v}_j(t_2) - \mathbf{v}_j(t_1)] \qquad \blacktriangleleft \qquad (3.2\text{-}8)$$

which also corresponds exactly to the theorem for a single particle.   For the special case in which the impulse $\int_{t_1}^{t_2} \mathbf{F}\, dt = 0$ we have the theorem of the conservation of linear momentum:

$$m\mathbf{v}_C(t_2) = m\mathbf{v}_C(t_1) \tag{3.2-9}$$

which states that the center of mass of a system of particles does not change its velocity if the time integral of the external forces vanishes.

If the impulse is of extremely short duration, as in impact (see page 81), we denote the time integral of the force by $\hat{\mathbf{F}}$.

ILLUSTRATIVE EXAMPLE 3.2-1

Two students, each weighing 160 lb, are standing at one end of a barge 20 ft long, weighing 400 lb and floating in quiet water.   (a) If both students run simultaneously and attain a takeoff speed of 10 ft/sec relative to the barge as they jump off the end, what is the speed imparted to the barge?   (b) If each student in turn runs and jumps off with a relative speed of 10 ft/sec, determine the speed imparted to the barge.   Any resistance by the water is to be neglected, so that there is no external force acting on the barge.
SOLUTION: (a) Let m_s be the mass of each student and m_b that of the barge.   With v_R as the relative velocity of the students with respect to the barge, and V_1 as that of the barge, the momentum of the students becomes $2m_s(v_R - V_1)$ to the right, and that of the barge $m_b V_1$ to the left (see Fig. 3.2-1).

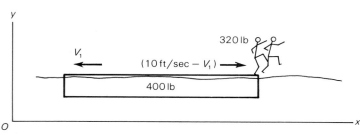

Fig. 3.2-1

The students and the barge form a "closed system of particles" whose momentum in the absence of external forces is conserved, and thus as the students run and jump off the barge simultaneously, starting with an initial momentum of zero, we have from Eq. (3.2-9)

$$320(10 - V_1) - 400V_1 = 0$$
$$V_1 = 4.45 \text{ ft/sec}$$

(b) As the first student runs to the right, the barge acquires a velocity of V_2 to the left, as shown in Fig. 3.2-2.   The momentum equation (3.2-9) then yields

$$160(10 - V_2) - (400 + 160)V_2 = 0$$

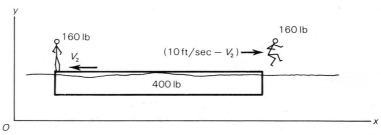

Fig. 3.2-2

which gives, for the velocity of the barge,

$$V_2 = 2.22 \text{ ft/sec}$$

As the first student jumps off, the second student and the barge constitute a new system with an initial momentum of $(400 + 160)/32.2 \times 2.22 = 1,242/32.2$ lb sec to the left. Immediately after the first student jumps off, the second student starts to run to the right, as shown in Fig. 3.2-3. The momentum of the new system remains constant at the

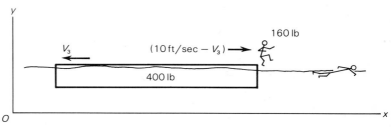

Fig. 3.2-3

initial value of $1,242/32.2$ lb sec, so that the momentum equation now yields

$$400V_3 - 160(10 - V_3) = 1,242$$

where V_3 is the new speed of the barge after the second student has jumped off. Solving for V_3, the final velocity of the barge is $V_3 = 5.08$ ft/sec, which is greater than $V_1 = 4.45$ ft/sec obtained in (a).

We conclude from this example that, in order to give the greatest velocity to the barge, it is more efficient for the two students to run separately than together.

Repeat the problem in symbols, without inserting numerical values, and discuss the solution.

ILLUSTRATIVE EXAMPLE 3.2-2
Two masses m_1 and m_2 (see Fig. 3.2-4) move in the absence of all forces other than their gravitational attraction. Derive the equation of motion of m_1 in coordinates with the origin placed in m_2.

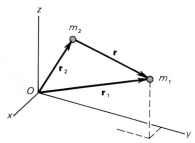

Fig. 3.2-4

SOLUTION: Letting O be a reference point fixed in an inertial system, the equations of motion for m_1 and m_2 are

$$m_1\ddot{\mathbf{r}}_1 = -\Gamma \frac{m_1 m_2}{r^3} \mathbf{r} \qquad (a)$$

$$m_2\ddot{\mathbf{r}}_2 = \Gamma \frac{m_1 m_2}{r^3} \mathbf{r} \qquad (b)$$

where $\mathbf{r}$ is a vector with the origin at m_2. Dividing Eq. (a) by m_1 and (b) by m_2 and sub-

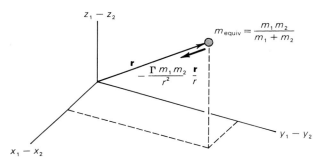

Fig. 3.2-5

tracting, we obtain (see Fig. 3.2-5)

$$\ddot{\mathbf{r}}_1 - \ddot{\mathbf{r}}_2 = \ddot{\mathbf{r}} = -\Gamma \frac{m_1 + m_2}{r^3} \mathbf{r} \qquad (c)$$

Multiplying Eq. (c) by $m_1 m_2/(m_1 + m_2)$, it may be written as

$$\frac{m_1 m_2}{m_1 + m_2} \ddot{\mathbf{r}} = -\Gamma \frac{m_1 m_2}{r^3} \mathbf{r} \qquad (d)$$

where the right side is equal to the gravitational force that, in the presence of m_2, acts on m_1. Comparing this with Newton's second law $\mathbf{F} = m\mathbf{a}$, Eq. (d) indicates that the motion of m_1 in coordinates tied to m_2 can be viewed as that of an equivalent mass of $m_1 m_2/(m_1 + m_2)$. Note that, if m_2 is infinitely larger than m_1, the equivalent mass reduces to m_1.

ILLUSTRATIVE EXAMPLE 3.2-3
A horizontal turntable rotating at constant speed ω has a straight frictionless slot through its center.   Two sliders m_1 and m_2 connected by an inextensible cord are allowed to slide outward from the center (see Fig. 3.2-6).   Show that the tension in the cord is independent of the position of the sliders.

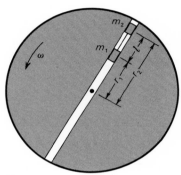

Fig. 3.2-6

SOLUTION: Consider the position of the two sliders to be r_1 and $r_2 = r_1 + l$, as shown in Fig. 3.2-6.   Letting F be the tension in the cord and a_{rel} the acceleration of the sliders relative to the disk, the force equation in the radial direction for each mass is

$$F = m_1(a_{\text{rel}} - r_1\omega^2) \tag{a}$$
$$-F = m_2(a_{\text{rel}} - r_2\omega^2) \tag{b}$$

Adding these equations, we obtain

$$0 = (m_1 + m_2)a_{\text{rel}} - \omega^2(m_1r_1 + m_2r_2)$$
$$a_{\text{rel}} = \frac{\omega^2(m_1r_1 + m_2r_2)}{m_1 + m_2} \tag{c}$$

Substituting Eq. (c) into (a), the equation for the tension F is found to be

$$F = m_1\left[\frac{\omega^2(m_1r_1 + m_2r_2)}{m_1 + m_2} - r_1\omega^2\right]$$
$$= \frac{\omega^2 m_1 m_2}{m_1 + m_2}(r_2 - r_1) = \omega^2 \frac{m_1 m_2}{m_1 + m_2} l \tag{d}$$

which is independent of the position.

PROBLEMS
3.2-1   Determine the center of mass of the system in the position indicated and its acceleration due to the given forces:

Mass	Position, ft	Force, $m \times$ ft/sec²
$8m$	$(3,-1,2)$	$(-1,3,-1)$
$4m$	$(1,2,-1)$	$(4,4,3)$
$2m$	$(4,3,6)$	$(2,5,1)$

3.2-2   A machine gun fires two hundred 8-oz bullets per minute into a sandbag.   If on the average a force of 100 lb is necessary to hold the sandbag in place, what is the velocity of the bullets?

3.2-3   Two barges 1 and 2 of weight w_1 and w_2 resting in calm water are connected by a cable of length l.   A windlass on barge 1 shortens the cable by a distance kl. Neglecting any resistance to motion, determine the distances moved by each barge.

3.2-4   A motor A is rotating with constant angular velocity ω (see Fig. P 3.2-4).   Determine the amplitude of the vibrations of 1 and 2.

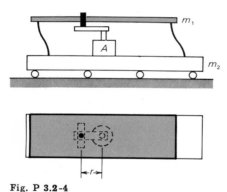

Fig. P 3.2-4

3.2-5   A platform of length l and mass m_p rests on rollers on a horizontal plane so that there is no resistance to motion in the horizontal direction (see Fig. P 3.2-5). At first a boy B and a girl G are standing together at rest with their center of

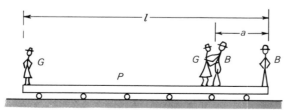

Fig. P 3.2-5

mass ($m_B + m_G$) at a distance a from the right end of the platform. After some time they quarrel and move to the ends of the platform, remaining stationary thereafter. How far does the platform move in this time? HINT: Solve this problem (a) as a system of particles, (b) by using the laws of motion for each mass.

3.2-6   A boy standing on a car 1 (mass m_1) jumps to another car 2 (mass m_2) with the horizontal velocity v_0 relative to car 1 (see Fig. P 3.2-6). What are the velocities of the cars afterward (the boy stands on car 2 afterward, relatively at rest)? The mass of the boy is m_b, and the cars are at rest at the beginning of the motion.

Fig. P 3.2-6

3.2-7   A man and a boy weighing 220 lb and 100 lb, respectively, stand at one end of a barge weighing 400 lb in calm water. Each can run with equal speed of 10 ft/sec relative to the barge. If each runs in turn and jumps off, which one should run first in order to give the barge the largest final velocity?

3.2-8   A pail of water resting on a weighing scale has a cork that is held submerged by a string. If the string breaks and the cork moves upward, does the scale read differently? HINT: Examine the motion of the center of mass of the combination of the water and the cork.

3.2-9   A boat weighing 300 lb is tied at the bow to a bridge across a stream. The flow of the stream exerts a 5-lb force on the boat. A man weighing 150 lb moves with an acceleration of 4 ft/sec² from the stern of the boat toward the bow. (a) Find the acceleration of the center of mass of the boat and man. (b) Using the result of (a), find the tension in the rope (horizontal) by which the boat is tied.

3.2-10   A man of weight w_1 jumps from a boat of weight w_2 with the horizontal velocity v_1 relative to inertial reference. The boat is at rest before the man jumps. Considering the man's takeoff to be instantaneous, (a) what is the velocity v_2 of the boat immediately after the man's jump? (b) After what time t and (c) at what distance s does the boat come to rest if it experiences a drag $D = cv^k$? It is sufficient to state the integral expressions for t and s.

3.2-11   A box of weight w_2 rests on a flatcar of weight w_1 with a coefficient of friction μ between them (see Fig. P 3.2-11). If the car runs into a stopping spring of stiffness k with speed v_0, determine the distance traveled by the car before the box starts to slide.

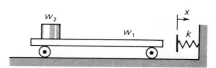

Fig. P 3.2-11

3.2-12   In Prob. 3.2-11 what is the maximum compression of the spring?

3.2-13   A box of weight w rests on a flatcar with a coefficient of friction μ between them (see Fig. P 3.2-13).   If through an impulse the car suddenly acquires a velocity v_0 in a very short time, determine how far the box slides before coming to rest relative to the car.   Assume that the car is so heavy compared with the box that the change in velocity v_0 of the car is negligible.

Fig. P 3.2-13

3.2-14   Solve Prob. 3.2-13 assuming the mass of the car to be finite.

3.2-15   Two masses m_1 and m_2 free to slide on a smooth rod are connected by a spring of stiffness k and unstretched length l (see Fig. P 3.2-15).   If at $t = 0$, $x_1 = 0$, $\dot{x}_1 = v_0$, $x_2 = l$, $\dot{x}_2 = 0$, show that at any time t their coordinates are

$$x_1 = \frac{v_0}{m_1 + m_2}\left(m_1 t + \frac{m_2}{\omega}\sin \omega t\right)$$

$$x_2 = l + \frac{v_0}{m_1 + m_2}\left(m_1 t - \frac{m_1}{\omega}\sin \omega t\right)$$

where $\omega = \sqrt{k(1/m_1 + 1/m_2)}$.

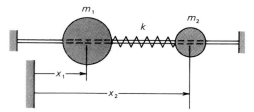

Fig. P 3.2-15

3.2-16   Two masses m_1 and m_2 rest on a smooth horizontal floor and are connected by a spring of stiffness k (see Fig. P 3.2-16).   If initially the spring is unstretched and a velocity v_0 is imparted to m_1, determine the motion of m_1 and m_2.

Fig. P 3.2-16

3.2-17   Masses m_1 and m_2 connected by a spring of stiffness k with unstretched length l in. can move along smooth horizontal guides l in. apart (see Fig. P 3.2-17). If the system is released from zero velocity with $x_1 = 0$ and $x_2 = b$, determine the maximum velocity of each mass.

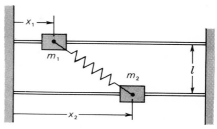

Fig. P **3.2-17**

3.2-18   A satellite consists of two equal masses tied together and compressing a spring of stiffness k between them a distance δ (see Fig. P 3.2-18).   Initially the satellite is in a circular orbit around the earth with a radius r.   If the tie is severed, find the new apogee heights of the two masses and their periods.

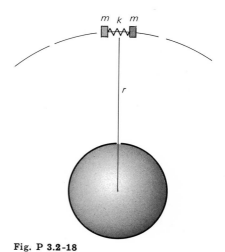

Fig. P **3.2-18**

3.2-19   Repeat Prob. 3.2-18 if the two masses are unequal, m_1 and m_2.

3.2-20   A uniform chain of length $2l$ and weight w hangs over a smooth horizontal peg (see Fig. P 3.2-20).   When released from an unbalanced position with a difference of level equal to $2x_0$, write the differential equation of motion using x from the position where $x_0 = 0$.   Determine the final velocity and the time required for the chain to leave the peg.

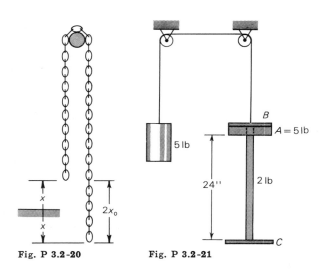

Fig. P 3.2-20   Fig. P 3.2-21

3.2-21   The system shown in Fig. P 3.2-21 is released from rest with A attached to B. After 1 sec the weight A is released from B and drops to C, after which it remains in contact with C.   Determine the time that it takes A to hit C.   Show that this time is the same regardless of when A is released.   The combined weight of B, C, and the connecting bar is 2 lb.

3.2-22   Two blocks are connected by a bar: block 1 (mass m_1) is sliding and block 2 (mass m_2) going on wheels down an inclined plane (see Fig. P 3.2-22).   Determine their acceleration and velocity as a function of time when $v(0) = 0$.

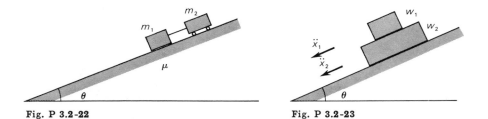

Fig. P 3.2-22   Fig. P 3.2-23

3.2-23   Two rectangular blocks are placed on an inclined plane, as shown in Fig. P 3.2-23. Let f_1 and f_2 be friction forces between w_1 and w_2, and w_2 and the plane, respectively.   (a) Show that, if $f_1 = f_2 = 0$, $\ddot{x}_1 = \ddot{x}_2$, and the two blocks slide together.

(b) For finite values of f_1 and f_2, under what condition is it possible to have $\ddot{x}_2 < \ddot{x}_1$?   (c) For finite values of f_1 and f_2, under what condition is it possible to have $\ddot{x}_2 > \ddot{x}_1$?   Verify your answers by means of free-body diagrams.

3.2-24   A mass m_2 lies on another mass m_1, as shown in Fig. P 3.2-24.   At the beginning of motion the distance between m_2 and the buffer A is c.   During motion m_2 reaches A, and after impact m_2 remains at A (relative to m_1).   How long does it take m_2 to travel distance c?

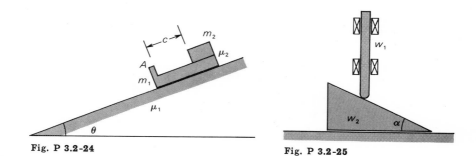

Fig. P 3.2-24   **Fig. P 3.2-25**

3.2-25   A bar of weight w_1 can move in a smooth vertical guide with its bottom end resting in a smooth wedge of weight w_2 and angle α (see Fig. P 3.2-25).   Determine the acceleration of the wedge when released from this position.

3.2-26   A small block of mass m is placed at height h on a smooth wedge of angle α that is resting on a smooth floor (see Fig. P 3.2-26).   If the mass of the wedge is M, determine the absolute motion of the block m when released.   What is the equation for the reaction of the floor on the wedge?   What is the equation for the normal reaction of the wedge on m?

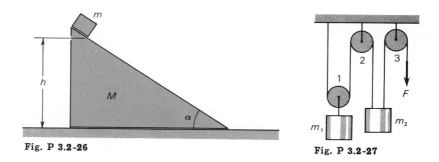

Fig. P 3.2-26   **Fig. P 3.2-27**

3.2-27   For the system shown in Fig. P 3.2-27 determine the acceleration of m_1 and m_2 when a force F is applied to the free end of the rope.   Also, compute the acceleration of the center of mass of the system.   Friction and the mass of the pulleys are neglected.

3.3 MOMENT OF MOMENTUM OF A SYSTEM OF PARTICLES

Again we describe the dynamic behavior of a closed system of particles with respect to an inertial frame of reference. Referring to Fig. 3.3-1, the

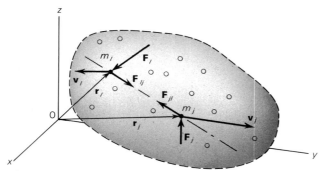

Fig. 3.3-1

moment of momentum of particle j with respect to point O fixed in an inertial reference frame, briefly called fixed point O, is

$$\mathbf{H}_{jo} = \mathbf{r}_j \times m_j \mathbf{v}_j \qquad (3.3\text{-}1)$$

Summing Eq. (3.3-1) over all n particles of the system, we obtain its total moment of momentum about O:

$$\mathbf{H}_O = \sum_{j=1}^{n} \mathbf{H}_{jo} = \sum_{j=1}^{n} \mathbf{r}_j \times m_j \mathbf{v}_j \qquad \blacktriangleleft \quad (3.3\text{-}2)$$

In general, as $\mathbf{r}_j$ and $\mathbf{v}_j$ change with time, so does $\mathbf{H}_O$.

We now investigate how $\mathbf{H}_O$ is affected by the moments of the external forces about the fixed reference point O. For a single particle m_j the moment of all forces acting on it, external and internal, is

$$\mathbf{M}_{jo} + \sum_{l=1}^{n} \mathbf{M}_{jlo} = \mathbf{r}_j \times \left(\mathbf{F}_j + \sum_{l=1}^{n} \mathbf{F}_{jl} \right) = \mathbf{r}_j \times \frac{d}{dt}(m_j \mathbf{v}_j) \qquad l \neq j \quad (3.3\text{-}3)$$

where Eqs. (3.2-1) and (3.2-5) have been used. Observing that the cross product $d\mathbf{r}_j/dt \times \mathbf{v}_j = \mathbf{v}_j \times \mathbf{v}_j = \mathbf{0}$, we may replace the right side of Eq. (3.3-3) by

$$\frac{d\mathbf{r}_j}{dt} \times m_j \mathbf{v}_j + \mathbf{r}_j \times \frac{d}{dt}(m_j \mathbf{v}_j)$$

which equals

$$\frac{d}{dt}(\mathbf{r}_j \times m_j \mathbf{v}_j) = \dot{\mathbf{H}}_{jo}$$

Hence
$$\mathbf{M}_{jo} + \sum_{l=1}^{n} \mathbf{M}_{jlo} = \frac{d\mathbf{H}_{jo}}{dt} = \dot{\mathbf{H}}_{jo} \qquad l \neq j \qquad (3.3\text{-}4)$$

so that the time rate of change of the moment of momentum of any single particle is equal to the moment of both the external and internal forces taken about the fixed reference point O.

In order to obtain the corresponding relation between the force moment and the time rate of change of the moment of momentum for the entire system of particles, we form the vector sum of $\mathbf{M}_{jo} + \sum_{l=1}^{n} \mathbf{M}_{jlo}$ over all n particles:

$$\sum_{j=1}^{n} \left(\mathbf{M}_{jo} + \sum_{l=1}^{n} \mathbf{M}_{jlo} \right) = \sum_{j=1}^{n} \mathbf{r}_j \times \left(\mathbf{F}_j + \sum_{l=1}^{n} \mathbf{F}_{jl} \right)$$

$$= \sum_{j=1}^{n} \frac{d\mathbf{H}_{jo}}{dt} = \frac{d\mathbf{H}_o}{dt} \qquad l \neq j \qquad (3.3\text{-}5)$$

Since in view of Eq. (2.1-4) and Fig. 3.3-1

$$\mathbf{r}_j \times \mathbf{F}_{jl} + \mathbf{r}_l \times \mathbf{F}_{lj} = \mathbf{0} \qquad (3.3\text{-}6)$$

the sum of the moments of all internal forces about the point O is zero:

$$\sum_{j=1}^{n} \left(\mathbf{r}_j \times \sum_{l=1}^{n} \mathbf{F}_{jl} \right) = \mathbf{0} \qquad l \neq j \qquad (3.3\text{-}7)$$

Therefore we arrive at the final result—see Eq. (2.4-3)—

$$\mathbf{M}_o = \sum_{j=1}^{n} \mathbf{r}_j \times \mathbf{F}_j = \frac{d\mathbf{H}_o}{dt} = \dot{\mathbf{H}}_o \qquad \blacktriangleleft \quad (3.3\text{-}8)$$

where $\mathbf{M}_o$ is the resultant moment of all external forces about O.

Although the internal forces do not influence the time rate of change of the total moment of momentum of the system, they do so for each particle of the system—see Eq. (3.3-3). Integration of Eq. (3.3-8) with respect to time yields the theorem of moment of momentum of a closed system about a fixed reference point O:

$$\int_{t_1}^{t_2} \mathbf{M}_o \, dt = \mathbf{H}_o(t_2) - \mathbf{H}_o(t_1) \qquad \blacktriangleleft \quad (3.3\text{-}9)$$

Equations (3.3-8) and (3.3-9) also hold when the moving center of mass C

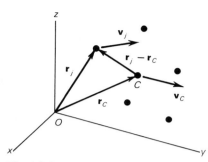

Fig. 3.3-2

replaces the fixed point O as reference point.   Referring to Fig. 3.3-2, we have

$$\mathbf{M}_O = \mathbf{M}_C + \mathbf{r}_C \times \mathbf{F} \qquad (3.3\text{-}10)$$

with $\mathbf{F}$ as the resultant of all external forces, and

$$\mathbf{H}_O = \mathbf{H}_C + \mathbf{r}_C \times m\mathbf{v}_C \qquad (3\text{-}3\text{-}11)$$

since
$$\mathbf{H}_C = \sum_{j=1}^{n} (\mathbf{r}_j - \mathbf{r}_C) \times m_j\mathbf{v}_j$$

$$= \sum_{j=1}^{n} \mathbf{r}_j \times m_j\mathbf{v}_j - \mathbf{r}_C \times \sum_{j=1}^{n} m_j\mathbf{v}_j \qquad (3.3\text{-}12)$$

Thus
$$\mathbf{H}_C = \mathbf{H}_O - \mathbf{r}_C \times m\mathbf{v}_C$$

Substituting Eqs. (3.3-10) and (3.3-11) in Eq. (3.3-8), we obtain

$$\mathbf{M}_C + \mathbf{r}_C \times \mathbf{F} = \dot{\mathbf{H}}_C + \mathbf{v}_C \times m\mathbf{v}_C + \mathbf{r}_C \times ma_C$$

or since $\mathbf{F} = ma_C$—see Eq. (3.2-7)—we have

$$\mathbf{M}_C = \dot{\mathbf{H}}_C \qquad (3.3\text{-}13)$$

or
$$\int_{t_1}^{t_2} \mathbf{M}_C\, dt = \mathbf{H}_C(t_2) - \mathbf{H}_C(t_1) \qquad \blacktriangleleft \quad (3.3\text{-}14)$$

Finally we derive another important relationship.   If we define $\mathbf{h}_C$ as the moment of momentum of the mass system with respect to its momentary center of mass C in a reference frame that is in pure translation with the velocity $\mathbf{v}_C$, such that it does not rotate with respect to an inertial frame, we obtain

$$\mathbf{h}_C = \sum_{j=1}^{n} (\mathbf{r}_j - \mathbf{r}_C) \times m_j(\mathbf{v}_j - \mathbf{v}_C) \qquad (3.3\text{-}15)$$

Expanding the right side of Eq. (3.3-15), we have

$$\mathbf{h}_C = \sum_{j=1}^{n} (\mathbf{r}_j - \mathbf{r}_C) \times m_j\mathbf{v}_j - \left(\sum_{j=1}^{n} \mathbf{r}_j m_j \right) \times \mathbf{v}_C + \mathbf{r}_C \times \mathbf{v}_C \sum_{j=1}^{n} m_j$$

Considering that $\sum\limits_{j=1}^{n} \mathbf{r}_j m_j = \mathbf{r}_C m$ and $\sum\limits_{j=1}^{n} m_j = m$, we see immediately that
—see Eq. (3.3-12)—

$$\mathbf{h}_C = \sum_{j=1}^{n} (\mathbf{r}_j - \mathbf{r}_C) \times m_j \mathbf{v}_j = \mathbf{H}_C \qquad (3.3\text{-}16)$$

and thus we also have—see Eq. (3.3-13)—

$$\mathbf{M}_C = \dot{\mathbf{h}}_C \qquad \blacktriangleleft \quad (3.3\text{-}17)$$

and
$$\int_{t_1}^{t_2} \mathbf{M}_C \, dt = \mathbf{h}_C(t_2) - \mathbf{h}_C(t_1) \qquad \blacktriangleleft \quad (3.3\text{-}18)$$

Equations (3.3-17) and (3.3-18) prove to be very useful in the treatment of rigid bodies, where the location of the center of mass C is fixed in the body.

ILLUSTRATIVE EXAMPLE 3.3-1

A dumbbell of masses m_1, m_2 connected by a rigid massless rod of length l is dropped without rotation, and mass m_1 strikes a ledge with velocity v (see Fig. 3.3-3). If m_1 rebounds with velocity c_1, determine the angular velocity of the rod immediately after impact and the impulse $\hat{F}$ imparted to the dumbbell by the ledge. All velocities are directed vertically.

SOLUTION: Denoting the velocities immediately before impact by v and after impact by c and employing coordinates as shown in Fig. 3.3-3, the momentum theorem—see Eq.

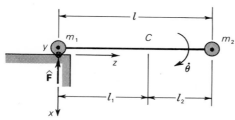

Fig. 3.3-3

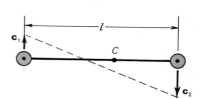

Fig. 3.3-4   Velocities after impact.

(3.2-9)—yields

$$\hat{F}_x = m_1 c_{1x} + m_2 c_{2x} - (m_1 + m_2) v_x$$

or with $c_{1x} = -c_1$ and $v_x = v$, as given above, as well as with $\hat{F}_x = -\hat{F}$, we have

$$\hat{F} = +m_1 c_1 - m_2 c_{2x} + (m_1 + m_2) v \qquad (a)$$

Noting from Fig. 3.3-4 that

$$\dot{\theta} = \frac{c_{2x} - c_{1x}}{l} = \frac{c_{2x} + c_1}{l} \qquad (b)$$

that is,
$$c_{2x} = l\dot{\theta} - c_1$$

Eq. (a) may be written

$$\hat{F} = -l\theta m_2 + (m_1 + m_2)(c_1 + v) \qquad (c)$$

For the determination of the two unknowns $\hat{F}$ and θ we need one more equation, which is offered by the moment-of-momentum theorem—see Eq. (3.3-14). Taking moments about the center of mass, we have

$$-l_1\hat{F}_x = -l_1 m_1 c_{1x} + l_2 m_2 c_{2x} - (-l_1 m_1 v_{1x} + l_2 m_2 v_{2x})$$

For $v_{1x} = v_{2x} = v$ the term in parentheses is zero, remembering that $m_1/m_2 = l_2/l_1$, and substituting $\hat{F}_x = -\hat{F}$, $c_{1x} = -c_1$, $c_{2x} = l\theta - c_1$, we obtain

$$l_1\hat{F} = c_1(l_1 m_1 - l_2 m_2) + m_2 l_2 l\theta \qquad (d)$$

Hence by means of Eqs. (c) and (d) and using the obvious relationships $l_1 + l_2 = l$, $l_1 = m_2 l/(m_1 + m_2)$, and $l_2 = m_1 l/(m_1 + m_2)$, we find

$$\hat{F} = m_1(c_1 + v_1) \qquad (e)$$

and

$$\theta = \frac{v + c_1}{l} \qquad (f)$$

Thus we have, furthermore—see Eq. (b)—

$$c_{2x} = l\theta - c_1 = v \qquad (g)$$

Taking moments about the point of impact instead of about the center of mass, the result (g) could be deduced immediately, and therefore the answers (e) and (f) could be written readily, using Eqs. (a) and (b).

ILLUSTRATIVE EXAMPLE 3.3-2

A massless rigid shaft of length L rotating with constant angular speed ω carries, on a rigid massless rod of length l, two particles, each of mass m, as shown in Fig. 3.3-5. Determine the bearing reactions, not considering the weight of the particles.

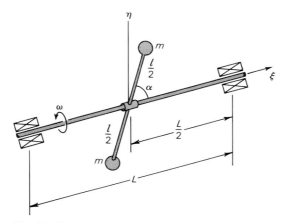

Fig. 3.3-5

SOLUTION:[1]   First we determine the moment of momentum $\mathbf{H}_O$ and then apply the relationship (3.3-8), yielding the moment $\mathbf{M}_O$ exerted by the bearing reactions.   With Eq. (3.3-2) we have

$$\mathbf{H}_O = \sum_{j=1}^{2} \mathbf{r}_j \times m_j \mathbf{v}_j \tag{a}$$

or with $\qquad \mathbf{r}_1 = l \cos \alpha\, \mathbf{i} + l \sin \alpha\, (\cos \omega t\, \mathbf{j} + \sin \omega t\, \mathbf{k}) \qquad \mathbf{r}_2 = -\mathbf{r}_1$

and $\qquad\qquad \mathbf{v}_1 = \dot{\mathbf{r}}_1 = \omega l \sin \alpha\, (-\sin \omega t\, \mathbf{j} + \cos \omega t\, \mathbf{k}) \qquad \mathbf{v}_2 = -\mathbf{v}_1$

and $\qquad\qquad\qquad\qquad m_1 = m_2 = m$

$\qquad \mathbf{H}_O = 2m\mathbf{r}_1 \times \mathbf{v}_1 = 2m\omega l^2 \sin^2 \alpha\, \mathbf{i} - 2m\omega l^2 \cos \alpha \sin \alpha\, (\cos \omega t\, \mathbf{j} + \sin \omega t\, \mathbf{k})$

Hence we find—see Eq. (3.3-8)—

$$\mathbf{M}_O = \dot{\mathbf{H}}_O = 2m\omega^2 l^2 \cos \alpha \sin \alpha\, (\sin \omega t\, \mathbf{j} - \cos \omega t\, \mathbf{k}) \tag{b}$$

Thus we obtain for the magnitude of $\mathbf{M}_O$

$$M_O = 2m\omega^2 l^2 \cos \alpha \sin \alpha \tag{c}$$

The bearing forces form a couple of moment $\mathbf{M}_O$, each force being of magnitude

$$F = \frac{M_O}{L} \tag{d}$$

The bearing forces rotate with the shaft, as seen from expression (b), such that they are always in a plane with masses m_1 and m_2.

Obtain the same results using the concept of centrifugal force.

PROBLEMS

3.3-1   Weights $w_1 > w_2$ are connected by a weightless pulley that is attached to a lever system with balancing weight w_3 (see Fig. P 3.3-1).   If the pulley wheel is

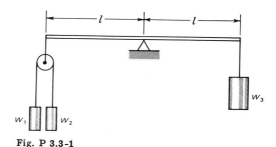

Fig. P 3.3-1

unlocked, how large must w_3 be in order to keep the lever balanced in the horizontal position?

3.3-2   If $w_3 = w_1 + w_2$, the lever balances with the pulley wheel locked.   If the pulley wheel is unlocked in this position, determine the acceleration of each weight (cf. Prob. 3.3-1).

---

[1] The solution is most easily obtained by means of the concept of centrifugal force.   However, for didactic reasons the problem is treated to demonstrate the application of the theory presented in this section.

3.3-3   Masses m_1 and m_2 falling through different heights strike the pans of a platform balance simultaneously with velocities v_1 and v_2, respectively, and thereafter stick to the pans (see Fig. P 3.3-3).   Determine the velocity of the pans of mass m each.

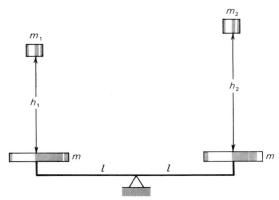

Fig. P 3.3-3

3.3-4   A particle m_2 attaches itself to the mass m_1 of a pendulum, as shown in Fig. P 3.3-4.   What is the velocity of the combined mass when the velocities of the two masses before impact were v_1 and v_2, respectively?

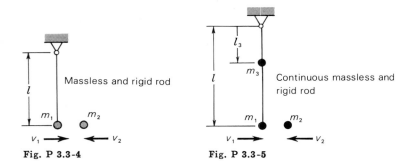

Fig. P 3.3-4   **Fig. P 3.3-5**

3.3-5   Answer the same question as in Prob. 3.3-4 when the pendulum consists of two masses, as shown in Fig. P 3.3-5.

3.3-6   The pendulum shown in Fig. P 3.3-5 is at rest before impact.   After masses m_1 and m_2 are combined, their common velocity is c.   What is the velocity of mass m_2 before impact?

3.3-7   A ball of mass m_1 is shot through the hole in mass m_2 in the pendulum shown in
          Fig. P 3.3-7.   Thereby the ball changes its velocity from v_1 to c_1.   If the pendu-
          lum is at rest before, what is its motion immediately after the ball passes through
          mass m_2?

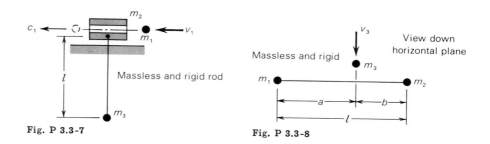

Fig. P 3.3-7   Fig. P 3.3-8

3.3-8   A dumbbell at rest on a horizontal table is struck by a particle of mass m_3
          traveling horizontally, as shown in Fig. P 3.3-8.   If the particle 3 attaches itself
          to the massless and rigid bar of the dumbbell, determine the motion of the three
          masses immediately after the impact.
3.3-9   What is the motion of the dumbbell shown in Fig. P 3.3-8 if the particle 3 bounces
          off the rod in the opposite direction with velocity c_3?
3.3-10   What are the velocities of masses m_1 and m_2 of Fig. P 3.3-8 if the rod breaks and
          mass m_3 continues in the same direction with diminished velocity c_3?
3.3-11   A mass m attached to a rigid massless beam of length l is hinged at O and is
          supported by a spring at a point a distance c from O.   A lump of putty of mass

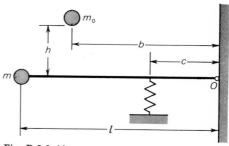

Fig. P 3.3-11

m_0 is dropped from a height h on the beam at a point a distance b from O.   Determine the angular velocity θ of the beam immediately after the putty strikes and
sticks to the beam.

3.4 WORK THEOREM

Remembering that every particle is simultaneously subjected to external and internal forces (see Fig. 3.4-1), we apply the work theorem, as derived

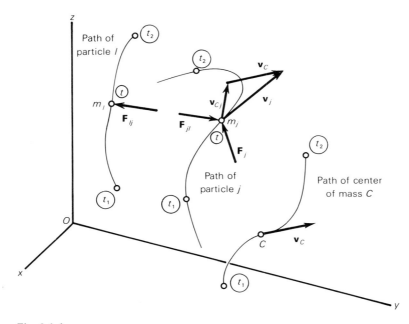

Fig. 3.4-1

in Sec. 2.5, to each particle m_j, which yields—see Eq. (2.5-7)—for the path between points 1 and 2

$$W_{j_{1,2}} = \int_{t_1}^{t_2} \left(\mathbf{F}_j + \sum_{l=1}^{n} \mathbf{F}_{jl} \right) \cdot \mathbf{v}_j \, dt = T_{j2} - T_{j1} = \tfrac{1}{2} m_j (v_{j2}^2 - v_{j1}^2) \qquad l \neq j$$

$$(3.4\text{-}1)$$

Summation of $W_{j_{1,2}}$ over all n particles with respect to j leads to the theorem that the work done by the external and internal forces on all n particles of a closed system is equal to the change of the total kinetic energy of the system:

$$W_{1,2} = \sum_{j=1}^{n} \left[\int_{t_1}^{t_2} \left(\mathbf{F}_j + \sum_{l=1}^{n} \mathbf{F}_{jl} \right) \cdot \mathbf{v}_j \, dt \right] = T_2 - T_1$$

$$= \sum_{j=1}^{n} \tfrac{1}{2} m_j (v_{j2}^2 - v_{j1}^2) \qquad l \neq j \quad \blacktriangleleft \quad (3.4\text{-}2)$$

Note that the influence of the internal forces $\mathbf{F}_{jl}$ does not vanish with summation, as in those cases in which the total momentum or the moment of momentum is calculated, because in spite of Eq. (3.1-1) we have, in general, $\mathbf{F}_{jl} \cdot \mathbf{v}_j + \mathbf{F}_{lj} \cdot \mathbf{v}_l \neq 0$. If all external forces have the potential U_e and all internal forces the potential U_i, that is, if the system of particles is conservative, then we have, with $U_e + U_i = U$ (see Sec. 2.5),

$$U_1 - U_2 = T_2 - T_1$$
or
$$U_1 + T_1 = U_2 + T_2$$
or
$$U + T = E = \text{const}$$

Equation (3.4-2) can be modified slightly if the velocity $\mathbf{v}_j$ of particle j is resolved as follows:

$$\mathbf{v}_j = \mathbf{v}_C + \mathbf{v}_{Cj}$$

where $\mathbf{v}_{Cj}$ is the velocity of particle j relative to the center of mass C. Because $\sum\limits_{j=1}^{n} \left(\sum\limits_{l=1}^{n} \mathbf{F}_{jl} \cdot \mathbf{v}_C \right) = \mathbf{v}_C \cdot \sum\limits_{j=1}^{n} \sum\limits_{l=1}^{n} \mathbf{F}_{jl} = 0$ with $l \neq j$ and $\mathbf{F} = \sum\limits_{j=1}^{n} \mathbf{F}_j$, Eq. (3.4-2) may be written

$$W_{1,2} = \int_{t_1}^{t_2} \mathbf{F} \cdot \mathbf{v}_C \, dt + \sum_{j=1}^{n} \int_{t_1}^{t_2} \left[\left(\mathbf{F}_j + \sum_{l=1}^{n} \mathbf{F}_{jl} \right) \cdot \mathbf{v}_{Cj} \right] dt$$
$$= T_2 - T_1 \qquad l \neq j \quad (3.4\text{-}3)$$

With $\mathbf{v}_j = \mathbf{v}_C + \mathbf{v}_{Cj}$, the kinetic energy T can also be written

$$T = \tfrac{1}{2} \sum_{j=1}^{n} m_j v_C^2 + \tfrac{1}{2} \sum_{j=1}^{n} m_j v_{Cj}^2 + \mathbf{v}_C \cdot \sum_{j=1}^{n} m_j \mathbf{v}_{Cj}$$
or
$$T = \tfrac{1}{2} m v_C^2 + \tfrac{1}{2} \sum_{j=1}^{n} m_j v_{Cj}^2 \qquad \blacktriangleleft \quad (3.4\text{-}4)$$

since $\sum\limits_{j=1}^{n} m_j \mathbf{v}_{Cj} = \mathbf{0}$.†

Equation (3.4-3) then permits the following interpretation. The first term of the equation is

$$\int_{t_1}^{t_2} \mathbf{F} \cdot \mathbf{v}_C \, dt = \int_{t_1}^{t_2} m \frac{d\mathbf{v}_C}{dt} \cdot \mathbf{v}_C \, dt = \int_{v_{C1}}^{v_{C2}} m \mathbf{v}_C \cdot d\mathbf{v}_C$$
$$= \tfrac{1}{2} m (v_{C2}^2 - v_{C1}^2) \qquad \blacktriangleleft \quad (3.4\text{-}5)$$

† Since $\sum\limits_{j=1}^{n} m_j \mathbf{v}_{Cj} = d \left(\sum\limits_{j=1}^{n} m_j \mathbf{r}_{Cj} \right) \Big/ dt = \mathbf{0}$ by definition of the center of mass—see Eqs. (3.2-3) and (2.1-8a).

Thus by comparing Eqs. (3.4-3) and (3.4-4), we conclude that

$$\sum_{j=1}^{n} \int_{t_1}^{t_2} \left[\left(\mathbf{F}_j + \sum_{l=1}^{n} \mathbf{F}_{jl} \right) \cdot \mathbf{v}_{Cj} \right] dt$$

$$= \frac{1}{2} \sum_{j=1}^{n} m_j (v_{Cj2}^2 - v_{Cj1}^2) \qquad l \neq j \quad \blacktriangleleft \quad (3.4\text{-}6)$$

or the work done by the external and internal forces along the path of each particle j relative to the center of mass equals the kinetic energy of all particles due to their relative motion to the center of mass. Equation (3.4-6) is independent of Eq. (3.4-5), and the fact that with Eq. (3.4-6) the velocities $\mathbf{v}_{Cj}$ relative to the center of mass can be determined irrespective of the motion of the center of mass is often helpful in the solution of problems.

ILLUSTRATIVE EXAMPLE 3.4-1

A grenade of mass m explodes in mid-air, scattering fragments in all directions (see Fig. 3.4-2). Assuming that the energy of explosion converted into kinetic energy is E,

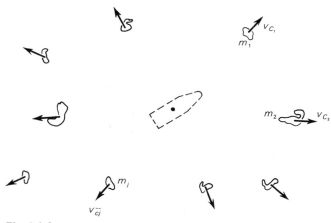

Fig. 3.4-2

determine the magnitude of the relative velocity $|\mathbf{v}_{Cj}|$ of the fragments immediately after the explosion.

SOLUTION: Equation (3.4-6) yields one equation for the determination of the relative velocities of the fragments. Since the work done by the weight during the explosion is negligible, the left side of Eq. (3.4-6) is simply E, which can be interpreted as the work done by internal forces during the explosion. Thus

$$\sum_{j=1}^{n} m_j v_{Cj}^2 = 2E$$

To proceed further, we must make an assumption as to the size and number of fragments. If we assume that the n fragments have equal mass m_j, then $m_j = m/n$ and

$$|\mathbf{v}_{C1}| = \cdots = |\mathbf{v}_{Cj}| = \cdots = |\mathbf{v}_{Cn}|$$

where

$$|\mathbf{v}_{Cj}| = \sqrt{\frac{2E}{m}}$$

which shows that the magnitude of the relative velocity is independent of the number of fragments; that is, all fragments are located at any instant after the explosion on a common sphere with the mass center as its center.

If two unequal fragments m_1 and m_2 result from the explosion $(m_1 + m_2 = m)$, we have

$$m_1 v_{C1}^2 + m_2 v_{C2}^2 = 2E \qquad \text{energy theorem}$$
$$m_1 \mathbf{v}_{C1} + m_2 \mathbf{v}_{C2} = 0 \qquad \text{momentum theorem}$$

The two fragments must then have equal and opposite momentum, or

$$|\mathbf{v}_{C2}| = \frac{m_1}{m_2} |\mathbf{v}_{C1}|$$

Eliminating v_{C2}^2 in the energy equation, we arrive at the result

$$|v_{C1}| = \sqrt{2 \frac{m_2}{m_1} \frac{E}{m}}$$

Similarly we obtain for $|v_{C2}|$

$$|v_{C2}| = \sqrt{2 \frac{m_1}{m_2} \frac{E}{m}}$$

ILLUSTRATIVE EXAMPLE 3.4-2

In a freight yard a car of mass m_1 runs into a standing car of mass m_2 with an impact speed of v_0 (see Fig. 3.4-3). The stiffness of the buffers that cushion the collision is k_1

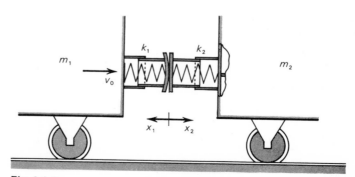

Fig. 3.4-3

and k_2, respectively.   In the absence of friction determine the maximum force F_{12} transmitted by the buffers.

SOLUTION: Consider that in the instant of maximum compression of the buffers both cars have the same velocity v_C, which is determined by means of the theorem of the conservation of momentum (no external forces):

$$m_1 v_0 = (m_1 + m_2) v_C$$

Thus

$$v_C = \frac{m_1}{m_1 + m_2} v_0 \qquad (a)$$

Furthermore we know that in the absence of friction the total energy of the system before the collision must equal the total energy at the instant of maximum compression of the buffers:

$$E = U_1 + T_1 = U_2 + T_2$$

Before the collision the total energy is solely the kinetic energy of car 1 $(U_1 = 0)$.   Thus

$$E = T_1 = \tfrac{1}{2} m_1 v_0^2 \qquad (b)$$

Denoting the maximum distance through which the buffers are compressed by x_1 and x_2, respectively, the potential energy stored in the buffer springs is

$$U_2 = \tfrac{1}{2}(k_1 x_1^2 + k_2 x_2^2) \qquad (c)$$

and we have as kinetic energy

$$T_2 = \tfrac{1}{2}(m_1 + m_2) v_C^2$$

or in view of Eq. (a)

$$T_2 = \frac{1}{2} \frac{m_1^2}{m_1 + m_2} v_0^2 \qquad (d)$$

Equation (c) can be rewritten if we consider that in accordance with Newton's third law

$$k_1 x_1 = k_2 x_2 = F_{12}$$

Thus we obtain

$$U_2 = \tfrac{1}{2} F_{12}(x_1 + x_2)$$

or with $x_1 = F_{12}/k_1$ and $x_2 = F_{12}/k_2$

$$U_2 = \tfrac{1}{2} F_{12}^2 \frac{k_1 + k_2}{k_1 k_2} \qquad (e)$$

Therefore the total energy is conserved if—see Eqs. (b), (d), and (e)—

$$T_1 - T_2 = U_2$$

or

$$\tfrac{1}{2} v_0^2 \left(m_1 - \frac{m_1^2}{m_1 + m_2} \right) = \tfrac{1}{2} F_{12}^2 \frac{k_1 + k_2}{k_1 k_2}$$

Thus

$$F_{12} = v_0 \sqrt{\frac{m_1 m_2}{m_1 + m_2} \frac{k_1 k_2}{k_1 + k_2}}$$

The result shows that with the assumption of linear buffer springs (spring force $= kx$) the force is proportional to the speed of collision. Is the result changed when car 2 is also in motion, such that the relative speed of the two cars remains v_0?

PROBLEMS

3.4-1   A spring of mass m and spring constant k is compressed into a cylinder of mass M a distance x from its unstretched position (see Fig. P 3.4-1). If the system is suddenly released, determine the maximum velocity of M and that of the end of the spring. The equivalent mass of the spring is $\frac{1}{3}m$ at the end of the spring.

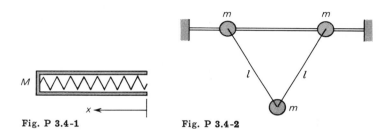

Fig. P 3.4-1   Fig. P 3.4-2

3.4-2   Three equal masses are connected as shown in Fig. P 3.4-2, with the two upper masses free to slide along a smooth horizontal rod and the third connected to the first two by strings of length l. If released from the equilateral position, determine the velocity with which the two upper masses collide.

3.4-3   Four masses connected by massless members of length l hinged at the ends are released from the position shown in Fig. P 3.4-3. Determine the equation for the angular velocity $\dot{\theta}$ of the connecting bars as a function of θ.

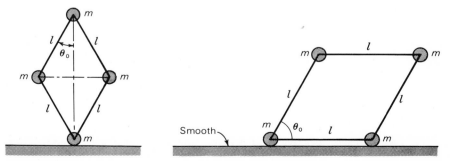

Fig. P 3.4-3   Fig. P 3.4-4

3.4-4   Four equal masses are connected by weightless bars of length l (see Fig. P 3.4-4). If the system is released from position θ_0, determine the angular velocity of the bars as a function of θ.

3.4-5   A weight w_1 is tied to a second weight w_2 by a cord of length l (see Fig. P 3.4-5) that is passed over a smooth peg ($l > 2h$). Determine the velocity of w_2 as a function of x if at the start w_2 is on an inclined plane at $x = 0$ ($w_1 > w_2$).

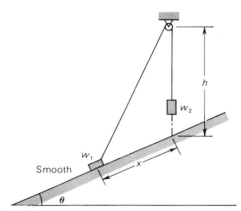

Fig. P 3.4-5

3.4-6   Referring to Fig. P 3.2-25, what is the velocity of the bar when it reaches the ground? Consider the bar at rest before it is released, with its lower end a distance h above the ground.

3.4-7   Referring to Fig. P 3.2-26, what is the velocity of the wedge when the small block of mass m touches the ground?

3.4-8   Referring to Fig. P 3.2-11, what is the maximum compression x_{max} of the spring if there is no friction between the box and the car?

3.4-9   Referring to Fig. P 3.2-15, consider the two masses at rest before mass m_1 acquires velocity $\dot{x}_1$ by a sudden impulse. What is the minimum distance $|x_2 - x_1|_{min}$ thereafter? The horizontal rod is long enough so that mass m_2 does not collide with the wall before the minimum distance is reached.

3.4-10 to 3.4-16   Determine the energy loss in Probs. 3.3-4 to 3.3-10 caused by the impact.

3.4-17   Determine the maximum angle through which the pendulum in Fig. P 3.3-5 swings after impact.

3.4-18   Let there be no friction between mass m_2 and its horizontal support in Fig. P 3.3-7. Determine the maximum angle through which the pendulum swings after the ball passes through mass m_2. What is the velocity of m_2 then?

3.4-19   An elevator of weight w_1 connected to a counterweight w_2 is moving upward at a constant speed of v (see Fig. P 3.4-19). Determine the power output required by the motor. If the elevator is also accelerating upward at $a < g$ when the speed is v, determine the power required at the instant.

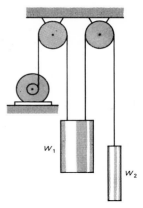

Fig. P 3.4-19

3.4-20   Two weights $w_1 > w_2$ are connected by a cord.   A third weight w_3 $(w_2 + w_3 > w_1)$ rides on w_2 and is removed as w_2 passes through an opening at A (see Fig. P 3.4-20).   Determine the distance h_2 at which w_1 and w_2 come to an instantaneous stop and the distance h_3 above A where they stop again.   The system is started at height h_1 with zero velocity.   Neglect the mass of the pulleys as well as friction, and disregard any bouncing of w_3.

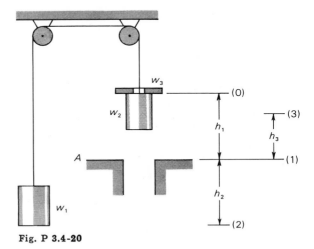

Fig. P 3.4-20

3.4-21   Two particles of mass m_1 and m_2 are connected by a rigid massless bar and held in position $\theta = 45°$ by a spring of stiffness k (see Fig. P 3.4-21).   The carriage on which this system is mounted has a mass m_3 and is constrained to move solely in the horizontal direction. If mass m_1 is displaced to the right a small distance ξ_0 from the equilibrium position ($\xi = \eta = 0$) and released, determine the motion of the three masses as a function of time. Friction is negligible, as well as the mass of rollers.

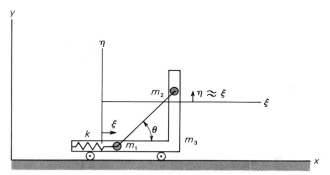

Fig. P 3.4-21

3.5 COLLISION OF TWO PARTICLES—STRAIGHT CENTRAL IMPACT

When two bodies collide, the impact, usually of short duration, changes the velocities of their centers of mass as well as their angular velocities (see Fig. 3.5-1). Furthermore, it causes a deformation of the two bodies, espe-

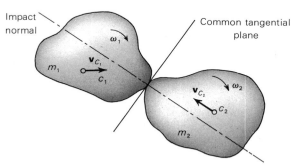

Fig. 3.5-1   General impact case.

cially in the neighborhood of the respective impact locations, and, in general, the bodies assume a state of vibration, because of the sudden and large impact forces. In most practical cases the problem is so complicated that drastic idealizations are necessary in order to obtain more or less reliable results with tolerable mathematical expense. We deal here with the simplest case, the straight central impact of two bodies; in Sec. 4.7 there is a more general treatment.

BASIC ASSUMPTIONS

We now list a number of basic assumptions some of which are rescinded in Sec. 4.7:

1   The angular velocities of both bodies are zero before their collision.

2   The impact normal contains both centers of mass (see Fig. 3.5-2). The impact normal is the straight line normal to the tangential plane that is common to both bodies at their point of contact.[1]

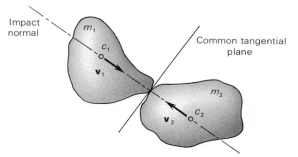

Fig. 3.5-2   Straight central impact.

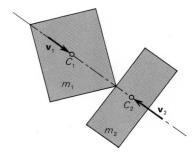

Fig. 3.5-3   Straight central impact (abnormal case).

[1] If one of the two bodies hits the surface of the other with a sharp edge, the tangential plane in the contact point of the second body is the common one. If, however, both bodies come into contact with edges, so that no tangential plane exists, the impact normal cannot be defined uniquely. But it is possible to formulate assumption 2 for straight central impact even in this case, for both centers of mass and the point of contact must be on a straight line that serves then as the impact normal (see Fig. 3.5-3).

3   The velocities of the centers of mass coincide immediately before impact with the impact normal.

4   The two bodies are considered rigid before and after their collision, but not during the impact period.   However, their mass distribution is not changed by the impact.

5   The impact duration t_i is considered infinitely short, so that the positions of the bodies immediately before and after the collision are identical. In this connection it may be stated that the actual impact duration for two identical steel balls having a diameter of 2 in. and a relative velocity of 3 ft/sec is about 10^{-4} sec.

Assumption 2 is responsible for the term *central impact*, and assumption 3 limits the general central impact to a *straight central impact*.   When both conditions 2 and 3 are satisfied, assumption 1 also holds after the collision. Evidently the straight central impact is most easily visualized as the collision of two spheres, as shown in Fig. 3.5-4.   The formulation of assumption 4

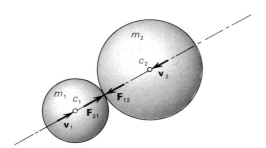

Fig. 3.5-4

leads immediately to the conclusion that it is necessary to consider the response of the bodies to their deformation during impact in order to explain their motion after the collision.

Finally, assumption 5 is an idealization of the fact that the duration of impact is usually very short, whereas the intensity of the average impact forces $\mathbf{F}_{12}$ and $\mathbf{F}_{21}$ is very large,[1] so that besides these two equal and opposite "internal" forces all external forces, such as the weight of the mass, can be ignored during the time of impact.

[1] For example, the average impact force in the case mentioned under assumption 5 amounts to approximately 2,000 lb.

COEFFICIENT OF RESTITUTION

The velocities of two bodies immediately before their collision is v_1 and v_2, and immediately after, c_1 and c_2, as shown in Fig. 3.5-5.   Because of

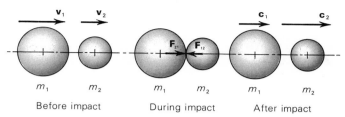

Before impact   During impact   After impact

Fig. 3.5-5

Newton's third law,[1] forces $\mathbf{F}_{12}$ and $\mathbf{F}_{21}$ are equal in magnitude and opposite in direction during impact.   Hence their total impulse is zero; that is, with $\int_0^{t_i} \mathbf{F}_{12}\, dt = \mathbf{\hat{F}}_{12}$ and $\int_0^{t_i} \mathbf{F}_{21}\, dt = \mathbf{\hat{F}}_{21}$ we have $\mathbf{\hat{F}}_{12} + \mathbf{\hat{F}}_{21} = 0$.   Thus the total momentum of the two-body system remains unchanged by the impact:

$$m_1\mathbf{v}_1 + m_2\mathbf{v}_2 = m_1\mathbf{c}_1 + m_2\mathbf{c}_2 \qquad \blacktriangleleft \quad (3.5\text{-}1)$$

With the motion of the two bodies being parallel to the impact normal at all times, it is convenient to replace the velocity vectors as well as the force vectors by their scalar quantities.   All velocities in the direction of $\mathbf{v}_1$ are then considered positive.   This sign convention also holds for the impulsive forces.   Thus we may write, instead of Eq. (3.5-1), letting the positive x direction coincide with the direction of $\mathbf{v}_1$,

$$m_1v_{1x} + m_2v_{2x} = m_1c_{1x} + m_2c_{2x} \qquad (3.5\text{-}2)$$

This represents only one equation for the two unknowns c_{1x} and c_{2x}.   In order to find the other, let us investigate the impact period more fully, which lasts the infinitesimal time t_i.   A deeper insight into the phenomenon of impact is gained if we split the duration of impact into two intervals t_I and t_{II} (see Fig. 3.5-6), where t_I covers the period of compression from first contact until maximum deformation of the two bodies.   At the end of this interval the relative velocity of the two bodies is zero.   The interval t_{II}

---

[1] Newton felt the necessity of pointing to the impact tests by C. Wren, the famous architect of St. Paul's Cathedral, in London (born 1632 in East Knoyle, Wilshire; died 1723 in Hampton Court), C. Huygens (born 1629 in The Hague; died there 1695), and J. Wallis (born 1661 in Ashford, Kent; died 1703 in Oxford) in order to give proof of the validity of his third law in the field of dynamics also.   It reflects the great interest of Newton's era in this problem that the three scientists presented the results of their work within a few weeks to the Royal Society in London: Wallis on November 26, 1668; Wren on December 17, 1668; and Huygens on January 4, 1669.

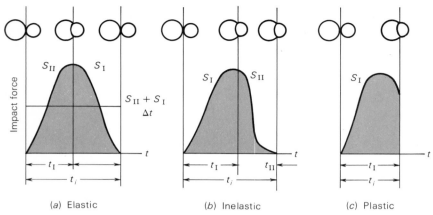

(a) Elastic   (b) Inelastic   (c) Plastic

Fig. 3.5-6

comprises the period of restitution from maximum deformation until cessation of contact. In the ideally elastic case we have $t_I = t_{II} = t_i/2$ (see Fig. 3.5-6a); in the inelastic case we have, in general, $t_I \neq t_{II}$ (see Fig. 3.5-6b); and the so-called plastic impact is characterized by $t_{II} = 0$ (see Fig. 3.5-6c), because the two bodies then remain in contact after the compression period. Corresponding to the two distinct intervals we also split the total impulse $\hat{\mathbf{F}}_{12} = -\hat{\mathbf{F}}_{21}$ (see Fig. 3.5-7) that is exchanged between the

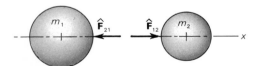

Fig. 3.5-7

two bodies into $\hat{\mathbf{F}}_{12}{}^I$ and $\hat{\mathbf{F}}_{12}{}^{II}$, which are defined as

$$\hat{\mathbf{F}}_{12}{}^I = \int_0^{t_I} \mathbf{F}_{12}\, dt \qquad \text{and} \qquad \hat{\mathbf{F}}_{12}{}^{II} = \int_{t_I}^{t_I+t_{II}} \mathbf{F}_{12}\, dt$$

Thus we have

$$\hat{\mathbf{F}}_{12} = \hat{\mathbf{F}}_{12}{}^I + \hat{\mathbf{F}}_{12}{}^{II}$$

Because $\hat{F}_{12} = \hat{F}_{21}$, and so on, we use the shorter symbols $\hat{F}_I$, $\hat{F}_{II}$, and $\hat{F}$, that is, $\hat{F}_{12}{}^I = \hat{F}_{21}{}^I = \hat{F}_I$, $\hat{F}_{12}{}^{II} = \hat{F}_{21}{}^{II} = \hat{F}_{II}$, and $\hat{F}_{12} = \hat{F}_{21} = \hat{F}$.

At the end of the compression period, the velocities of the two bodies are equal. Designating this common velocity by v_C, the change of momentum of each body is

$$m_1(v_{Cx} - v_{1x}) = -\hat{F}_\mathrm{I} \qquad (3.5\text{-}3)$$

and

$$m_2(v_{Cx} - v_{2x}) = \hat{F}_\mathrm{I} \qquad (3.5\text{-}4)$$

respectively. By adding the two equations, we eliminate $\hat{F}_\mathrm{I}$ and obtain

$$v_{Cx} = \frac{m_1 v_{1x} + m_2 v_{2x}}{m_1 + m_2} \qquad \blacktriangleleft \quad (3.5\text{-}5)$$

Thus v_{Cx} turns out to be the velocity of the center of mass of the two-body system, which remains unchanged by the collision.

We now consider the period of restitution and write, in accordance with Eqs. (3.5-3) and (3.5-4) for the change in the momentum of each mass,

$$m_1(c_{1x} - v_{Cx}) = -\hat{F}_\mathrm{II} \qquad (3.5\text{-}6)$$

$$m_2(c_{2x} - v_{Cx}) = \hat{F}_\mathrm{II} \qquad (3.5\text{-}7)$$

These two equations yield no additional information, for their addition leads only to

$$v_{Cx} = \frac{m_1 c_{1x} + m_2 c_{2x}}{m_1 + m_2} \qquad \blacktriangleleft \quad (3.5\text{-}8)$$

which, in conjunction with Eq. (3.5-5), is equivalent to Eq. (3.5-2) and thus does not yield the still wanted second equation for the two unknowns c_{1x} and c_{2x}.

In order to proceed, we have to assume a relation between impulse $\hat{F}_\mathrm{I}$ during the compression period and impulse $\hat{F}_\mathrm{II}$ during the period of restitution; that is, we have to make an assumption regarding the response of the two bodies to their impact deformation. The simplest possible relation serving this purpose is

$$\hat{F}_\mathrm{II} = e\hat{F}_\mathrm{I} \qquad \blacktriangleleft \quad (3.5\text{-}9)$$

Since it is due to Newton, it is now known as *Newton's hypothesis*. The coefficient e is called the coefficient of restitution, which depends chiefly on the materials of the two bodies, their size, and their relative velocity. With Eq. (3.5-9) we obtain from Eqs. (3.5-3) and (3.5-6) and from Eqs. (3.5-4) and (3.5-7), respectively,

$$c_{1x} - v_{Cx} = e(v_{Cx} - v_{1x})$$

$$c_{2x} - v_{Cx} = e(v_{Cx} - v_{2x})$$

Thus by subtraction we arrive at the result

$$e = \frac{c_{1x} - c_{2x}}{v_{2x} - v_{1x}} \qquad \blacktriangleleft \quad (3.5\text{-}10)$$

which states that the ratio between the relative velocities immediately after and before the collision is equal to the coefficient of restitution. In the ideally elastic case (see Fig. 3.5-6a) we have $\hat{F}_{\mathrm{I}} = \hat{F}_{\mathrm{II}}$ or $e = 1$, in the inelastic case (see Fig. 3.5-6b) $0 < \hat{F}_{\mathrm{II}} < \hat{F}_{\mathrm{I}}$ or $0 < e < 1$, and in plastic impact $\hat{F}_{\mathrm{II}} = 0$ or $e = 0$.

With Eqs. (3.5-2) and (3.5-10) the velocity of each mass immediately after the collision is found to be

$$c_{1x} = v_{1x} - \frac{(1 + e)(v_{1x} - v_{2x})}{1 + m_1/m_2} \qquad \blacktriangleleft \quad (3.5\text{-}11)$$

$$c_{2x} = v_{2x} + \frac{(1 + e)(v_{1x} - v_{2x})}{1 + m_2/m_1} \qquad \blacktriangleleft \quad (3.5\text{-}12)$$

Finally the energy loss during impact is found from the difference of the kinetic energy before and after the collision:

$$\Delta T = \tfrac{1}{2}(m_1 v_1{}^2 + m_2 v_2{}^2) - \tfrac{1}{2}(m_1 c_1{}^2 + m_2 c_2{}^2) \qquad (3.5\text{-}13)$$

or after substitution of Eqs. (3.5-11) and (3.5-12)

$$\Delta T = \tfrac{1}{2}(1 - e^2) \frac{m_1 m_2}{m_1 + m_2} (v_{1x} - v_{2x})^2 \qquad \blacktriangleleft \quad (3.5\text{-}14)$$

Other forms of Eq. (3.5-13) are

$$\Delta T = \frac{1}{2} \frac{1 - e^2}{e^2} \frac{m_1 m_2}{m_1 + m_2} (c_{1x} - c_{2x})^2 \qquad (3.5\text{-}15)$$

and $\qquad \Delta T = \frac{1}{2} \frac{1 - e}{1 + e} [m_1(c_{1x} - v_{1x})^2 + m_2(c_{2x} - v_{2x})^2] \qquad (3.5\text{-}16)$

Equations (3.5-14) to (3.5-16) are in agreement with the fact that the energy loss is zero for elastic impact ($e = 1$) and attains its largest value for plastic impact ($e = 0$). For the latter case discuss Eq. (3.5-15).

Finally we state two relations for the total impulse:

$$\hat{F} = \hat{F}_{\mathrm{I}}(1 + e) = \frac{m_1 m_2}{m_1 + m_2} (1 + e)(v_{1x} - v_{2x}) \qquad (3.5\text{-}17)$$

$$\hat{F} = - \frac{m_1 m_2}{m_1 + m_2} \frac{1 + e}{e} (c_{1x} - c_{2x}) \qquad (3.5\text{-}18)$$

SPECIAL CASE A—STRAIGHT IMPACT OF A PARTICLE AGAINST A WALL
Considering the mass m_2 of the wall as infinitely large compared with the mass m_1 of the striking body, we find from Eq. (3.5-12) the obvious result that $c_{2x} = v_{2x}$, or if the wall was at rest before the impact, that is, $v_{2x} = 0$, it remains so: $c_{2x} = 0$. Furthermore Eq. (3.5-11) yields

$$c_{1x} = v_{1x} - (1 + e)(v_{1x} - v_{2x}) \qquad (3.5\text{-}19)$$

or for $v_{2x} = 0$

$$c_{1x} = -e v_{1x} \qquad \blacktriangleleft \quad (3.5\text{-}20)$$

This equation is often used to determine the coefficient of restitution by dropping a small sphere on a smooth plane from a height h. Rebounding, the sphere attains a height $h' < h$, because of the inevitable loss of mechanical energy during impact. The velocity of the sphere immediately before impact is $v_{1z} = \sqrt{2gh}$, and immediately after, it must be $c_{1z} = -\sqrt{2gh'}$ in order to reach height h'. Thus we have from Eq. (3.5-20)

$$e = \sqrt{\frac{h'}{h}} \qquad (3.5\text{-}21)$$

SPECIAL CASE B—OBLIQUE IMPACT OF A PARTICLE AGAINST A ROUGH WALL
For a particle striking a rough wall obliquely (friction $\neq 0$) with coefficient of restitution e, the horizontal components of the velocity before and after impact are no longer equal (see Fig. 3.5-8). Assuming this relationship to

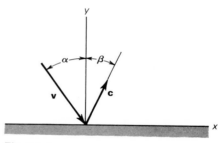

Fig. 3.5-8

be $c_x/v_x = 1 - \lambda$, we show that $\tan \beta / \tan \alpha = (1/e)(1 - \lambda)$. Referring to Fig. 3.5-8, we have

$$\tan \alpha = \left| \frac{v_x}{v_y} \right|$$

$$\tan \beta = \left| \frac{c_x}{c_y} \right| = \left| \frac{c_x}{ev_y} \right|$$

Thus

$$\frac{\tan \beta}{\tan \alpha} = \frac{1}{e} \left| \frac{c_x}{v_y} \right| \cdot \left| \frac{v_y}{v_x} \right| = \frac{1}{e}(1 - \lambda)$$

Letting $\hat{\mathbf{F}}$ be the total impulse and resolving it in the x and y directions, we have $\hat{\mathbf{F}} = \hat{\mathbf{F}}_x + \hat{\mathbf{F}}_y$:

$$\hat{F}_x = m(c_x - v_x) = -m\lambda v_x = -m\lambda v \sin \alpha$$
$$\hat{F}_y = m(c_y - v_y) = mv_y(1 + e) = m(1 + e)v \cos \alpha$$

Thus, by combining these two components, the equation for the total impulse becomes

$$|\mathbf{\hat{F}}| = mv \sqrt{\lambda^2 \sin^2 \alpha + (1 + e)^2 \cos^2 \alpha}$$

For the frictionless case, $\lambda = 0$, this equation reduces to

$$|\mathbf{\hat{F}}| = mv(1 + e) \cos \alpha$$

ILLUSTRATIVE EXAMPLE 3.5-1

Consider two small ivory balls, as shown in Fig. 3.5-9, of equal mass $m_1 = m_2 = m$. Determine their velocities c_1 and c_2 immediately after impact if e is $15/16$. What is the energy loss?

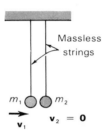

Massless strings

m_1 m_2

v_1 $v_2 = 0$

Fig. 3.5-9

SOLUTION: The energy loss is most easily found from Eq. (3.5-14):

$$\Delta T = \frac{1}{2}\left[1 - \left(\frac{15}{16}\right)^2\right]\frac{m}{2}v_1^2 = \frac{31}{512}\frac{m}{2}v_1^2$$

Thus only about 6 percent of the initial kinetic energy is lost.

Equation (3.5-11) shows that after the collision the velocity of mass 1 is reduced to

$$c_1 = 1/32 v_1$$

and from Eq. (3.5-12) we find that mass 2 has, by the impact, acquired the velocity

$$c_2 = 31/32 v_1$$

It is easily seen that in the ideally elastic case ($e = 1$) we find that $\Delta T = 0$, $c_1 = 0$, and $c_2 = v_1$; that is, the kinetic energy, as well as the momentum, is then entirely transferred from mass 1 to mass 2.

ILLUSTRATIVE EXAMPLE 3.5-2

In a forging operation, performed by a hammer hitting metal on an anvil (see Fig. 3.5-10), the object is to transform as great a part of the kinetic energy of the falling hammer as possible into energy that is dissipated in changing the shape of the metal. Hence we must aim at making the ratio between the energy loss ΔT and the kinetic energy of the hammer before impact as large as possible.

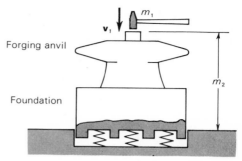

Fig. 3.5-10

SOLUTION: Denoting the mass of the hammer by m_1 and that of the combined metal, anvil, and foundation by m_2,† we have, as the kinetic energy of the system before impact,

$$T = \tfrac{1}{2}m_1 v_1^2$$

For $v_2 = 0$, Eq. (3.5-14) yields the energy loss

$$\Delta T = \tfrac{1}{2}(1 - e^2)\,\frac{m_1 m_2}{m_1 + m_2}\,v_1^2$$

Defining $\Delta T/T = \eta$ as the degree of efficiency of the forging operation we find the relation

$$\eta = (1 - e^2)\,\frac{m_2}{m_1 + m_2}$$

which shows that η approaches the ideal value 1 when $e \to 0$ and $m_2 \to \infty$, that is, when the rebound of the hammer is avoided as much as possible (hot forging) and the combined weight of the metal, anvil, and foundation is made considerably larger than that of the hammer.

PROBLEMS

3.5-1   A bullet weighing 0.10 lb with a muzzle velocity of 2,000 ft/sec is fired parallel to a 30° inclined plane and into a block weighing 2 lb (see Fig. P 3.5-1). If the bullet remains embedded in the block, how far up the inclined plane does the block go? Assume friction to be zero.

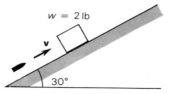

Fig. P 3.5-1

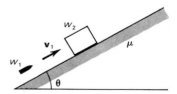

Fig. P 3.5-2

† Consider the foundation block to be supported by springs for the sake of shock isolation.

3.5-2   A bullet of weight w_1 shot parallel to an inclined plane strikes a block of weight w_2 with velocity v_1 and is embedded in it (see Fig. P 3.5-2). If the block moves 5 ft up the plane and the coefficient of friction between it and the block is μ, determine the velocity of the bullet.

3.5-3   A bullet of mass m strikes a block of wood of mass M and is embedded in it (see Fig. P 3.5-3). M and the embedded bullet travel distances s_1 and s_2 together before coming to rest. Determine the corresponding time.

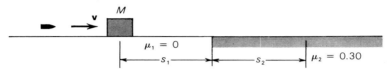

Fig. P 3.5-3

3.5-4   A bullet weighing 0.065 lb approaches a wooden target 1 in. thick weighing 2.2 lb with a velocity of 1,800 ft/sec (see Fig. P 3.5-4). After passing through the target, the velocity of the bullet is 500 ft/sec. What is the velocity of the target? Determine the energy lost. If the target is suspended as a simple pendulum 10 ft long, through what angle does it travel?

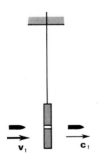

Fig. P 3.5-4

3.5-5   A bullet of mass m with velocity v strikes a sack of sand of mass M supported as a simple pendulum. If the sand with the embedded bullet swings to a maximum angle of θ_0, determine the velocity of the bullet and the loss of kinetic energy.

3.5-6   A pile driver of weight w_1 falls through a height h on a pile of weight w_2 (see Fig. P 3.5-6). The impact is plastic, and the pile is driven down a distance δ. Assuming the ground resistance to be constant, determine its value.

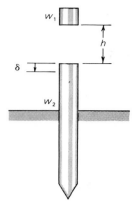

Fig. P 3.5-6

3.5-7   A pile weighing 400 lb is driven by the 1,000-lb weight of a pile driver that falls
         through a distance of 8 ft and moves with the pile.   What is the loss of kinetic
         energy?   If the pile is driven 2 in. by the impact, determine the average resistance
         of the ground.

3.5-8   A pile hammer of weight w_h strikes a pile with velocity v, the impact being plastic.
         If the weight of the pile is w_p and the ground resistance is assumed to be a con-
         stant R, determine the equation for the distance x through which the pile moves.

3.5-9   A drop hammer of weight w_1 falls through a height h on a base of weight w_2 sup-
         ported on a nest of springs that deflect x_0 in. under the static weight of w_2.
         If w_1 moves with w_2 without rebound, determine the maximum force transmitted
         to the floor.

3.5-10   A box weighing 10 lb slides to the right on a smooth horizontal floor with a
         velocity of 12 ft/sec (see Fig. P 3.5-10).   At a given position an 8-lb block of
         putty drops into the box from a height of 2 ft.   After impact the box and putty
         strike a horizontal spring, compressing it 6 in. before being brought to rest.
         Determine the modulus k of the spring.

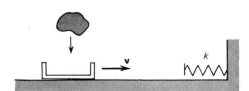

Fig. P 3.5-10

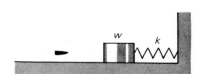

Fig. P 3.5-11

3.5-11   A bullet weighing 0.12 lb and traveling with a speed of 2,000 ft/sec strikes a
         20-lb block of wood and remains embedded in it (see Fig. P 3.5-11).   The block
         is attached to a spring of stiffness 8 lb/in. that is unstrained in the original
         position.   Determine the maximum compression of the spring.

3.5-12   The block in Prob. 3.5-11 is now placed on a rough floor, and the experiment repeated.   If the maximum compression of the spring is 10 in., determine the coefficient of friction between the block and the floor.

3.5-13   A mass m_0 strikes another mass m resting on a spring, after falling through a height h, and the two masses then move together as a single mass (see Fig. P 3.5-13).   Determine the maximum deflection of the spring.

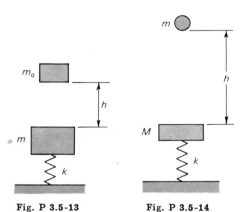

Fig. P 3.5-13   Fig. P 3.5-14

3.5-14   A ball of mass m falls through a height h on a mass M supported by a spring of stiffness k (see Fig. P 3.5-14).   If no energy is lost during impact, determine the velocity acquired by m and M immediately after impact and the deflection of M.

3.5-15   If in Prob. 3.5-14 m is a lump of putty that sticks to M, determine the velocity acquired by M.   What is the maximum displacement of M?

3.5-16   A steel ball of mass m_1 is shot against a steel block of mass m_2 attached to a spring of stiffness k (see Fig. P 3.5-16).   If the coefficient of restitution between the ball and the block is e and the ball strikes the block with velocity v_1, determine the maximum distance x that the spring is compressed.   Under what condition does the velocity of the ball become zero after impact?

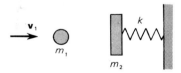

Fig. P 3.5-16

3.5-17   The system in Fig. P 3.5-17 is released from rest from the position shown.   The 10-lb weight passes through the hole in the bracket, but the 8-lb rider remains on the bracket without rebound.   Determine the maximum distance x measured from the starting position to which the 10-lb weight descends.   To what height h above the bracket does the 10-lb weight return?   Account for the loss in height.

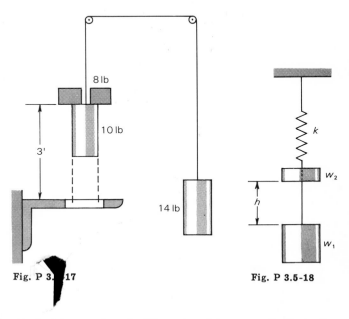

Fig. P 3.5-17   Fig. P 3.5-18

3.5-18   A weight w_1 is attached to a spring of stiffness k and hangs vertically in the equilibrium position (see Fig. P 3.5-18).   Another weight w_2 falls from rest through a height h and collides with weight w_1 without rebound.   Deduce the subsequent motion of the weights.

3.5-19   Two masses m_1 and m_2 are in motion on a frictionless horizontal table.   Mass m_2 follows mass m_1 on the same line with speed $v_2 > v_1$.   (a) Which conditions (velocity and mass ratio) have to be satisfied in order that after collision $c_2 = 0$? The coefficient of restitution is e.   (b) What is the least ratio of v_2/v_1 for c_2 to become zero?

3.5-20   Three billiard balls are lined up along a straight line with distance d between them (see Fig. P 3.5-20).   A fourth ball strikes the first one along the same line with velocity v.   Assuming elastic impact, describe the motion of the balls. If distance d is reduced to zero, so that the three balls are touching each other, what is the resulting motion?

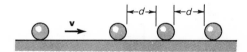

Fig. P 3.5-20

3.5-21   Four billiard balls of radius r are spaced $4r$ apart between their centers. If the first ball is given a velocity v, determine the motion of all the balls as the impact progresses to the right. Assume $e = 0.80$.

3.5-22   The masses $m_1 < m_2 < m_3$ are on a straight line, and m_1 strikes m_2 with velocity v_1, after which m_2 strikes m_3. Assuming elastic impact $e = 1$, determine (a) the velocity of m_1 after impact, (b) the velocity of m_2 after impact with m_3, and (c) the velocity of m_3. Determine the value of m_2 that gives the greatest velocity to m_3, and determine the maximum velocity of m_3.

3.5-23   A dumbbell of two equal masses m rests on a horizontal frictionless table (see Fig. P 3.5-23). A third mass M traveling with velocity v normal to l strikes one of the masses, the coefficient of restitution for the impact being e. We wish to know the velocity of each mass after impact. State the unknowns of the problem, and write the number of equations necessary for their solution, indicating the principle behind each.

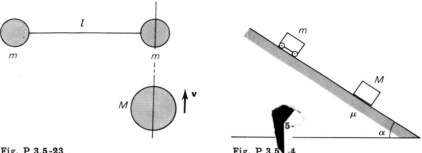

Fig. P 3.5-23   Fig. P 3.5-24

3.5-24   A car of mass m rolls down an inclined plane of angle α and strikes a second mass M with velocity v (see Fig. P 3.5-24). If $\mu > \tan \alpha$, determine the distance s traveled by M, assuming $e = 1$. How far up the incline does m rebound $(M > m)$?

3.5-25   A mass m_1 supported as a simple pendulum of length l is raised through an angle θ and allowed to strike a mass m_2 resting on the floor with coefficient of friction μ (see Fig. P 3.5-25). If the coefficient of restitution between m_1 and m_2 is e, determine the distance through which m_2 travels before coming to rest. What is the rebound angle of m_1?

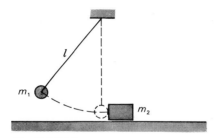

Fig. P 3.5-25

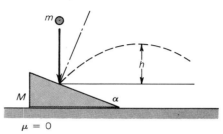

Fig. P 3.5-26

3.5-26   A small steel ball is dropped on a solid steel wedge with velocity v_0 (see Fig. P 3.5-26). Neglecting friction and assuming $e = 0.80$ for normal impact, determine the height h above the impact point to which it rebounds. What is the velocity acquired by the wedge?

3.5-27   A steel ball rolls off a step of height h_0 with horizontal velocity v_0 (see Fig. P 3.5-27). If it bounces on a floor for which the coefficient of restitution $e < 1$ and the coefficient of friction $\mu = 0$, determine the equation for the horizontal distance traveled by the ball before bouncing stops.

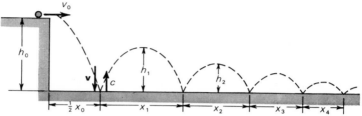

Fig. P 3.5-27

3.6   BODY OF VARIABLE MASS

The concept of a body refers here to finite bodies in translation to whose mass an influx of mass is impinging, or vice versa. As examples of the former, we mention the air intake of a jet engine, and of the latter, the rocket, a balloon dropping ballast, and the like. The dynamic problem presented by the phenomenon of the mass remaining no longer constant but changing with time is examined from the following point of view. The increasing mass can be viewed as receiving the incoming mass elements dm by means of a continuous series of infinitesimal plastic impacts. Thereby each mass element assumes a new velocity in common with the body to which it is attached, the instant that it makes its contact. The fact that frequently, for example, in the case of rockets, the mass is decreased, because of a continuous discharge of matter, is simply taken into account by introducing dm as negative.

Taking this viewpoint of continuous infinitesimal impacts, we consider, at time t, the infinitesimal time interval dt in which the mass element dm, having the velocity $\mathbf{v}_0$, attaches itself to a body that, at time t, has the mass $m(t)$ and travels at this time with the velocity $\mathbf{v}$. Thus at time t, immediately before the mass element attaches itself, the total momentum is

$$m(t)\mathbf{v} + dm\ \mathbf{v}_0$$

At time $t + dt$ the mass of the body is $m(t) + dm$, and its velocity has changed to $\mathbf{v} + d\mathbf{v}$. So the change of momentum in the time interval dt is

$$[m(t) + dm](\mathbf{v} + d\mathbf{v}) - [m(t)\mathbf{v} + dm\ \mathbf{v}_0]$$

We assume that an external force $\mathbf{F}$ acts during the infinitesimal time interval dt on the body. Hence the momentum theorem yields

$$\mathbf{F}\,dt = [m(t) + dm](\mathbf{v} + d\mathbf{v}) - [m(t)\mathbf{v} + dm\,\mathbf{v}_0)]$$
$$= m(t)\,d\mathbf{v} + (\mathbf{v} - \mathbf{v}_0)\,dm \qquad (3.6\text{-}1)$$

where the term $dm\,d\mathbf{v}$ has been discarded as an infinitesimal quantity of second order. Thus the equation of motion for a particle of variable mass can be written

$$\mathbf{F} = m(t)\frac{d\mathbf{v}}{dt} + (\mathbf{v} - \mathbf{v}_0)\frac{dm}{dt} \qquad \blacktriangleleft \quad (3.6\text{-}2)$$

or

$$\mathbf{F} = \frac{d}{dt}[m(t)\mathbf{v}] - \dot{m}(t)\mathbf{v}_0 \qquad \blacktriangleleft \quad (3.6\text{-}3)$$

Letting $\mathbf{v}_0 - \mathbf{v} = \mathbf{u}$ represent the relative velocity of the added mass dm with respect to $m(t)$ and defining the quantity

$$\mathbf{u}\frac{dm}{dt} = \mathbf{R} \qquad (3.6\text{-}4)$$

as the kinetic reaction of the added mass dm, we obtain from Eq. (3.6-2)

$$\mathbf{F} + \mathbf{R} = m(t)\frac{d\mathbf{v}}{dt} \qquad \blacktriangleleft \quad (3.6\text{-}5)$$

an expression that states that the vector sum of the external force and the kinetic reaction equals the instantaneous mass times the acceleration. The direction of the kinetic reaction coincides with that of the relative velocity $\mathbf{u}$ when dm/dt is positive—for example, the air intake of a jet engine—and it is opposite to $\mathbf{u}$ when dm/dt is negative—for example, the jet discharged from a jet engine.

Since the rocket is a variable-mass system of considerable importance, some special comments are in order at this point. For a rocket (see Fig. 3.6-1), $m(t)$ decreases with time; hence dm/dt is a negative quantity. The velocity $\mathbf{u} = \mathbf{v}_0 - \mathbf{v}$ is the relative velocity of the ejected gas with respect to

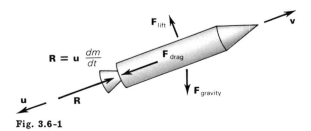

Fig. 3.6-1

the rocket, that is, the jet velocity.   The absolute velocity of the ejected gas is $\mathbf{v}_0 = \mathbf{v} + \mathbf{u}$, and it can be in the direction of $\mathbf{v}$ or opposite to it, depending on the magnitude and direction of $\mathbf{u}$.

The thrust of the rocket is nothing but the kinetic reaction $\mathbf{R} = \mathbf{u}\, dm/dt$—defined in Eq. (3.6-4)—and since dm/dt is negative, $\mathbf{R}$ and $\mathbf{u}$ are opposite to each other.   Therefore, if the gas is ejected in a direction opposite to that of the rocket motion, $\mathbf{R}$ is accelerating the rocket, and if the gas is ejected in the direction of flight, $\mathbf{R}$ is decelerating its motion, as in the case of a retro-rocket. We also deduce from Eq. (3.6-4) that the direction of the thrust can be altered by changing the direction of the gas jet, thereby changing the course of the rocket.   Note that the thrust $\mathbf{R}$ is proportional to the jet velocity $\mathbf{u}$ of the ejected gases.   Therefore, the increase of the jet velocity through the development of "exotic" fuels is of decisive importance for the improvement of the rocket's efficiency.

ILLUSTRATIVE EXAMPLE 3.6-1
A rocket is fired vertically from the earth's surface.   Determine the equation for its velocity v_z, assuming that its fuel is burned at a constant rate and ejected with a constant relative speed (jet speed) $u_z = -u_{\text{jet}}$, as shown in Fig. 3.6-2.

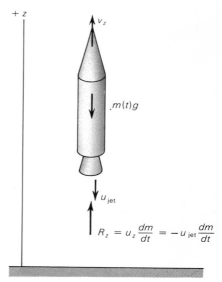

Fig. 3.6-2

SOLUTION: With $F_z = -mg$ (neglecting the variation of g) and $u_z = -u_{\text{jet}}$, Eq. (3.6-5) becomes

$$-m(t)g - u_{\text{jet}}\frac{dm}{dt} = m(t)\frac{dv_z}{dt} \tag{a}$$

Multiplying by $dt/m(t)$ and rearranging, we evaluate the integrals

$$\int_0^{v_z} dv_z = -u_{\text{jet}} \int_{m_0}^{m} \frac{dm}{m} - g \int_0^t dt \qquad (b)$$

which assumes that the rocket with initial mass m_0 starts at time $t = 0$ with zero velocity. Thus the velocity equation becomes

$$v_z = u_{\text{jet}} \ln \frac{m_0}{m} - gt \qquad (c)$$

where g has been assumed to be a constant. On account of the term $-gt$, v_z becomes larger as less time is used to burn the fuel.

Use formula (c) to show that the final velocity v_{z2} of a two-stage rocket is

$$v_{z2} = u \left(\ln \frac{m_0}{m_1} + \ln \frac{m_1 - m_d}{m_2 - m_d} \right) - g(t_1 + t_d + t_2)$$

where m_0 = initial mass of rocket
$m_0 - m_1$ = fuel burned in first stage of rocket during time t_1
$\quad m_d$ = dead mass of discarded first stage
$m_2 - m_1$ = fuel burned in second stage during time t_2
$\quad t_d$ = time used to discard burnout first stage

Discuss the merits of the two-stage rocket compared with a one-stage rocket consuming the same amount of fuel.

ILLUSTRATIVE EXAMPLE 3.6-2

Although we saw in Illustrative Example 3.6-1 that, in order to obtain the largest velocity for a rocket in vertical flight, it is desirable to burn the fuel in as short a time as possible, practical considerations favor a flight under constant acceleration equal to the maximum allowable value a_0, as dictated by the structure or the passengers. Determine the required mass variation for this condition.

SOLUTION: Equation (3.6-5) with $F = -mg$ and $R = u_x \, dm/dt$ may be written

$$-mg + u_x \frac{dm}{dt} = m(t) \frac{dv_x}{dt}$$

To maintain constant acceleration, $dv_x/dt = a_0$, and the equation of motion for vertical flight becomes

$$-m(t)g + u_x \frac{dm}{dt} = m(t)a_0$$

or
$$u_x \frac{dm}{m(t)} = (a_0 + g) \, dt \qquad (a)$$

Assuming u remains constant, and integrating, we obtain the result

$$u_x \ln \frac{m(t)}{m_0} = (a_0 + g)t$$

or
$$\frac{m(t)}{m_0} = e^{[(a_0+g)/u_x]t} \qquad (b)$$

where $m_0 = m(t = 0)$ and u_x is a negative quantity (see Fig. 3.6-3).

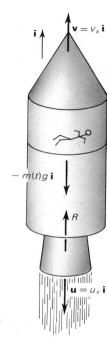

Fig. 3.6-3

Thus the time rate of fuel consumption is—see Eq. (a)—

$$\frac{dm}{dt} = m(t)\,\frac{a_0 + g}{u_x} = m_0\,\frac{a_0 + g}{u_x}\,e^{[(a_0+g)/u_x]t} \tag{c}$$

Again consider u_x negative.

ILLUSTRATIVE EXAMPLE 3.6-3
Consider the three-engine jet plane, shown in Fig. 3.6-4, flying at an airspeed of $V = 500$ mph.   The jet velocity is $u_{\text{jet}} = 1{,}460$ ft/sec, and the total cross-sectional area

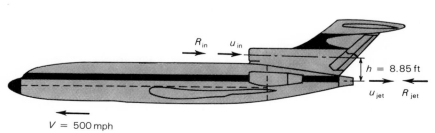

Fig. 3.6-4

of the air intakes is $A = 29.5$ ft^2.   The fuel consumption is 6.5 lb/sec.   Determine the thrust of the three engines.

SOLUTION: At the intakes dm/dt is positive and equal to the mass per second of the incoming air.   Thus we have, considering that the intake speed is equal to the airspeed of the plane ($u_{in} = V$),

$$\left(\frac{dm}{dt}\right)_{in} = \rho V A = \frac{2.5 \times 10^{-3} \times 500 \times 5{,}280 \times 29.5}{3{,}600} = 54.08 \text{ lb sec/ft}$$

Thus the thrust normal to the intakes (opposite to the flight direction) is—see Eq. (3.6-4)—

$$R_{in} = \rho V^2 A = 54.08 \times \frac{500 \times 5{,}280}{3{,}600} = 39.67 \times 10^3 \text{ lb}$$

At the nozzles dm/dt is negative and equal to the mass per second of the incoming air plus the fuel mass per second:

$$\frac{dm}{dt} = -(54.08 + 0.20) \text{ lb sec/ft}$$

Therefore the jet thrust is opposite the jet velocity $u_{jet} = 1{,}460$ ft/sec; that is, in flight direction

$$R_{jet} = 54.28 \times 1{,}460 = 79.25 \times 10^3 \text{ lb}$$

Hence the total thrust is

$$R = R_{jet} - R_{in} = (79.25 - 39.67)10^3 = 39.58 \times 10^3 \text{ lb}$$

in flight direction.   Besides, a clockwise couple (lifting the nose of the airplane) is exerted by the center engine (one-third of the total engine power), whose moment is

$$M = \tfrac{1}{3}\rho V^2 A h = \frac{8.85}{3} (39.67) \times 10^3 = 117 \times 10^3 \text{ ft lb}$$

What is the horsepower developed by the three engines at the given airspeed if the wind moves with the airplane at 100 mph?

PROBLEMS

3.6-1   A jet engine takes in air at a rate $\dot{m}_a$, compresses it and mixes it with kerosene at a rate $\dot{m}_k$, and ejects the ignited mixture at a speed u relative to the nozzle. If the jet plane is traveling at a speed v, show that the thrust of the engine is

$$R = \dot{m}_k u + \dot{m}_a (u - v)$$

3.6-2   A jet-propelled airplane has a constant speed of 600 mph in horizontal flight. The engine consumes air at a rate of 200 lb/sec at this speed and uses fuel at a rate of 2.0 lb/sec.   The exhaust gas has a relative speed of 2,200 ft/sec at atmospheric pressure.   Determine the total drag of the airplane and the useful power of the engine at this speed.

3.6-3   A jet-propelled airplane is traveling at a constant speed of $V = 650$ mph in horizontal flight.   The jet engine consumes air through the intake scoop at a rate of 160 lb/sec and uses fuel at a rate of 1.42 lb/sec.   The gases are exhausted at a relative nozzle speed of $u = 2{,}400$ ft/sec at atmospheric pressure.   Write the force equation for the airplane, defining all symbols used.   Determine the thrust T of the engine, the total drag D of the airplane, and the useful power P of the engine.

3.6-4   Sand is dumped on a flat car of weight w moving under a constant force P at a rate of 100 lb/sec (see Fig. P 3.6-4).   Determine the acceleration of the car.

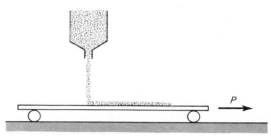

Fig. P 3.6-4

3.6-5   A uniform chain of weight w and length l suspended from one end with the other just touching the floor is released from this position.   Determine the force exerted on the floor as a function of the distance x of the upper end from its starting point.

3.6-6   A chain of mass per unit length μ and length l is in a pile on top of a table and is allowed to fall through a hole, each link being set in motion impulsively with $u = 0$.   Determine the equation for the velocity of the chain, and find the final velocity as the last link falls through the hole.   What are the time elapsed and the energy dissipated?

3.6-7   It is proposed to arrest the landing speed v_0 of a carrier plane of mass M by engaging a heavy chain of mass μ per unit length that is piled in a heap below the deck, as shown in Fig. P 3.6-7.   Determine the velocity of the plane when entire length l of the chain has been pulled out.

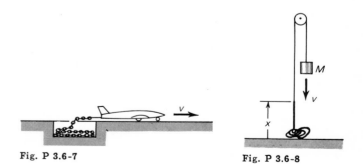

Fig. P 3.6-7   **Fig. P 3.6-8**

3.6-8   A thin string runs over a smooth peg and connects a mass M and a heavy rope of mass μ per unit length (see Fig. P 3.6-8).   At $t = 0$ the rope rests entirely on the ground in a heap. Set up the differential equation of motion in terms of v, the velocity of M, and its displacement x. Reduce this to a first-order differential equation for $v^2(x)$.

3.6-9   The V-2 rocket had an initial weight of 20 tons, including 13 tons of fuel. If the fuel is all burned in 2 min and the exhaust velocity of the fuel relative to the nozzle is 6,500 ft/sec, determine, neglecting air resistance and change in gravity, (a) the velocity at $t = 2$ min when fired vertically, (b) the height at $t = 2$ min, (c) the maximum height attained.

3.6-10   The theoretical velocity of a certain rocket defined by the equation

$$v = u \ln \frac{m_0}{m_f}$$

is 8,000 ft/sec. When shot vertically, the initial and burnout weights are 20,000 and 4,000 lb, with a burnout time of 40 sec. What are the vertical velocity and altitude attained at burnout? Assume $g =$ const.

3.6-11   An experimental sled weighing 90 lb, including 60 lb of fuel, moves along a straight track inclined at 15° with the horizontal. If the rocket gas has an exhaust velocity of 1,500 ft/sec relative to the nozzle and all the fuel is used up in 2 min, determine the maximum velocity attained. How far up the incline does it go?

3.6-12   The efficiency of a rocket can be defined as the ratio of the thrust power Rv to the thrust power plus the rate at which the kinetic energy is lost in the exhaust jet. Show that the equation for the efficiency is

$$\eta = \frac{2v/u}{1 + (v/u)^2}$$

where u is the velocity of the jet relative to the rocket. Under what condition is the efficiency maximum?

3.6-13   Since the ratio $r = v/u$ for a rocket flight must vary from zero to some terminal value r_1, a mean value defined by the equation

$$\eta_{\text{mean}} = \frac{1}{r_1} \int_0^{r_1} \eta \, dr$$

has been suggested as a quantity more representative of the flight efficiency. Show that the mass ratio corresponding to the maximum mean efficiency is equal to $m_f/m_0 = 0.693$, where m_f and m_0 are the final and the initial masses of the rocket.

3.6-14   A rocket of initial mass m_0 is fired vertically. The exhaust rate and the exhaust velocity relative to the nozzle are constant, and the final mass at burnout is m_f. Neglecting air drag and variation in g, show that for a given m_0, m_f, $\dot{m}$, and u the greatest maximum altitude is attained when the fuel is used in the shortest time.

3.6-15   Water is pouring into a tank at a rate of 100 lb/min from a height of 16 ft. The tank, which weighs 50 lb, rests on a platform scale. What is the scale reading after $\frac{1}{2}$ min? Assume the kinetic energy of the water after impact to be zero.

3.7 LAGRANGE'S EQUATIONS

We now derive Lagrange's equations, beginning with the case of a conservative system, where all impressed external forces and all internal forces have a potential.   The sum of the system's kinetic and potential energies is then a constant:

$$T + U = E = \text{const}$$

or the total differential of E vanishes:

$$dE = d(T + U) = dT + dU = 0 \tag{3.7-1}$$

Lagrange's[1] equations constitute one of the cornerstones of the imposing edifice of analytical mechanics, which is dealt with at length in other volumes.   Here our treatment is brief, but it is sufficient to introduce those who are not going on to the study of advanced mechanics to the basic approach and the fundamental merits of Lagrange's method.

Our simple derivation is based on Eq. (3.7-1).[2]   We consider a system of particles having N degrees of freedom.   Then N independent coordinates $q_1, q_2, \ldots, q_N$ suffice to describe the configuration of the system at all times.   We take, for example, two particles connected by a massless rigid bar and constrained to move on a plane (see Fig. 3.7-1).   This system has

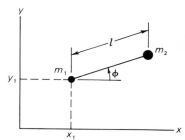

Fig. 3.7-1

three degrees of freedom ($N = 3$), and its configuration can be described, for example, by the three independent coordinates $q_1 = x_1$, $q_2 = y_1$, $q_3 = \phi$. Since the coordinates q_i ($i = 1, 2, \ldots, N$) are mostly not only cartesian but often involve angles and other geometric and mechanical quantities also, they are called generalized coordinates.

It is easily shown that the kinetic energy is a function of the generalized coordinates q_i and the generalized velocities $\dot{q}_i$:

$$T = T(q_1, q_2, \ldots, q_N; \dot{q}_1, \dot{q}_2, \ldots, \dot{q}_N)$$

[1] Joseph Louis Comte de Lagrange (born 1736 in Torino, Italy; died 1813 in Paris).
[2] For a system of one degree of freedom there is no need to derive Lagrange's equations; $dE/dt = 0$ serves the same purpose for such a conservative system.

and thus the differential of T is

$$dT = \sum_{i=1}^{N} \frac{\partial T}{\partial q_i} dq_i + \sum_{i=1}^{N} \frac{\partial T}{\partial \dot{q}_i} d\dot{q}_i \tag{3.7-2}$$

The following mathematical manipulations aim at eliminating the differentials $d\dot{q}_i$ from Eq. (3.7-2).

We consider a system of n particles assembled in such a way that the system has N degrees of freedom ($N \leq 3n$). Defining the instantaneous position of each particle of mass m_j by the vector $\mathbf{r}_j$, we may express all n vectors in terms of N generalized coordinates q_i:

$$\mathbf{r}_j = \mathbf{r}_j(q_1, q_2, \ldots, q_N) \qquad j = 1, 2, \ldots, n$$

Hence the velocity of each particle is

$$\mathbf{v}_j = \dot{\mathbf{r}}_j = \sum_{i=1}^{N} \frac{\partial \mathbf{r}_j}{\partial q_i} \dot{q}_i \qquad j = 1, 2, \ldots, n$$

Thus we may write, for the kinetic energy of the entire system,

$$T = \tfrac{1}{2} \sum_{j=1}^{N} m_j \mathbf{v}_j \cdot \mathbf{v}_j = \tfrac{1}{2} \sum_{j=1}^{n} \left(\sum_{i=1}^{N} \frac{\partial \mathbf{r}_j}{\partial q_i} \dot{q}_i \right) \cdot \left(\sum_{i=1}^{N} \frac{\partial \mathbf{r}_j}{\partial q_i} \dot{q}_i \right)$$

The evaluation of this expression then yields the kinetic energy as the quadratic form

$$T = \tfrac{1}{2} \sum_{i=1}^{N} \sum_{k=1}^{N} a_{ik} \dot{q}_i \dot{q}_k \qquad a_{ik} = a_{ki} \tag{3.7-3}$$

where the coefficients a_{ik} are, in general, functions of the generalized coordinates q_i.

We take the example of Fig. 3.7-1. There we have, for the kinetic energy,

$$\begin{aligned} T &= \tfrac{1}{2} m_1 (\dot{x}_1{}^2 + \dot{y}_1{}^2) + \tfrac{1}{2} m_2 [(\dot{x}_1 - l \sin \phi \, \dot{\phi})^2 + (\dot{y}_1 + l \cos \phi \, \dot{\phi})^2] \\ &= \tfrac{1}{2} [(m_1 + m_2)\dot{x}_1{}^2 + (m_1 + m_2)\dot{y}_1{}^2 + m_2 l^2 \dot{\phi}^2 - 2m_2 l \sin \phi \, \dot{x}_1 \dot{\phi} \\ &\qquad\qquad\qquad\qquad\qquad\qquad\qquad\qquad + 2m_2 l \cos \phi \, \dot{y}_1 \dot{\phi}] \\ &= \tfrac{1}{2} [(m_1 + m_2)\dot{q}_1{}^2 + (m_1 + m_2)\dot{q}_2{}^2 + m_2 l^2 \dot{q}_3{}^2 \\ &\qquad\qquad\qquad + 2(-m_2 l \sin q_3)\dot{q}_1 \dot{q}_3 + 2(m_2 l \cos q_3)\dot{q}_2 \dot{q}_3] \end{aligned}$$

Thus the coefficients a_{ik} turn out to be

$$\begin{aligned} a_{11} &= a_{22} = \tfrac{1}{2}(m_1 + m_2) & a_{33} &= \tfrac{1}{2}m_2 l^2 \\ a_{12} &= a_{21} = 0 & a_{13} &= a_{31} = -m_2 l \sin q_3 \\ a_{23} &= a_{32} = m_2 l \cos q_3 \end{aligned}$$

Equation (3.7-3) now leads to a relationship that proves to be quite instrumental in the derivation of Lagrange's equations. Differentiating Eq. (3.7-3) with respect to the generalized velocity $\dot{q}_i$, then multiplying by $\dot{q}_i$, and then summing over i from 1 up to N yields

$$\sum_{i=1}^{N} \frac{\partial T}{\partial \dot{q}_i} \dot{q}_i = \sum_{i=1}^{N} \sum_{k=1}^{N} a_{ik} \dot{q}_k \dot{q}_i = 2T$$

or

$$2T = \sum_{i=1}^{N} \frac{\partial T}{\partial \dot{q}_i} \frac{dq_i}{dt} \qquad (3.7\text{-}4)$$

Employing Eq. (3.7-4), we now form the differential of $2T$ and find, observing the product rule in differential calculus,

$$d(2T) = 2\,dT = \sum_{i=1}^{N} d\left(\frac{\partial T}{\partial \dot{q}_i}\right) \frac{dq_i}{dt} + \sum_{i=1}^{N} \frac{\partial T}{\partial \dot{q}_i} d\dot{q}_i$$

or treating dt in the first term like a scalar parameter,

$$2\,dT = \sum_{i=1}^{N} \frac{d}{dt}\left(\frac{\partial T}{\partial \dot{q}_i}\right) dq_i + \sum_{i=1}^{N} \frac{\partial T}{\partial \dot{q}_i} d\dot{q}_i \qquad (3.7\text{-}5)$$

Subtracting Eq. (3.7-2) from this equation, we obtain

$$dT = \sum_{i=1}^{N} \left[\frac{d}{dt}\left(\frac{\partial T}{\partial \dot{q}_i}\right) - \frac{\partial T}{\partial q_i}\right] dq_i \qquad (3.7\text{-}6)$$

and we recognize that through these mathematical manipulations the differentials $d\dot{q}_i$ have been eliminated.

Considering that the potential U of the given external forces and of the internal forces is simply a function of the generalized coordinates q_i, that is, $U(q_1, q_2, \ldots, q_N)$, we find that

$$dU = \sum_{i=1}^{N} \frac{\partial U}{\partial q_i} dq_i$$

and thus we have with Eqs. (3.7-1) and (3.7-6)

$$d(T + U) = \sum_{i=1}^{N} \left[\frac{d}{dt}\left(\frac{\partial T}{\partial \dot{q}_i}\right) - \frac{\partial T}{\partial q_i} + \frac{\partial U}{\partial q_i}\right] dq_i = 0 \qquad (3.7\text{-}7)$$

Now, since the N generalized coordinates q_i are independent of one another, this is also the case for the differentials dq_i,[†] and therefore Eq. (3.7-7) is satisfied only if

$$\frac{d}{dt}\left(\frac{\partial T}{\partial \dot{q}_i}\right) - \frac{\partial T}{\partial q_i} + \frac{\partial U}{\partial q_i} = 0 \qquad i = 1, 2, \ldots, N \quad \blacktriangleleft \quad (3.7\text{-}8)$$

Equations (3.7-8) are Lagrange's equations for the case in which all forces (external and internal) have a potential. They can be somewhat modified

† This is not so in the so-called nonholonomic cases, mainly concerning rolling bodies.

by introducing the lagrangian $L = T - U$. Since $\partial U / \partial \dot{q}_i = 0$, Eqs. (3.7-8) can then be written

$$\frac{d}{dt}\left(\frac{\partial L}{\partial \dot{q}_i}\right) - \frac{\partial L}{\partial q_i} = 0 \qquad i = 1, 2, \ldots, N \qquad \blacktriangleleft \quad (3.7\text{-}9)$$

Now, when the system is also subjected to given forces which do not have a potential or whose potential is not readily known, we have instead of Eq. (3.7-1)

$$d(T + U) = dW \tag{3.7-10}$$

where dW is the work of these forces when the system is subjected to an arbitrary infinitesimal displacement. Since any arbitrary infinitesimal displacement may be described by the independent differentials dq_i of the generalized coordinates, dW can be expressed as

$$dW = \sum_{i=1}^{N} Q_i \, dq_i \tag{3.7-11}$$

where the quantities Q_i are known as the generalized forces associated with the generalized coordinates q_i. From Eq. (3.7-11) we see that Q_i has the dimension of a force moment when q_i represents an angle.

With Eqs. (3.7-7), (3.7-10), and (3.7-11) we then obtain Lagrange's equations, valid for systems of bodies subjected simultaneously to potential and nonpotential forces:

$$\frac{d}{dt}\left(\frac{\partial T}{\partial \dot{q}_i}\right) - \frac{\partial T}{\partial q_i} + \frac{\partial U}{\partial q_i} = Q_i \qquad i = 1, 2, \ldots, N \qquad \blacktriangleleft \quad (3.7\text{-}12)$$

This form of Lagrange's equations is used, for example, for spring-mass systems, where the elastic spring forces have a potential and where the potential of the given external forces is not known or not stated (see, e.g., Prob. 3.7-7).

The advantage that Lagrange's equations offer in establishing the equations of motion is twofold. First, we need only to formulate the two scalar quantities, namely, kinetic energy T and potential energy U, in terms of the generalized coordinates q_i and velocities $\dot{q}_i$. This is mostly simpler than the direct establishment of vectorial relationships, offered by Newton's second axiom.

Second, in the absence of friction, the forces of reaction, for example, those due to frictionless guides or to frictionless hinged rigid rods connecting two bodies, can be completely disregarded in the formulation of the equations of motion. This is evident from Eq. (3.7-11), considering that the left side of the equation represents the infinitesimal work done by all forces acting on the system when it is subjected to the infinitesimal displacement dq_i. Now, since all these displacements are compatible with the constraints of the system, the forces of reaction caused by these (ideal, frictionless) constraints do no work and thus do not enter into the determination of the generalized forces Q_i. From this circumstance we derive the great advantage that an ideal (frictionless) mechanical system consisting of a number of bodies can now be treated as a whole without the free-body technique otherwise necessary in order to establish the equations of motion of the system. A short example may demonstrate how the generalized forces Q_i are easily determined by means of the principle of virtual work.

ILLUSTRATIVE EXAMPLE 3.7-1

We consider the plane mechanism shown in Fig. 3.7-2, where massless rigid rods carry a system of mass particles in such a way that the system has only two degrees of freedom. The mechanism is subjected to the moments and forces displayed in Fig. 3.7-2. Determine the corresponding generalized forces.

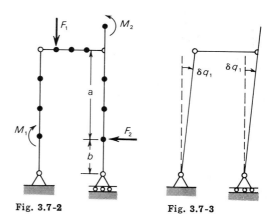

Fig. 3.7-2   Fig. 3.7-3

SOLUTION: Since the plane mechanism has two degrees of freedom, any infinitesimal displacement of the mechanism can be obtained by a superposition of the two independent virtual displacements δq_1 and δq_2 shown in Figs. 3.7-3 and 3.7-4. Hence the generalized force Q_1 is obtained by letting the forces and moments, shown in Fig. 3.7-2, do virtual work along the virtual displacement δq_1:

$$Q_1\, \delta q_1 = (M_1 - M_2)\, \delta q_1 - F_2 b\, \delta q_1$$

or

$$Q_1 = M_1 - M_2 - F_2 b$$

Likewise,

$$Q_2\, \delta q_2 = M_2\, \frac{\delta q_2}{a+b} - F_2\, \frac{a}{a+b}\, \delta q_2$$

or

$$Q_2 = \frac{M_2 - F_2 a}{a+b}$$

Since q_1 represents an angle, Q_1 has the dimension of a force moment and Q_2 the dimension of a force, q_2 being a linear displacement. The force F_1 does not enter at all, since it does no virtual work, whether the virtual displacement is δq_1 or δq_2; thus F_1 does no work whatever the infinitesimal displacement of the mechanism, shown in Fig. 3.7-2, may be, since the displacement of F_1 due to δq_1 and δq_2, respectively, is infinitesimally small of second order.

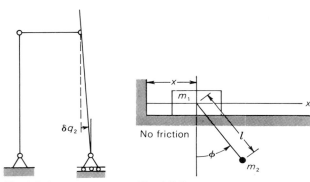

Fig. 3.7-4   **Fig. 3.7-5**

ILLUSTRATIVE EXAMPLE 3.7-2
Let us establish the differential equations for the pendulum assembly shown in Fig. 3.7-5. With the two generalized coordinates $q_1 \equiv x$ and $q_2 \equiv \phi$ the kinetic energy is

$$T = \frac{m_1 \dot{x}^2}{2} + \frac{m_2}{2} [(\dot{x} + l\dot{\phi} \cos \phi)^2 + (l\dot{\phi} \sin \phi)^2]$$

$$= \frac{m_1 + m_2}{2} \dot{x}^2 + \frac{m_2}{2} l(l\dot{\phi}^2 + 2\dot{\phi}\dot{x} \cos \phi)$$

and the potential energy (the reference level is insignificant here) is

$$U = -m_2 gl \cos \phi$$

Thus the lagrangian becomes

$$L = T - U = \frac{m_1 + m_2}{2} \dot{x}^2 + \frac{m_2}{2} l(l\dot{\phi}^2 + 2\dot{\phi}\dot{x} \cos \phi) + m_2 gl \cos \phi$$

Note that $L(\dot{x}, \phi, \dot{\phi})$ does not depend on x explicitly.
   Hence $\partial L / \partial x = 0$, and in view of Eq. (3.7-9)

$$\frac{\partial L}{\partial \dot{x}} = (m_1 + m_2)\dot{x} + m_2 l\dot{\phi} \cos \phi = \text{const} \qquad (a)$$

This result states that the x component of the total momentum does not change—which was expected, because of the absence of external forces in the x direction.

With

$$\frac{\partial L}{\partial \dot{\phi}} = m_2 l(l\dot{\phi} + \dot{x}\cos\phi) \qquad \text{and} \qquad \frac{\partial L}{\partial \phi} = -m_2 l(\dot{\phi}\dot{x} + g)\sin\phi$$

Eq. (3.7-9) yields

$$\ddot{\phi} + \ddot{x}\frac{\cos\phi}{l} + \frac{g}{l}\sin\phi = 0 \tag{b}$$

For $\ddot{x} = 0$, this equation is, of course, identical to that for the simple mathematical pendulum. From Eq. (a) we obtain

$$\ddot{x} = -\frac{m_2}{m_2 + m_2}\, l(\ddot{\phi}\cos\phi - \dot{\phi}^2\sin\phi)$$

or for small oscillations $\dot{\phi}^2 \approx 0$, $\sin\phi \approx \phi$, and $\cos\phi \approx 1$

$$\ddot{x} = -\frac{m_2}{m_1 + m_2}\, l\ddot{\phi}$$

and thus Eq. (b) becomes

$$\frac{m_1}{m_1 + m_2}\,\ddot{\phi} + \frac{g}{l}\,\phi = 0 \tag{c}$$

Discuss this equation also for the limiting case $m_1 \to \infty$.

PROBLEMS

For all problems belonging to Sec. 3.7 use Lagrange's equations.

3.7-1   Establish the equations of motion for Prob. 3.2-4.

3.7-2   Establish the equations of motion for Prob. 3.2-17.

3.7-3   Establish the equations of motion for the system shown in Fig. P 3.7-3 (small displacements).

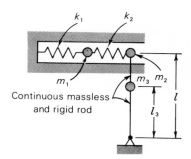

Fig. P 3.7-3

3.7-4   Consider that a horizontal force $F = F_0 \sin \omega t$ acts on mass m_3 in Prob. 3.7-3.

3.7-5   Establish the equations of motion for the system shown in Fig. P 3.4-4.

3.7-6   Establish the equations of motion for the system shown in Fig. P 3.4-4 if the masses are tied to each other by two equal diagonal springs of spring constant k. The unstretched length of each spring is $\sqrt{2}\, l$.

3.7-7   Establish the equations of motion for the double pendulum shown in Fig. P 3.7-7.

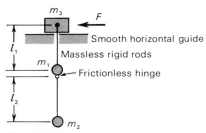

Fig. P 3.7-7

3.7-8   Amplify the equations of motion for Prob. 3.7-7 when there is dry friction between mass m_3 and the horizontal guide.

3.7-9   Figure P 3.7-9 represents the drastically simplified substitute system for a rectangular machine-foundation table supported by four elastic columns. The four equal masses m are connected by rigid massless ties so that they always stay in one plane. All four columns have the same spring constant k. Establish the equations of motion for the table for small vertical displacements.

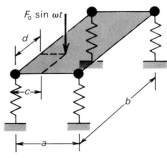

Fig. P 3.7-9

3.7-10   Establish the homogeneous equations of motion when the four masses in Fig. P 3.7-9 are m_1, m_2, m_3, m_4, and the four spring constants of the columns are k_1, k_2, k_3, k_4, respectively. How must these masses and spring constants be related to one another in order that the equations of motion can be written easily in decoupled form?

3.7-11   A dumbbell satellite is in plane motion under the influence of the earth's gravity
(see Fig. P 3.7-11).   The length of the massless bar is very small compared with
the distance r (earth-satellite).   Derive the equations of motion.   Notice the
coupling between the translational motion of the satellite's center of mass and
the plane libration.

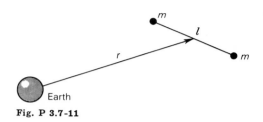

Fig. P 3.7-11

3.7-12   Establish the equations of motion for Prob. 3.4-21 by means of Lagrange's
equations.

RIGID BODIES IN PLANE MOTION

4.1 GENERAL CONSIDERATIONS

It is only a small step from the treatment of a closed system of particles to that of a rigid body, since we may consider a rigid body a special case of an assembly of mass particles in which the distance between any two, j and l, does not change; that is, $|\mathbf{r}_{jl}| = \text{const.}$ Actually a perfectly rigid body does not exist. It is an idealization of a real body, however, that leads to the most useful results if we are interested only in the motion of a body as a whole. For example, a rocket is treated as a rigid body when we are interested in the computation of its flight path although it is really a very flexible structure, containing liquids and the like. On the other hand, if we are concerned with the stresses and strains in the structure of the rocket, we have to abandon its idealization as a rigid body and treat it in terms of a far more complex model of a deformable body.

Hence the basic relationships obtained in Chap. 3 are more than sufficiently general in scope for the purposes of rigid-body dynamics to be treated here and in Chap. 6. It seems useful, therefore, at the beginning, to compile the fundamental equations derived in Chap. 3:

$$(a) \qquad \mathbf{F} = \frac{d\mathbf{G}}{dt} = \frac{d}{dt}(m\mathbf{v}_C) \qquad (3.2\text{-}7)$$

where $\mathbf{F}$ is the resultant of all forces acting on the rigid body and $\mathbf{G} = m\mathbf{v}_C$ is its momentum, with $\mathbf{v}_C$ denoting the velocity of its center of mass; and

$$(b) \qquad \mathbf{M}_0 = \dot{\mathbf{H}}_0 \qquad (3.3\text{-}8)$$

where $\mathbf{M}_0$ is the moment of all forces acting on the rigid body with respect to the reference point 0 fixed in an inertial frame and $\mathbf{H}_0$ is the moment of momentum of the rigid body referred to the same point. Furthermore, we have the corresponding relationship

$$(c) \qquad \mathbf{M}_C = \dot{\mathbf{H}}_C \qquad (3.3\text{-}13)$$

where the center of mass of the rigid body serves as reference point. In rigid-body dynamics the most benefit is derived from the associated relationship

$$(d) \qquad \mathbf{M}_C = \dot{\mathbf{h}}_C \qquad (3.3\text{-}17)$$

where $\mathbf{h}_C$ is defined as the moment of momentum of the rigid body with respect to its center of mass, computed in a reference frame that translates[1] with velocity $\mathbf{v}_C$ relative to an inertial reference body.

Next we repeat the definition of the concept of kinetic energy:

$$T = \tfrac{1}{2}mv_C^2 + \tfrac{1}{2} \sum_{j=1}^{n} m_j v_{Cj}^2 \qquad (3.4\text{-}4)$$

where $\mathbf{v}_{Cj} = \mathbf{v}_j - \mathbf{v}_C$ is the velocity of particle j with respect to a reference frame[1] translating with velocity $\mathbf{v}_C$ in an inertial frame.   Finally let us quote the work theorem as expressed by Eqs. (3.4-5) and (3.4-6):

$$\int_{t_1}^{t_2} \mathbf{F} \cdot \mathbf{v}_C \, dt = \tfrac{1}{2}m(v_{C2}^2 - v_{C1}^2) \qquad (3.4\text{-}5)$$

where the meanings of $\mathbf{F}$ and $\mathbf{v}_C$ have been defined above, and

$$\int_{t_1}^{t_2} \sum_{j=1}^{n} \left[\left(\mathbf{F}_j + \sum_{l=1}^{n} \mathbf{F}_{jl} \right) \cdot \mathbf{v}_{Cj} \right] dt = \tfrac{1}{2} \sum_{j=1}^{n} m_j(v_{Cj2}^2 - v_{Cj1}^2) \quad (3.4\text{-}6)$$

The second equation applied to a rigid body becomes far less complicated, however, because in a rigid body all mass particles remain at a constant distance from one another.   Consequently the work of the internal forces $\mathbf{F}_{jl}$ vanishes, because they do work only along the relative displacement between particles j and l, which is zero in a rigid body.

It would now be quite in order to apply these fundamental relationships directly to the general motion of a rigid body.   However, it is far easier to evaluate the right sides of Eqs. (3.3-8), (3.3-17), (3.4-5), and (3.4-6) for a rigid body[2] in plane motion.   This is one reason that we treat the special case of plane motion first.   The other is that from the standpoint of engineering this special case is overwhelmingly important.   Throughout the discussion the reader should remember, however, that both the special case of plane motion and the general motion of rigid bodies simply represent exemplary applications of the fundamental relationships derived in Chap. 3.

4.2   KINEMATICS OF RIGID BODIES IN PLANE MOTION

DEFINITION OF PLANE MOTION

A rigid body L is in plane motion with respect to a reference frame K if every point in the body L undergoes motion in planes that are parallel to one another.   We let one of these planes be identified with the xy plane, so that all points of body L that lie on a line parallel to the z axis must have the same velocity and acceleration relative to reference frame K in which the cartesian x, y, z system is fixed.   It is therefore sufficient to describe the

---

[1] That is, a reference frame not rotating with respect to an inertial frame although it may be in accelerated motion with respect to the latter, because, in general, $\mathbf{v}_C \neq$ const.

[2] Subject to certain limitations (see the beginning of Sec. 4.3).

plane motion of body L with respect to reference frame K by considering the motion of a plane fixed in body L, say the $\xi\eta$ plane, whose normal vector $\mathbf{1}_\zeta$ is at all times parallel to the direction of the unit vector $\mathbf{k}$ (see Fig. 4.2-1).

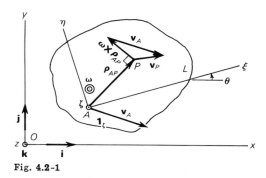

Fig. 4.2-1

Furthermore, we lay the $\xi\eta$ plane directly on the xy plane so that $z = \zeta$, and we place the origin of the $\xi\eta$ plane in an arbitrary body-fixed reference point A. Since we sometimes find it useful to describe the motion of body L with respect to reference frame K in body-fixed $\xi\eta$ coordinates, we are then confronted with the situation alluded to in Sec. 1.1, that the coordinate system used for the description of the motion is not tied to reference frame K with respect to which the motion is defined.

INSTANTANEOUS CENTER OF VELOCITY

In plane motion, the position of a body L with respect to a reference frame K is defined in terms of the location of some arbitrary reference point A on the body L and the angle θ between the coordinate axis ξ, fixed in L, and the x axis, fixed in the reference body K (see Fig. 4.2-1). Thus the plane motion of body L in reference frame K is defined by the velocity $\mathbf{v}_A$ of point A with respect to K and by the time rate of change $\dot\theta$ of the angular position of body L with respect to reference body K. The two quantities $\mathbf{v}_A$ and $\dot\theta$ then permit the computation of the velocity $\mathbf{v}_P$ of any point P, fixed in L, with respect to K. In order to establish a vectorial relationship for the computation of $\mathbf{v}_P$, we introduce a reference frame J that translates relative to reference frame K with the velocity $\mathbf{v}_A$. With respect to J body L then carries out a pure rotation (see Fig. 4.2-2) with $\dot\theta$ about an axis that "penetrates" body L at point A normal to the $\xi\eta$ plane, and thus also normal to the xy plane. Therefore, the velocity $\mathbf{v}_{AP} = \mathbf{v}_P - \mathbf{v}_A$ of point P with respect

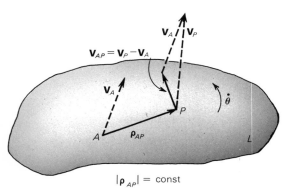

Fig. 4.2-2   Motion of point P in reference frame J.

to reference frame J is

$$|\mathbf{v}_{AP}| = |\varrho_{AP}| \times |\dot\theta|$$

and is directed normal to ϱ_{AP} compatible with the sense of $\dot\theta$, where ϱ_{AP} denotes the position vector from point A to point P, both fixed in body L (see Fig. 4.2-2). Now, if we define the angular velocity of body L in its plane motion with respect to body K in the vectorial form

$$\boldsymbol{\omega} = \dot\theta \mathbf{1}_{\zeta}$$

then we may describe the velocity $\mathbf{v}_{AP}$ as

$$\mathbf{v}_{AP} = \boldsymbol{\omega} \times \varrho_{AP} \qquad \blacktriangleleft \quad (4.2\text{-}1)$$

and thus the velocity $\mathbf{v}_P$ of point P with respect to reference frame K is

$$\mathbf{v}_P = \mathbf{v}_A + \boldsymbol{\omega} \times \varrho_{AP} \qquad \blacktriangleleft \quad (4.2\text{-}2)$$

The introduction of the angular velocity as a vectorial quantity might, at first, seem quite arbitrary. However, the results obtained in Eq. (4.2-1) are in accordance with the definition of the velocity $\mathbf{v}_{AP}$. The question of whether the vectorial concept of the angular velocity is also legitimate in the case of three-dimensional motion is discussed in Sec. 5.1 and is answered affirmatively. But, for the time being, no such general proof is necessary, as long as we confine our treatment to plane motion.

Before going on, we show that the angular velocity $\boldsymbol{\omega}$ of body L with respect to reference frame K does not depend on the choice of point A. Referring to Fig. 4.2-3, where we depict, in addition to A, another reference point B, we find, with B as reference point, analogous to Eq. (4.2-2),

$$\mathbf{v}_P = \mathbf{v}_B + \boldsymbol{\Omega} \times \varrho_{BP} \qquad (4.2\text{-}3)$$

Here $\boldsymbol{\Omega} = \dot\beta \mathbf{1}_{\zeta}$ is the vector of the angular velocity defining the rotational

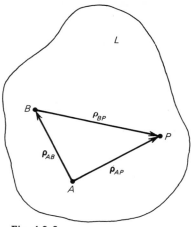

Fig. 4.2-3

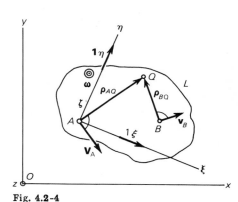

Fig. 4.2-4

motion of L with respect to K when point B is chosen as reference point fixed in L. We now show that $\mathbf{\Omega} \equiv \boldsymbol{\omega}$. In accordance with Eq. (4.2-2)

$$\mathbf{v}_B = \mathbf{v}_A + \boldsymbol{\omega} \times \boldsymbol{\varrho}_{AB}$$

Substitution of this equation into Eq. (4.2-3) then yields

$$\mathbf{v}_P = \mathbf{v}_A + \boldsymbol{\omega} \times \boldsymbol{\varrho}_{AB} + \mathbf{\Omega} \times \boldsymbol{\varrho}_{BP} \qquad (4.2\text{-}4)$$

Considering that $\boldsymbol{\varrho}_{AP} = \boldsymbol{\varrho}_{AB} + \boldsymbol{\varrho}_{BP}$, Eq. (4.2-4) is compatible with Eq. (4.2-2) only if $\mathbf{\Omega} \equiv \boldsymbol{\omega}$. Hence the angular velocity of body L with respect to reference frame K is a kinematic property of body L not dependent on the choice of the reference point in L.

It is now necessary to find a special point Q on the $\xi\eta$ plane for which $\mathbf{v}_Q = \mathbf{0}$ with respect to the xy plane. In view of Eq. (4.2-2) the vector $\boldsymbol{\varrho}_{AQ}$ from reference point A to point Q has to satisfy the equation

$$0 = \mathbf{v}_A + \boldsymbol{\omega} \times \boldsymbol{\varrho}_{AQ} \qquad (4.2\text{-}5)$$

Thus $\mathbf{v}_A = -\boldsymbol{\omega} \times \boldsymbol{\varrho}_{AQ}$, and the vector $\boldsymbol{\varrho}_{AQ}$ is, by the definition of $\boldsymbol{\omega}$, in the $\xi\eta$ plane and normal to $\mathbf{v}_A$. Hence Q can be found by drawing a line of length v_A/ω normal to $\mathbf{v}_A$ from point A. The sense of direction of this line is such that the sense of rotation and the direction of $\mathbf{v}_A$ are compatible.

Point Q can, of course, also be located by drawing normals from the velocity vectors of two arbitrary body-fixed points A and B, as shown in Fig. 4.2-4.

Because the velocity of body-fixed point Q is zero, body L can be viewed by an observer on the xy plane as performing, at this instant, a pure rotation about a perpendicular axis through Q. Since at the next instant point Q may well be a different point on the $\xi\eta$ plane, that is, in body L, we call this axis the *instantaneous axis of rotation* of body L with respect to reference body K, and Q the *instantaneous center of velocity*. It must be noted that the acceleration of body point Q with respect to the xy plane is usually not zero. One can, however, find a point in the $\xi\eta$ plane, the so-called *instantaneous center of acceleration*, whose acceleration is zero with respect to the xy plane. For example, in a wheel rolling at constant velocity the center of acceleration is at every instant in the center of the wheel, and the instantaneous center of velocity is the point of contact with the track (see Sec. 1.4).

If $\boldsymbol{\omega}$ and $\mathbf{v}_A$ are known, then the components of $\boldsymbol{\varrho}_{AQ}$ measured in the $\xi\eta$ plane are found by writing Eq. (4.2-5) in cartesian coordinates:

$$v_{A\xi}\mathbf{1}_\xi + v_{A\eta}\mathbf{1}_\eta = -\omega_\zeta\mathbf{1}_\zeta \times (\xi_Q\mathbf{1}_\xi + \eta_Q\mathbf{1}_\eta)$$
$$= -\omega_\zeta\xi_Q\mathbf{1}_\eta + \omega_\zeta\eta_Q\mathbf{1}_\xi$$

Hence, by equating components, we obtain

$$\xi_Q = -\frac{v_{A\eta}}{\omega_\zeta} \qquad \eta_Q = \frac{v_{A\xi}}{\omega_\zeta} \tag{4.2-6}$$

Equations (4.2-6) reveal that three quantities $v_{A\eta}$, $v_{A\xi}$, and ω_ζ are sufficient to define the position of the instantaneous center of velocity. From Fig. 4.2-4 the reader knows that the directions of $\mathbf{v}_A$ and $\mathbf{v}_B$ also, and hence the two quotients $v_{A\eta}/v_{A\xi}$ and $v_{B\eta}/v_{B\xi}$, suffice to define the instantaneous center Q. However, the magnitude of at least one of the velocities, say $\mathbf{v}_A$, is necessary to determine the angular velocity $\boldsymbol{\omega}$ of body L relative to reference body K:

$$|\boldsymbol{\omega}| = \frac{|\mathbf{v}_A|}{|\boldsymbol{\varrho}_{AQ}|} \tag{4.2-7}$$

Once the instantaneous center Q is known, the velocity of any point P in the $\xi\eta$ plane is simply

$$\mathbf{v}_P = \boldsymbol{\omega} \times \boldsymbol{\varrho}_{QP} \tag{4.2-8}$$

CENTRODES

As the body L moves, the position vector $\boldsymbol{\varrho}_{AQ}$ of the instantaneous center Q also changes, thereby generating a curve in the $\xi\eta$ plane called the body[1] centrode (polhode). Likewise the points in the xy plane that coincide with Q eventually describe a different curve, known as the space[1] centrode (herpolhode). The body centrode need not lie within the material body L itself, as evident in Illustrative Example 4.2-1.

---

[1] This term stems from the usage of considering the reference body K to be fixed in "space." Therefore points, curves, and the like, fixed in K are called space-fixed points and curves, respectively. In contrast, points and curves fixed in body L are called body-fixed points and curves, respectively. For the sake of brevity we follow this usage whenever convenient.

The plotting of the centrodes by an experimental procedure may be demonstrated by the simple example of a wheel (body L) rolling without slipping over a path fixed in body K (see Fig. 4.2-5). The wheel is drawn

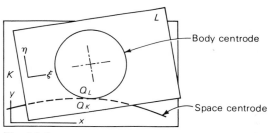

Fig. 4.2-5

on transparent paper ($\xi\eta$ plane in body L) and laid over a sheet (xy plane in reference body K) with the path drawn on it.

In the case of no slipping between the wheel and the path the velocity of the contact point Q fixed in the wheel with respect to the reference body K is zero, and thus Q is an instantaneous center. We mark this point on both sheets by penetrating them with a needle that acts as the instantaneous axis of rotation. The mark on the transparent sheet is the body point Q_L, and the one on the lower sheet, with the path, is the space point Q_K. We then rotate the sheets relative to each other through a very small angle and pierce them both again at the contact point of the wheel and the path, and so on. It is quite obvious that in this example all pinholes on the lower sheet (xy plane) lie on the path, which is therefore identical to the space centrode, and all pinholes on the upper sheet ($\xi\eta$ plane) lie on the circumference of the wheel, which is therefore the body centrode. This simple method is applicable to complicated plane motions (except, even momentarily, pure translations, where the instantaneous center lies in infinity), and it is a convenient tool for showing that any plane motion of two bodies, say two parts of a mechanism, relative to each other can be reduced to a rolling motion like a wheel on a path if their respective centrodes that belong to this plane motion are tied to them. The body centrode can then be viewed as the "wheel" that rolls without slipping on the space centrode.

ILLUSTRATIVE EXAMPLE 4.2-1

A bar of length l (body L) slides in the xy plane with its ends along the x and y axes fixed in body K, respectively. Determine the space and body centrodes, and plot these curves.

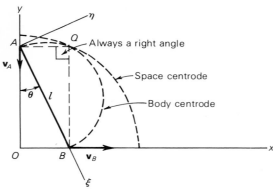

Fig. 4.2-6

SOLUTION: We attach the $\xi\eta$ plane to the bar, as shown in Fig. 4.2-6, with the ξ axis along the axis of the bar. Since the velocities $\mathbf{v}_A$ and $\mathbf{v}_B$ of the end points of the bar are always vertical and horizontal, respectively, the angle formed by the intersection of their normals at the instantaneous center Q is always a right angle. Hence the body centrode is a half circle spanning the sliding bar, and since $(AQ)^2 + (BQ)^2 = l^2 = $ const, the space centrode is a quarter circle about point O with a radius equal to l.

ANGULAR ACCELERATION AND ACCELERATION OF A BODY POINT
Equation (4.2-2) showed that the velocity $\mathbf{v}_P$ of a body point P may be expressed as

$$\mathbf{v}_P = \mathbf{v}_A + \boldsymbol{\omega} \times \boldsymbol{\varrho}_{AP} \qquad (4.2\text{-}2)$$

In order to find the acceleration of P with respect to reference frame K, we first study its motion again in reference frame J, which translates with velocity $\mathbf{v}_A$ relative to frame K. Thus point P describes, with respect to frame J, a circular path with point A as its center (see Fig. 4.2-2). From Chap. 1 we know that the acceleration $\mathbf{a}_{AP}$ of P with respect to frame J is then readily expressed by two vector components, one in tangential direction and the other in centripetal direction, pointing in the direction of A:

$$\mathbf{a}_{AP} = -\dot{\theta}^2\boldsymbol{\varrho}_{AP} + |\boldsymbol{\varrho}_{AP}|\ddot{\theta}\mathbf{1}_\theta \qquad \text{cf. Eq. (1.4-9a)}$$

where $\mathbf{1}_\theta$ is defined as unit vector normal to $\boldsymbol{\varrho}_{AP}$ pointing in the positive θ direction.

Now we define the angular acceleration of body L with respect to K (and, of course, also with respect to frame J, which is relative to K in pure translatory motion) as the vector quantity

$$\dot{\boldsymbol{\omega}} = \ddot{\theta}\mathbf{1}_\zeta$$

which is in accordance with the definition of $\boldsymbol{\omega} = \dot{\theta}\mathbf{1}_\zeta$, since $\dot{\mathbf{1}}_\zeta = \mathbf{0}$ as $\mathbf{1}_\zeta$ is always normal to the xy plane fixed in reference body K. Then we express

$\mathbf{a}_{AP}$ by the vectorial relationship—see Eq. (1.4-9a)—

$$\mathbf{a}_{AP} = -\omega^2 \boldsymbol{\varrho}_{AP} + \dot{\boldsymbol{\omega}} \times \boldsymbol{\varrho}_{AP} \qquad (4.2\text{-}9)$$

Considering that the acceleration of all points in J with respect to K is equal to the acceleration $\mathbf{a}_A$ of point A, we find the acceleration of body point P with respect to reference frame K to be

$$\mathbf{a}_P = \mathbf{a}_A + \mathbf{a}_{AP} = \mathbf{a}_A + \dot{\boldsymbol{\omega}} \times \boldsymbol{\varrho}_{AP} - \omega^2 \boldsymbol{\varrho}_{AP} \qquad (4.2\text{-}10)$$

ILLUSTRATIVE EXAMPLE 4.2-2

Referring to Fig. 4.2-6, determine the angular velocity $\boldsymbol{\omega}$, the angular acceleration $\dot{\boldsymbol{\omega}}$, and the acceleration $\mathbf{a}_B$ of point B when $\mathbf{v}_A = -v_A\mathbf{j}$ is constant.

SOLUTION: Inspection of Fig. 4.2-6 yields immediately the angular rate of the bar AB:

$$\omega_\zeta = \omega_z = \frac{v_A}{l \sin \theta} \qquad \text{counterclockwise}$$

In order to determine $\mathbf{a}_B$ and $\dot{\boldsymbol{\omega}}$, we use Eq. (4.2-10):

$$\mathbf{a}_B = \mathbf{a}_A + \dot{\boldsymbol{\omega}} \times \boldsymbol{\varrho}_{AB} - \omega^2 \boldsymbol{\varrho}_{AB}$$

where
$$\boldsymbol{\varrho}_{AB} = l(\sin \theta \, \mathbf{i} - \cos \theta \, \mathbf{j})$$

is the body-fixed position vector drawn from point A to point B. Thus we have, considering also that $\mathbf{a}_A$ was assumed to be zero and that $\mathbf{a}_B = a_B\mathbf{i}$,

$$a_B\mathbf{i} = (\dot{\omega}_z\mathbf{k}) \times (\sin \theta \, \mathbf{i} - \cos \theta \, \mathbf{j})l - \frac{v_A{}^2}{l^2 \sin^2 \theta} l(\sin \theta \, \mathbf{i} - \cos \theta \, \mathbf{j})$$

We see immediately that this vector equation is equivalent to the two scalar equations below and therefore sufficient to determine the two unknowns a_B and $\dot{\omega}_z$:

$$a_B - \dot{\omega}_z l \cos \theta = -\frac{v_A{}^2}{l \sin \theta}$$

$$\dot{\omega}_z l \sin \theta = -\frac{v_A{}^2}{l} \frac{\cos \theta}{\sin^2 \theta}$$

Thus
$$\dot{\omega}_z = -\frac{v_A{}^2}{l^2} \frac{\cos \theta}{\sin^3 \theta}$$

and
$$a_B = -\frac{v_A{}^2}{l \sin^3 \theta}$$

Plot these results.

ILLUSTRATIVE EXAMPLE 4.2-3

The center of a double gear (see Fig. 4.2-7) has a velocity of 6 in./sec to the right. Determine the velocity of the upper rack when (a) the lower rack is fixed, (b) the velocity of the lower rack is 3 in./sec to the left.

SOLUTION: (a) With the lower rack fixed in the xy plane, the contact point Q (see Fig. 4.2-7a) is the instantaneous center. The angular velocity of the gear is then

$$\omega = \frac{6 \text{ in./sec}}{3 \text{ in.}} = 2 \text{ rad/sec clockwise}$$

and the velocity of point P on the upper rack is

$$v_P = (3 + 5) \text{ in.} \times 2 \text{ rad/sec} = 16 \text{ in./sec to the right}$$

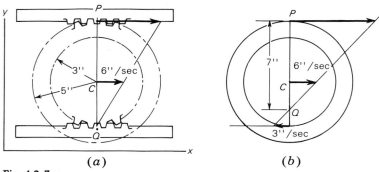

Fig. 4.2-7

(b) When the velocity of the lower rack is 3 in./sec to the left, the instantaneous center Q is located as the point of zero velocity, which is $\frac{2}{3} \times 3$ in. = 2 in. below C (see Fig. 4.2-7b).   The angular velocity of the gear is then

$$\omega = \frac{6 \text{ in./sec}}{2 \text{ in.}} = 3 \text{ rad/sec clockwise}$$

and the velocity of P is

$$v_P = 7 \text{ in.} \times 3 \text{ rad/sec} = 21 \text{ in./sec to the right}$$

PROBLEMS

4.2-1   A bar $AB = 3$ ft is moving in a plane.   At a given instant, the velocities of A and B are $v_A = 2$ ft/sec directed 60° clockwise from line A to B and v_B directed 30° clockwise from line A to B.   Determine the angular velocity of the bar at this instant, giving its rotation sense.

4.2-2   In the position shown in Fig. P 4.2-2, an arm AB has a constant angular velocity of 10 rpm.   Determine the angular velocity of BC.

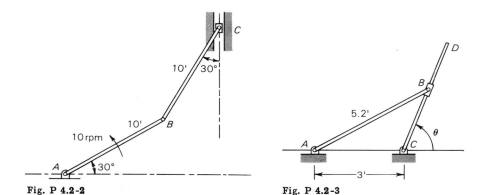

Fig. P 4.2-2   **Fig. P 4.2-3**

4.2-3 An arm CD is rotating at a constant counterclockwise velocity of 2 rad/sec (see Fig. P 4.2-3). Determine the angular velocity of AB when $\theta = 60°$.

4.2-4 An arm OA is rotating clockwise with an angular velocity of 15 rad/sec. Determine the velocity of point C for the position shown in Fig. P 4.2-4.

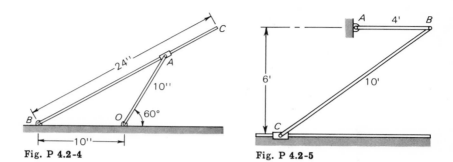

Fig. P 4.2-4   Fig. P 4.2-5

4.2-5 At a given instant AB is horizontal, and $v_C = 15$ ft/sec to the right (see Fig. P 4.2-5). Determine the velocity of B and the angular velocity of AB.

4.2-6 In the position shown in Fig. P 4.2-6, $\omega_{AB} = 1.2$ rad/sec counterclockwise, and bar BC is horizontal. Determine the velocity v_C and the angular velocity ω_{BC} of bar BC.

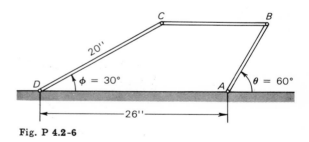

Fig. P 4.2-6

4.2-7 An arm AB in the position shown in Fig. P 4.2-7 has an angular velocity of $\omega_{AB} = 2$ rad/sec counterclockwise. Determine ω_{BC}, v_C, and ω_{DC}.

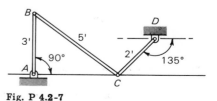

Fig. P 4.2-7

4.2-8   A cubical block $ABCD$ moves in a vertical plane with two of its sides in contact with the corners E and F (see Fig. P 4.2-8). When $\theta = 30°$, the angular velocity of the block is 4 rad/sec counterclockwise. Determine the velocities of A, B, C, and D.

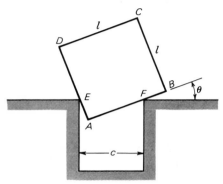

Fig. P 4.2-8

4.2-9   A four-slotted Geneva wheel executes intermittent rotary motion ϕ under continuous motion θ of a drive wheel and pin (see Fig. P 4.2-9). By choosing the distance between the centers to be $b = \sqrt{2}\,a$, the angular velocity of the Geneva wheel is zero as the pin enters or leaves a slot. Determine the angular velocity ϕ of the Geneva wheel.

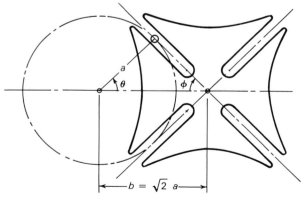

Fig. P 4.2-9

4.2-10   In the position shown in Fig. P 4.2-10, the angular velocity and acceleration of a crank OA are $\omega = 4$ rad/sec and $\dot{\omega} = 6$ rad/sec². Determine the velocity and acceleration of B and the angular velocity and acceleration of the connecting rod.

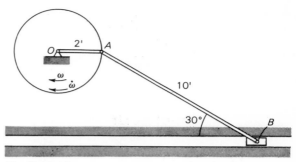

Fig. P 4.2-10

4.2-11   In the position shown in Fig. P 4.2-11, ω_{AB} = 2 rad/sec clockwise and $\dot{\omega}_{AB}$ = 30 rad/sec² clockwise.   Determine the acceleration of block C.

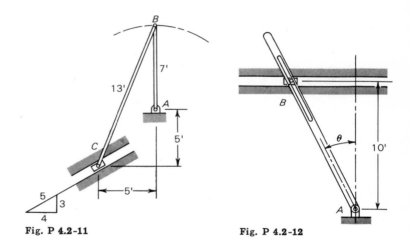

Fig. P 4.2-11   **Fig. P 4.2-12**

4.2-12   When $\theta = \tan^{-1} \frac{3}{4}$, a slider B has a velocity of 6 in./sec to the left and an acceleration of 2 in./sec² to the right (see Fig. P 4.2-12).   Determine the angular velocity and angular acceleration of AB.

4.2-13   Sliders A and B, connected by a 20-in. bar, move along guides that make an angle of 30° with each other.   In the position shown in Fig. P 4.2-13, slider A has a

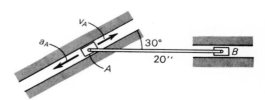

Fig. P 4.2-13

velocity of 40 in./sec up and an acceleration of 8 in./sec² down. Determine (a) the angular velocity of AB, (b) the angular acceleration of AB and the linear acceleration of slider B.

4.2-14   In the position shown in Fig. P 4.2-14, A has a velocity of 2 ft/sec down and an acceleration of 5 ft/sec² up. Determine the angular acceleration of AB.

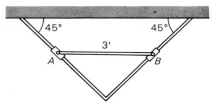

Fig. P 4.2-14

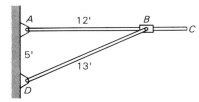

Fig. P 4.2-15

4.2-15   At a given instant, a bar AC is horizontal, and a bar DB has an angular velocity of 3 rad/sec clockwise and an angular acceleration of 2 rad/sec² counterclockwise (see Fig. P 4.2-15). Determine (a) the velocity of slider B relative to bar AC and the angular velocity of AC, (b) the angular acceleration of bar AC.

4.2-16   A bar AB 10 ft long is connected to sliders at the ends that move along vertical and inclined guides, as shown in Fig. P 4.2-16. If slider B is moving upward with a constant velocity of $v_B = 5$ ft/sec, determine ω_{AB}, $\dot{\omega}_{AB}$, v_A, and a_A when $\theta = 60°$.

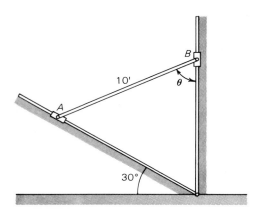

Fig. P 4.2-16

4.2-17   Two wheels are connected by a connecting rod BC, as shown in Fig. P 4.2-17. The left wheel rotates clockwise at a constant speed of 2 rad/sec. For the position shown, determine (a) the angular velocity of BC, that is, ω_{BC}; (b) ω_{DC}; (c) $\dot{\omega}_{DC}$; and (d) $\dot{\omega}_{BC}$.

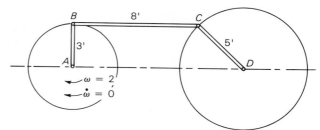

Fig. P 4.2-17

4.2-18 A bar AC has a slider B that is pinned to the rim of a wheel with a 5-ft radius (see Fig. P 4.2-18). At the position shown, $\theta = 30°$, and B is directly above O. With ω and $\dot{\omega}$ as given, determine ω_{AC}, $\dot{\omega}_{AC}$, and a_B relative to bar AC.

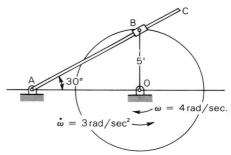

Fig. P 4.2-18

4.2-19 A slotted disk rotates counterclockwise at a constant speed of 15 rad/sec (see Fig. P 4.2-19). An arm AB rotates counterclockwise relative to the disk, and in the position $\theta = 30°$ has the values of $\dot{\theta} = 10$ rad/sec and $\ddot{\theta} = -20$ rad/sec². Determine the acceleration of a slider P.

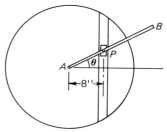

Fig. P 4.2-19

4.2-20 If in Prob. 4.2-19 the wheel has an angular acceleration of 2 rad/sec² in the clockwise direction, determine the acceleration of P for the position shown.

4.2-21   The arm $OB = r$ of a quick-return mechanism is driven at constant angular velocity $\dot\theta$ (see Fig. P 4.2-21).   Determine the equations for the angular velocity ω of the arm AB and the velocity of the slider B relative to the arm AB.

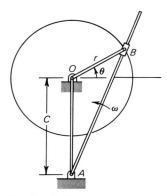

Fig. P 4.2-21

4.2-22   For the quick-return mechanism shown in Fig. P 4.2-22, determine x, $\dot x$, and $\ddot x$ as functions of time.   At what angle ϕ is $\dot x$ a maximum?   If t_1 and t_2 are the time durations for the longest and shortest strokes of the cycle, determine the ratio b/r for $t_1/t_2 = 2$.   For $n = 50$ rpm, $r = 5$ in., $L = 21$ in., and $b = 8$ in., deter-

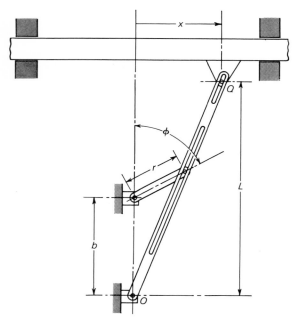

Fig. P 4.2-22

mine the values of x, $\dot{x}$, and $\ddot{x}$ for $\phi = 30°$. Plot the approximate phase plane $\dot{x} = f(x)$.

4.2-23 A slider C moves in a circular slot of radius r on a wheel rotating with angular velocity ω (see Fig. P 4.2-23). If $\dot{\omega} = 0$ and $\theta = $ const, determine the velocity and acceleration of C relative to a fixed reference, and determine ω_{AB} and $\dot{\omega}_{AB}$.

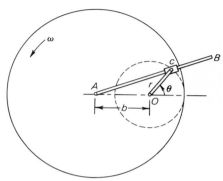

Fig. P 4.2-23

4.2-24 An arm AB, in the position shown in Fig. P 4.2-24, has an angular velocity $\omega_{AB} = 2$ rad/sec and an angular acceleration $\dot{\omega}_{AB} = 3$ rad/sec². Determine $\dot{\omega}_{BC}$ and $\dot{\omega}_{DC}$.

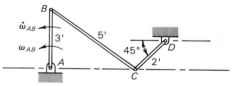

Fig. P 4.2-24

4.2-25 Determine the angular acceleration of member BC in Prob. 4.2-6 when $\dot{\omega}_{AB} = 2.0$ rad/sec² counterclockwise.

4.2-26 A bar AB of length l moves with its ends along a horizontal floor and inclined wall, as shown in Fig. P 4.2-26. When $\theta = 30°$, A has a velocity v_A to the right and an acceleration a_A to the left. Determine ω_{AB}, v_B, $\dot{\omega}_{AB}$, and a_B.

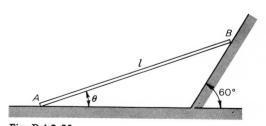

Fig. P 4.2-26

4.2-27   A bar AB of length l is hinged at A (see Fig. P 4.2-27).   A wedge of angle ϕ pushes up against B with constant horizontal velocity $\dot{s}$.   Determine θ.

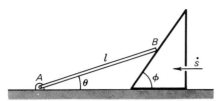

Fig. P 4.2-27

4.2-28   An arm OC of a planetary gear assembly rotates clockwise at constant angular velocity ω rad/sec (see Fig. P 4.2-28).   Determine the velocity and acceleration of points A, B, C in the small wheel for the large wheel at rest.

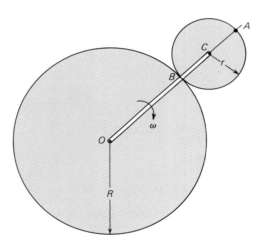

Fig. P 4.2-28

4.2-29   If in Prob. 4.2-28 the large wheel of radius R is given a constant angular velocity $\dot{\phi}$ counterclockwise and the arm OC rotates with ω as before, determine the new velocities and accelerations of A, B, C.

4.2-30   A small wheel of radius r rolls without sliding on the inside of a large wheel of radius R that is stationary (see Fig. P 4.2-30).   Determine the velocity and acceleration of a point P on the rim of the small wheel, which has a constant angular velocity ω.

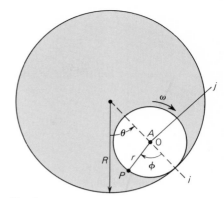

Fig. P 4.2-30

4.2-31 Solve Prob. 4.2-30 when the constant angular velocity of the large wheel is ω_1 (clockwise) and that of the small wheel relative to the large wheel is ω_2 (constant and clockwise).

4.2-32 In Prob. 4.2-31 what value of ω_2 results in the acceleration of any point P on the rim of the small wheel to be directed to the center of the large wheel? Assume both angular velocities to be constant.

4.2-33 The outer race of a roller bearing rotates with constant angular velocity θ (see Fig. P 4.2-33). For no sliding, determine the angular velocity of the roller and the linear velocity of its center. The inner race is held stationary.

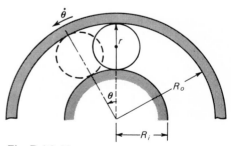

Fig. P 4.2-33

4.2-34 For the roller bearing in Prob. 4.2-33 the outer race is held stationary and the inner race is rotated at an angular velocity θ. Determine the angular velocity of the roller and the linear velocity of its center. Compare with Prob. 4.2-33.

4.2-35 In the gear system shown in Fig. P 4.2-35, the driving gear of radius R rotates with angular velocity ω and angular acceleration $\dot{\omega}$ clockwise. The arm $OA = 3R$ rotates about O with the same angular velocity and acceleration counterclock-

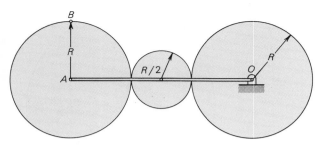

Fig. P 4.2-35

wise.   Determine the velocity and acceleration of point B on the driven wheel in the position shown.

4.2-36   A slider C has a velocity of 10 in./sec to the left when in the position shown in Fig. P 4.2-36.   Determine the instantaneous center Q of bar BC and the angular velocities of bars AB and BC.

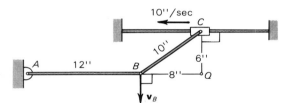

Fig. P 4.2-36

4.3   CENTER OF MASS; MOMENT OF INERTIA

In dealing with the dynamics of plane motion, we limit our discussion in this chapter to rigid bodies that have a plane of symmetry concerning their mass distribution.   This plane, therefore, contains the center of mass and is identified with the body-fixed $\xi\eta$ plane, which during the body's motion is always to coincide with the space-fixed xy plane.   For the sake of brevity we define such a body as a "plane" body.   It is shown in Sec. 6.4[1] that a far broader class of bodies behaves in plane motion exactly like the "plane" body defined here.   Furthermore, all forces are to act so that their resultant is always in the plane of symmetry, or if the force system is reduced to a force couple, its moment vector is in the z direction.   Hence we may immediately project all forces on the plane of symmetry, thereby obtaining an equivalent force system, and thus the position vectors $\mathbf{r}$ and $\boldsymbol{\varrho}$[†] are drawn in

---

[1] There it is shown [see Eqs. (6.4-3)] that any body with a central principal axis normal to the plane of motion behaves like the "plane" body defined above.

[†] Of course, the same notation would be achieved if we defined the vectors $\mathbf{r}$ and $\boldsymbol{\varrho}$ as position vectors drawn normal to the z and ζ axis respectively to the forces in their actual location.

the xy and $\xi\eta$ planes respectively to arbitrary points on the lines of action of the forces.

The presence of the plane of symmetry has, furthermore, the following important consequence. If we consider the rigid body made up of mass elements dm that are represented as cylinders or prisms of infinitesimal cross sections (see Fig. 4.3-1), then because of the symmetry each mass element

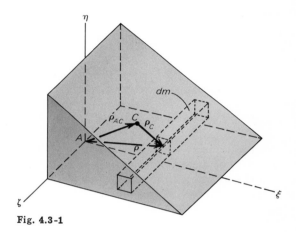

Fig. 4.3-1

has its center of mass in the $\xi\eta$ plane, and hence the location of this mass element with respect to the arbitrary origin A of the $\xi\eta\zeta$ frame is fully defined by the vector ϱ drawn in the $\xi\eta$ plane from A to the center of mass of the element dm.

In the special case of the body shown in Fig. 4.3-2, where there is rotational

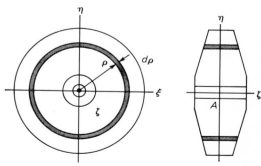

Fig. 4.3-2

symmetry with respect to the ζ axis, the mass element dm is best chosen as a concentric cylinder of thickness $d\rho$.

In Sec. 2.1 the center of mass of a rigid body was defined as—see Eqs. (2.1-8)—

$$\varrho_{AC} = \frac{\int_m \varrho \, dm}{\int_m dm} = \frac{\int_m \varrho \, dm}{m} \qquad \blacktriangleleft \quad (4.3\text{-}1)$$

Substituting for ϱ (see Fig. 4.3-1)

$$\varrho = \varrho_{AC} + \varrho_C \qquad (4.3\text{-}2)$$

we find

$$\varrho_{AC} = \frac{\int_m \varrho_{AC} \, dm + \int_m \varrho_C \, dm}{m} = \varrho_{AC} + \frac{\int_m \varrho_C \, dm}{m}$$

Thus

$$\int_m \varrho_C \, dm = 0 \qquad \blacktriangleleft \quad (4.3\text{-}3)$$

which establishes the fact that the so-called first moment of the mass about its center of mass C is zero.

In the dynamic problems in this chapter we encounter a further property of the rigid body expressed by the second moment of the mass, which is usually called the moment of inertia[1] about the ζ axis:

$$I_A = \int_m \varrho \cdot \varrho \, dm = \int_m \rho^2 \, dm \qquad (4.3\text{-}4a)$$

or

$$I_A = \int_m (\xi^2 + \eta^2) \, dm \qquad (4.3\text{-}4b)$$

Substituting $\varrho = \varrho_{AC} + \varrho_C$, we obtain the equation

$$I_A = \rho_{AC}^2 m + 2\varrho_{AC} \cdot \int_m \varrho_C \, dm + \int_m \rho_C^2 \, dm \qquad (4.3\text{-}5a)$$

or

$$I_A = I_C + \rho_{AC}^2 m \qquad \blacktriangleleft \quad (4.3\text{-}5b)$$

where we employed Eq. (4.3-3) and the definition

$$I_C = \int_m \rho_C^2 \, dm \qquad \blacktriangleleft \quad (4.3\text{-}6)$$

This relationship is known as the *parallel-axes theorem*.[2]   Equation (4.3-5b) also reveals that, of all parallel reference axes ζ, that containing the center of mass C yields the smallest moment of inertia.

Often the moment of inertia of a body about the center of mass axis is given in terms of the mass m of the body and a quantity k_C called the *radius*

---

[1] For an interpretation of this term see the footnote associated with Eq. (4.4-10).

[2] The parallel-axes theorem was formulated by J. Steiner (born 1796 in Solothurn, Switzerland; died 1863 in Bern).

of gyration with respect to the center of mass axis and defined by the equation

$$k_C = \sqrt{\frac{I_C}{m}} \qquad \blacktriangleleft \quad (4.3\text{-}7)$$

If we define, in addition, the radius of gyration of a body about a parallel axis through a point A as

$$k_A = \sqrt{\frac{I_A}{m}} \qquad (4.3\text{-}8)$$

we have—see Eq. (4.3-5b)—the following relationship between the radii of gyration:

$$k_A{}^2 = k_C{}^2 + \rho_{AC}{}^2 \qquad \blacktriangleleft \quad (4.3\text{-}9)$$

where ρ_{AC} is the distance between the two parallel axes.

ILLUSTRATIVE EXAMPLE 4.3-1
Determine the moment of inertia of a homogeneous circular sector of uniform thickness, shown in Fig. 4.3-3, about an axis through B normal to its face.

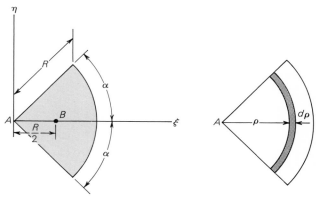

Fig. 4.3-3

SOLUTION: Since it is easiest to determine the moment of inertia about the center of the circular sector A, we first compute I_A.   However, it is then not permissible to apply the parallel-axes theorem directly to obtain I_B, since it is applicable only for transfer from the center of mass.[1]   Thus we have to follow the sequence

$$I_C = I_A - m\xi_C{}^2 \qquad (a)$$

[1] See Eqs. (4.3-5) and consider that $\displaystyle\int_m \varrho_B \, dm$ vanishes only if B happens to coincide with the center of mass.

η_C being zero, since the symmetry axis was chosen as the ξ axis and then

$$I_B = I_C + m\left(\xi_C - \frac{R}{2}\right)^2$$

$$= I_A + m\left[\left(\xi_C - \frac{R}{2}\right)^2 - \xi_C^2\right] \qquad (b)$$

In order to determine I_A, we form a concentric element of mass $dm = 2\alpha\mu\rho\,d\rho$, where μ is the mass per unit area of the sector. Then from Eqs. (4.3-4) we obtain

$$I_A = 2\alpha\mu\int_0^R \rho^3\,d\rho = \tfrac{1}{2}\alpha\mu R^4 = m\frac{R^2}{2} \qquad (c)$$

considering that $m = \mu\alpha R^2$.

With Eq. (b) we then have

$$I_B = m\left[\frac{R^2}{2} + \left(\xi_C - \frac{R}{2}\right)^2 - \xi_C^2\right]$$

where

$$\xi_C = \frac{2}{3}\frac{R}{\alpha}\sin\alpha$$

(see the Appendix).

ILLUSTRATIVE EXAMPLE 4.3-2
Determine the center of mass and the radius of gyration k_A of a cylinder of radius R and mass m, with a semicircular section of radius r cut out, as shown in Fig. 4.3-4.

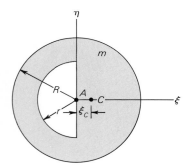

Fig. 4.3-4

SOLUTION: The center of mass of the cut-out semicircular area is at $\bar\xi = -4r/3\pi$ and $\bar\eta = 0$ (see the Appendix), and its mass is $m_1 = \mu(\pi r^2/2)$, where μ is the mass per unit area of the cross section. The mass of the cylinder with the section cut out is then

$$m = \mu\left(\pi R^2 - \frac{\pi r^2}{2}\right) = \mu\pi R^2\left[1 - \frac{1}{2}\left(\frac{r}{R}\right)^2\right]$$

Because of symmetry, the center of mass lies along the ξ axis and is found from the first moment about A as follows:

$$\xi_C = \frac{[-\mu(\pi r^2/2)][-\tfrac{4}{3}(r/\pi)]}{\mu\pi R^2[1 - \tfrac{1}{2}(r/R)^2]} = \frac{\tfrac{2}{3}(r/\pi)(r/R)^2}{1 - \tfrac{1}{2}(r/R)^2}$$

The moment of inertia about the ζ axis through A can be found simply by subtracting the moment of inertia of the cut-out section from that of the solid circular cylinder. Since the polar radius of gyration of a solid circular cylinder is $R/\sqrt{2}$, the moment of inertia of the cylinder shown in Fig. 4.3-4 is

$$I_\zeta = (\mu \pi R^2) \frac{R^2}{2} - \frac{1}{2}(\mu \pi r^2) \frac{r^2}{2}$$

$$= \frac{\mu \pi R^4}{2} \left[1 - \frac{1}{2} \left(\frac{r}{R} \right)^4 \right]$$

$$= \frac{mR^2}{2} \frac{1 - \frac{1}{2}(r/R)^4}{1 - \frac{1}{2}(r/R)^2}$$

Thus the radius of gyration is

$$k_\zeta = \sqrt{\frac{I_\zeta}{m}} = \frac{R}{\sqrt{2}} \sqrt{\frac{1 - \frac{1}{2}(r/R)^4}{1 - \frac{1}{2}(r/R)^2}}$$

This result can be checked for the limiting cases.   When $r/R = 0$, we obtain

$$I_\zeta = m \frac{R^2}{2}$$

where m is the mass of the solid cylinder.   When $r/R = 1.0$, we again obtain

$$I_\zeta = m \frac{R^2}{2}$$

where m is now the mass of the half cylinder.

PROBLEMS

4.3-1   Determine the moment of inertia of a uniform cylinder of constant mass μ per unit length, radius R, and length L about its axis.

4.3-2   Determine the moment of inertia of a uniform circular tube of mass μ per unit length, inner and outer radii R_1 and R_2, and length L about its axis.   Deduce the case for a thin tube.

4.3-3   Determine the moment of inertia of a uniform thin rod of length L about an axis (a) through its center and normal to the rod, (b) through its end and normal to the rod.

4.3-4   A thick cylinder is halved through its diameter, as shown in Fig. P 4.3-4.   Determine I_ζ.

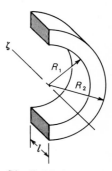

Fig. P 4.3-4

4.3-5   A solid wheel has a rim with a trapezoidal cross section, as shown in Fig. P 4.3-5. Determine I_ξ and I_ζ.

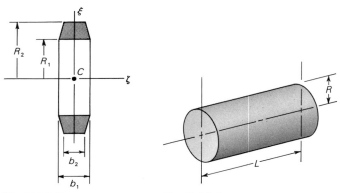

Fig. P 4.3-5   Fig. P 4.3-6

4.3-6   Determine the moment of inertia of a uniform solid cylinder of radius R, length L, and mass m about a diameter at one end (see Fig. P 4.3-6).   Express the result in terms of the mass m and its radius of gyration.

4.3-7   A uniform disk has a half-disk section punched out, as shown in Fig. P 4.3-7. Determine the moment of inertia about an axis normal to the disk passing through its center A, and express it in the form $I_A = K(\mu\pi R^4)$, where μ is the mass per unit area and K is to be determined (the Appendix may be used).

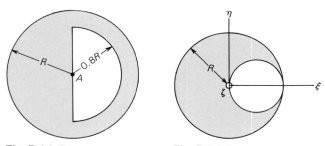

Fig. P 4.3-7   Fig. P 4.3-8

4.3-8   A uniform circular plate of thickness h and radius R has a hole of diameter R cut out of it, as shown in Fig. P 4.3-8.   Determine I_ζ.

4.3-9   A uniform rectangular block abc has one-fourth of its volume removed, as shown in Fig. P 4.3-9.   Determine I_ζ.

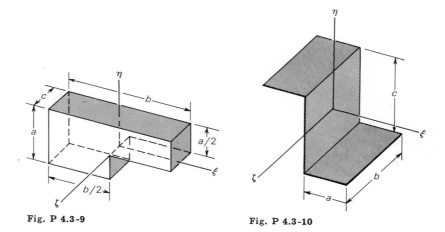

Fig. P 4.3-9   Fig. P 4.3-10

4.3-10   Determine I_ζ for the Z section shown in Fig. P 4.3-10.   Assume the thickness to
be negligible and the total mass to be m.

4.3-11   Assume the three-bladed propeller shown in Fig. P 4.3-11 to consist of three thin
uniform bars, and calculate I_ζ.

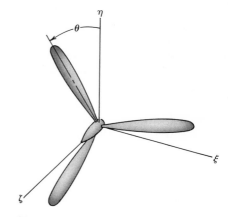

Fig. P 4.3-11

4.4 DYNAMICS OF A RIGID BODY[1] IN PLANE MOTION

LAWS OF MOTION AND MOMENTUM

With reference to Fig. 4.4-1 we have $\mathbf{r} = \mathbf{r}_C + \varrho_C$.   Hence

$$\int_m \mathbf{r} \, dm = \int_m \mathbf{r}_C \, dm + \int_m \varrho_C \, dm$$

[1] Our considerations are limited to "plane" bodies as defined at the beginning of Sec. 4.3.

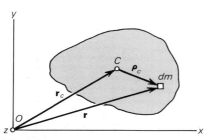

Fig. 4.4-1

In view of Eq. (4.3-3) and because $\mathbf{r}_C$ is not a variable as far as integration with respect to the mass of the body is concerned, this integration yields

$$\int_m \mathbf{r} \, dm = \mathbf{r}_C m \tag{4.4-1}$$

The time rate of change of Eq. (4.4-1) is then

$$\int_m \dot{\mathbf{r}} \, dm = m\dot{\mathbf{r}}_C$$

or

$$\int_m \mathbf{v} \, dm = m\mathbf{v}_C = \mathbf{G} \tag{4.4-2}$$

Thus the total momentum $\mathbf{G}$ of the rigid body is equal to its entire mass m multiplied by the velocity $\mathbf{v}_C$ of its center of mass. Equation (4.4-2) defines only the direction and the magnitude, and not the "line of action" of the momentum vector $\mathbf{G}$. Only in the case of pure translation does the resultant $\mathbf{G}$ of the infinitesimal momenta $d\mathbf{G} = \mathbf{v} \, dm$ contain the center of mass (see page 52).

Rigid bodies being simply a special system of particles, the equations of Sec. 3.2 also apply to the motion of rigid bodies. Thus Eq. (3.2-7) is also the expression for the law of motion of the center of mass of a rigid body:

$$\mathbf{F} = \frac{d\mathbf{G}}{dt} = \frac{d}{dt}(m\mathbf{v}_C) \tag{3.2-7}$$

For $dm/dt = 0$ we then have

$$\mathbf{F} = m\mathbf{a}_C \qquad \blacktriangleleft \quad (4.4\text{-}3)$$

where $\mathbf{F}$ is the resultant of all external[1] forces, that is, surface and body forces to which a rigid body is subjected. Integration of Eq. (4.4-3) with respect to time over the interval $\langle t_1 t_2 \rangle$ yields the expression for the theorem of momentum:

$$\int_{t_1}^{t_2} \mathbf{F} \, dt = m[\mathbf{v}_C(t_2) - \mathbf{v}_C(t_1)] \qquad \blacktriangleleft \quad (4.4\text{-}4)$$

---

[1] The resultant of all the distributed internal forces in a body is zero, in accordance with Newton's third law.

THEOREM OF MOMENT OF MOMENTUM OF A RIGID BODY IN PLANE MOTION
From our treatment of the dynamics of a system of particles we know that

$$\mathbf{M}_O = \dot{\mathbf{H}}_O \qquad \text{identical to Eq. (3.3-8)} \qquad (4.4\text{-}5)$$

where $\mathbf{M}_O$ is the moment of all external forces about a point O fixed in an inertial reference frame, in short about the space-fixed point O. $\mathbf{H}_O$ denotes the moment of momentum of all n particles about O:

$$\mathbf{H}_O = \sum_{j=1}^{n} \mathbf{r}_j \times m_j \mathbf{v}_j \qquad \text{identical to Eq. (3.3-2)}$$

As we remarked above, a rigid body may be considered simply a special case of a system of particles, that is, a system of an infinite number of infinitesimal mass elements dm that do not change their position relative to one another. Hence we obtain for the moment of momentum of a rigid body (see Fig. 4.4-1) about the space-fixed point O

$$\mathbf{H}_O = \int_m \mathbf{r} \times \dot{\mathbf{r}} \, dm$$

or with $\dot{\mathbf{r}} = \mathbf{v} = \mathbf{v}_C + \boldsymbol{\omega} \times \boldsymbol{\varrho}_C$ and $\mathbf{r} = \mathbf{r}_C + \boldsymbol{\varrho}_C$ and $\int_m \boldsymbol{\varrho}_C \, dm = \mathbf{0}$,

$$\mathbf{H}_O = \mathbf{r}_C \times m\mathbf{v}_C + \int_m \boldsymbol{\varrho}_C \times (\boldsymbol{\omega} \times \boldsymbol{\varrho}_C) \, dm = \mathbf{r}_C \times m\mathbf{v}_C + \mathbf{h}_C \quad \blacktriangleleft \quad (4.4\text{-}6)$$

Equation (4.4-6) defines $\mathbf{h}_C$ as the moment of momentum of a rigid body with respect to its center of mass in a reference frame that translates with velocity $\mathbf{v}_C$ relative to an inertial reference frame—see Eq. (3.3-15).

In plane motion ($\boldsymbol{\omega} \perp \boldsymbol{\varrho}_C$) we have $\boldsymbol{\varrho}_C \times (\boldsymbol{\omega} \times \boldsymbol{\varrho}_C) = \omega \rho_C^2$, and thus Eq. (4.4-6) may be reduced to

$$\mathbf{H}_O = \mathbf{r}_C \times m\mathbf{v}_C + \boldsymbol{\omega} \int_m \rho_C^2 \, dm$$

or with
$$\int_m \rho_C^2 \, dm = I_C \qquad \text{See Eq. (4.3-6)}$$

$$\mathbf{H}_O = \mathbf{r}_C \times m\mathbf{v}_C + \boldsymbol{\omega} I_C \qquad (4.4\text{-}7)$$

Hence, in view of Eq. (4.4-6) we have

$$\mathbf{h}_C = \boldsymbol{\omega} I_C$$

Differentiating Eq. (4.4-7) with respect to time, we obtain

$$\dot{\mathbf{H}}_O = \mathbf{v}_C \times m\mathbf{v}_C + \mathbf{r}_C \times m\mathbf{a}_C + \dot{\boldsymbol{\omega}} I_C$$

and thus Eq. (4.4-5) becomes

$$\mathbf{M}_O = \mathbf{r}_C \times m\mathbf{a}_C + \dot{\boldsymbol{\omega}} I_C \qquad \blacktriangleleft \quad (4.4\text{-}8)$$

If the space-fixed point O is also fixed in the body, as in a body rotating about a fixed axis normal to the xy plane, then we have $\mathbf{v}_C = \boldsymbol{\omega} \times \mathbf{r}_C$ and thus

$$\mathbf{H}_O = \omega(r_C{}^2 m + I_C)$$

or since $\mathbf{r}_C$ is now a body-fixed vector ρ_{OC}, we may write, in view of Eq. (4.3-6), with

$$I_O = \rho_{OC}{}^2 m + I_C = r_C{}^2 m + I_C$$
$$\mathbf{H}_O = \omega I_O \tag{4.4-9}$$

Referring to Eq. (4.4-5), we then have

$$\mathbf{M}_O = \dot{\omega} I_O \tag{4.4-10}[1]$$

when the point O is simultaneously space- and body-fixed.

We now consider that $m\mathbf{a}_C = \mathbf{F}$—see Eq. (4.4-3)—where $\mathbf{F}$ is the resultant of all external forces acting on a rigid body. Thus we find the moment of all external forces about the center of mass C to be

$$\mathbf{M}_C = \mathbf{M}_O - \mathbf{r}_C \times \mathbf{F} = \mathbf{M}_O - \mathbf{r}_C \times m\mathbf{a}_C$$

Therefore we immediately obtain from Eq. (4.4-8) the relationship

$$\mathbf{M}_C = \dot{\omega} I_C = \dot{\mathbf{h}}_C \tag{4.4-11}$$

which is completely analogous to Eq. (4.4-10), although the center of mass C may be in quite arbitrary plane motion. Equations (4.4-3) and (4.4-11) constitute the fundamental relationships in determining the motion of rigid bodies in their plane of symmetry. A useful formulation of the theorem of moment of momentum is found by integrating Eq. (4.4-11) with respect to time:

$$\int_{t_1}^{t_2} \mathbf{M}_C \, dt = [\omega(t_2) - \omega(t_1)]I_C = (\omega_2 - \omega_1)I_C \quad \blacktriangleleft \tag{4.4-12}$$

When the reference point O is space-fixed as well as body-fixed, we may likewise write—see Eq. (4.4-10)—

$$\int_{t_1}^{t_2} \mathbf{M}_O \, dt = (\omega_2 - \omega_1)I_O \quad \blacktriangleleft \tag{4.4-13}$$

Sometimes it may be advantageous to use a body-fixed reference point A other than the center of mass. Then we no longer have the simple relationship (4.4-11). But instead of starting from the beginning we develop the theorem of moment of momentum for an arbitrary body-fixed reference point A from Eq. (4.4-11). We first consider (see Fig. 4.4-2) that the moments of all external forces about points C and A are related as

$$\mathbf{M}_C = \mathbf{M}_A - \varrho_{AC} \times \mathbf{F}$$

[1] Referring to the footnote on page 204, the reader now understands the term *moment of inertia*, since I_O is shown to be equal to the amount of the force moment M_O necessary to overcome the body's rotary inertia, subjecting it to unit angular acceleration.

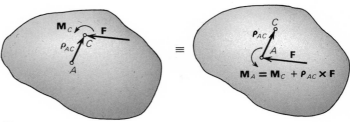

Fig. 4.4-2

or in view of Eq. (4.4-3)

$$\mathbf{M}_C = \mathbf{M}_A - \boldsymbol{\varrho}_{AC} \times (m\mathbf{a}_C) \qquad (4.4\text{-}14)$$

Besides, we know from the parallel-axes theorem—see Eq. (4.3-6)—that

$$I_C = I_A - \rho_{AC}{}^2 m$$

Thus we may substitute for Eq. (4.4-11)

$$\mathbf{M}_A - \boldsymbol{\varrho}_{AC} \times (m\mathbf{a}_C) = \dot{\omega}I_A - \dot{\omega}\rho_{AC}{}^2 m \qquad (4.4\text{-}15)$$

Now, it is easily verified that

$$\dot{\omega}\rho_{AC}{}^2 = \boldsymbol{\varrho}_{AC} \times (\dot{\omega} \times \boldsymbol{\varrho}_{AC}) \qquad (4.4\text{-}16)$$

since $\dot{\omega}$ is normal to $\boldsymbol{\varrho}_{AC}$ in plane motion. Furthermore we have—see Eq. (4.2-10)—

$$\mathbf{a}_C = \mathbf{a}_A + \dot{\omega} \times \boldsymbol{\varrho}_{AC} - \omega^2\boldsymbol{\varrho}_{AC} \qquad (4.4\text{-}17)$$

Substituting Eqs. (4.4-16) and (4.4-17) into Eq. (4.4-15) yields

$$\mathbf{M}_A - [\boldsymbol{\varrho}_{AC} \times \mathbf{a}_A + \boldsymbol{\varrho}_{AC} \times (\dot{\omega} \times \boldsymbol{\varrho}_{AC}) - \underbrace{\boldsymbol{\varrho}_{AC} \times \omega^2\boldsymbol{\varrho}_{AC}}_{=0}]m$$

$$= \dot{\omega}I_A - \boldsymbol{\varrho}_{AC} \times (\dot{\omega} \times \boldsymbol{\varrho}_{AC})m$$

Therefore $\qquad \mathbf{M}_A = \dot{\omega}I_A + \boldsymbol{\varrho}_{AC} \times m\mathbf{a}_A \qquad \blacktriangleleft \quad (4.4\text{-}18)$

It is readily seen that Eq. (4.4-18) reduces to Eq. (4.4-11) when A and C coincide ($\boldsymbol{\varrho}_{AC} = \mathbf{0}$). Equation (4.4-18) is especially useful when the acceleration of the reference point A is in line with the direction of $\boldsymbol{\varrho}_{AC}$. We consider, for example, a wheel rolling downhill, as shown in Fig. 4.4-3. Taking the instantaneous center as reference point A, then $\mathbf{a}_A$ points to the center of mass C if the wheel's center and its center of mass coincide. Thus $\boldsymbol{\varrho}_{AC} \times \mathbf{a}_A = \mathbf{0}$. The choice of the instantaneous center is advantageous, since the moment of the unknown reactions (tangential and normal) about A is zero and M_A is found to be simply

$$M_A = mgr \sin \alpha$$

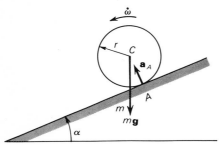

Fig. 4.4-3

With $I_A = mr^2/2 + mr^2 = 3mr^2/2$,† we then have, as the equation of motion,

$$mgr \sin \alpha = \frac{3mr^2\dot{\omega}}{2}$$

or

$$\dot{\omega} = \frac{2}{3} \frac{g \sin \alpha}{r}$$

The usefulness of the instantaneous center as reference point A, compared with the center of mass C as reference point, is lost to a great extent when the center of mass is eccentric and $\varrho_{AC} \times \mathbf{a}_A$ is no longer zero.

ILLUSTRATIVE EXAMPLE 4.4-1
A monorail car with the dimensions shown in Fig. 4.4-4 is driven by the front[1] wheel. If the coefficient of friction between the wheel and the rail is $\mu = 0.60$, determine the maximum acceleration possible for the car.

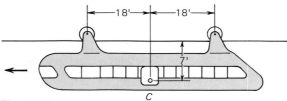

Fig. 4.4-4

SOLUTION: In the free-body diagram of Fig. 4.4-5 the force $\mu N_A = 0.6 N_A$ is the maximum horizontal force possible, exerted on the front wheel at A by the rails.   The diagram

† Assuming the wheel to be a homogeneous disk of mass m.
[1] Why not the rear wheel, like most cars?

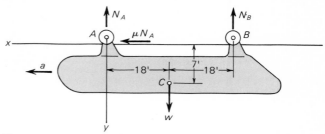

Fig. 4.4-5

further shows that there are three unknowns: the forces N_A, N_B and the acceleration $\mathbf{a}$, which is the same for all points of the car. For their determination we can establish three equations. Since $\mathbf{a} = \mathbf{a}_C = a_x\mathbf{i} + 0\mathbf{j}$, we have from Eq. (4.4-3)

$$\sum F_x = \mu N_A = \frac{w}{g}\, a_x \tag{a}$$

$$\sum F_y = -N_A - N_B + w = 0 \tag{b}$$

The third equation is supplied by taking the moment about some axis normal to the plane of motion and by recognizing that the angular acceleration is zero, that is, $\dot{\omega} \equiv 0$. If we choose the center of mass C as the moment center, Eq. (4.4-11) yields

$$M_C = (18)N_B + (7)\mu N_A - (18)N_A = 0 \tag{c}$$

If we take point A as the arbitrary reference point, then Eq. (4.4-18) applies, and with the term $\rho_{AC} \times m\dot{\mathbf{v}}_A = -(7)(w/g)a_x\mathbf{k}$ (see Fig. 4.4-5), we obtain

$$M_A = (36)N_B - (18)w = -(7)\frac{w}{g}\, a_x \tag{d}$$

Either (c) or (d) can be used together with (a) and (b), and their solution yields

$$N_A = \frac{18w}{36 - 7\mu} = 0.566w$$

$$N_B = w - N_A = 0.434w$$

$$a_x = \mu g \frac{N_A}{w} = \mu \frac{18g}{36 - 7\mu} = 0.340g$$

ILLUSTRATIVE EXAMPLE 4.4-2

The point of support A of a simple pendulum, shown in Fig. 4.4-6, is given an arbitrary motion $x_A(t)$. Demonstrate the use of Eq. (4.4-18) by taking the moment about the point A in order to establish the equation of motion of the pendulum.

SOLUTION: The equation to be used is

$$\mathbf{M}_A = I_A\dot{\boldsymbol{\omega}} + \varrho_{AC} \times m\dot{\mathbf{v}}_A \qquad \text{See Eq. (4.4-18)}$$

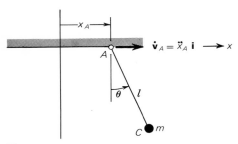

Fig. 4.4-6

which, applied to this problem, becomes

$$-mgl \sin \theta = ml^2\ddot{\theta} + (l \cos \theta)m\ddot{x}_A$$

Rearranging,

$$\ddot{\theta} + \frac{g}{l} \sin \theta = -\frac{\ddot{x}_A}{l} \cos \theta$$

If only small amplitudes are produced by the excitation, this equation is reduced to

$$\ddot{\theta} + \frac{g}{l} \theta = -\frac{\ddot{x}_A}{l}$$

ILLUSTRATIVE EXAMPLE 4.4-3
A roller of mass m and moment of inertia I_C, shown in Fig. 4.4-7, is given a horizontal impulse $\hat{F}_x$ of infinitesimal duration a distance z from the center C. (a) What value

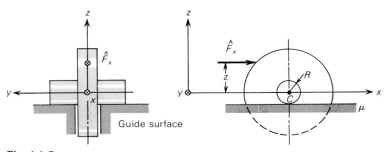

Fig. 4.4-7

must z have so the roller is in a state of pure rolling (without sliding) from the very beginning?   (b) Assuming dry friction with the frictional coefficient μ, determine the condition of z such that the roller eventually rolls in the negative x direction.   At what time is the direction of the velocity v_{Cx} reversed?

SOLUTION: (a) At time $t = 0$ we have the following momentum and moment-of-momentum relations:

$$\hat{F}_x = mv_{Cx_0} \qquad \text{See Eq. (4.4-4)} \qquad (a)$$

$$z\hat{F}_x = I_C\omega_{y_0} \qquad \text{See Eq. (4.4-12)} \qquad (b)$$

In view of the condition for pure rolling,

$$v_{Cx} = \omega_y R \qquad (c)$$

we immediately obtain, by division of Eqs. (b) and (a), after substituting Eq. (c) in Eq. (a),

$$z = \frac{I_C}{mR} \qquad (d)$$

(b) For every other value of z we first have mixed sliding and rolling. For $z > I_C/mR$ the rotation of the roller is faster than that required for pure rolling. Hence friction acts in counterclockwise direction until the state of pure rolling is reached. Thus reversal of the motion is impossible for $z > I_C/mR$. Therefore we have to consider only the case of $z < I_C/mR$.

We may then write, for the change of momentum and of moment of momentum during the time t after the initial impulse,

$$-\mu mgt = m(v_{Cx} - v_{Cx_0}) \qquad \text{See Eq. (4.4-4)} \qquad (e)$$

$$\mu mgRt = I_C(\omega_y - \omega_{y_0}) \qquad \text{See Eq. (4.4-12)} \qquad (f)$$

The reversal of the direction v_{Cx} may occur if, after the lapse of time t_1, v_{Cx} has become zero. Then we have from Eq. (e)

$$t_1 = \frac{v_{Cx_0}}{\mu g} \qquad (g)$$

However, the reversal can take place only if at time t_1 the roller is rotating counterclockwise. Now, counterclockwise rotation at this time is possible only if we already had it at time $t = 0$. This is so, because the friction μmg, which is acting in the negative x direction, diminishes the counterclockwise rotation with increasing time. Thus the time t_2 necessary to make the rotation zero must be larger than the time t_1.

We find t_2 from Eq. (f) by setting $\omega_y = 0$:

$$t_2 = -\frac{I_C\omega_{y_0}}{\mu mgR}$$

or with

$$I_C = \frac{\hat{F}_x z}{\omega_{y_0}} \qquad \text{Eq. (b)}$$

$$I_C = \frac{mv_{Cx_0}z}{\omega_{y_0}} \qquad \text{Eq. (a)}$$

$$t_2 = -\frac{v_{Cx_0}}{\mu gR}z \qquad (h)$$

Equation (h) shows immediately that ω_y can become zero only for a negative value of z, since t_2 must be positive. Furthermore, the condition $t_2 > t_1$ requires, in view of Eq. (g), that

$$|z| > |R| \qquad z < 0$$

Hence, if the roller is given a horizontal impulse in the x direction below the guide surface, it starts to run in the negative x direction at time $t_1 = v_{Cx_0}/\mu g$. For the special case of $z = -R$ it then stops moving entirely.

PROBLEMS

4.4-1   The car and uniform block shown in Fig. P 4.4-1 are moving at a speed of 32.2 ft/sec. In what time can the car be brought to rest at constant deceleration if the block neither tips over nor slides? The coefficient of friction between the car and block is 0.40.

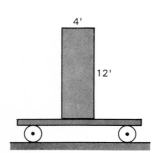

Fig. P 4.4-1

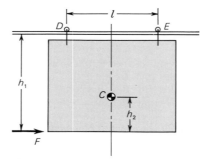

Fig. P 4.4-2

4.4-2   The sliding garage door shown in Fig. P 4.4-2 is rolled open by a force F applied at the bottom. Determine the force F that causes one of the wheels to lift off the track.

4.4-3   With F applied to a cart a, it is observed that a block b begins to tip backward at an acceleration of 4 ft/sec^2 (see Fig. P 4.4-3). Assuming friction between a and b to be large enough to prevent sliding, determine h and F when $w_a = 200$ lb, $w_b = 386.4$ lb, and $w_c = 96.6$ lb.

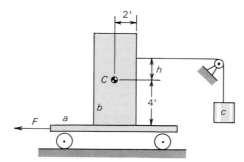

Fig. P 4.4-3

4.4-4   A sliding door a weighs 1,000 lb, and an attached weight b, 200 lb (see Fig. P 4.4-4). Draw the free-body diagram of a and b. Determine the acceleration of the door and the reaction of the track on the rollers.

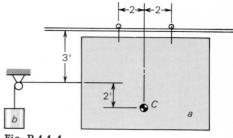

Fig. P 4.4-4

4.4-5   If the coefficient of friction between a wheel and a rail is 0.6 and the drive motor is in front (see Fig. P 4.4-5), determine the maximum velocity that a streetcar can attain in time t starting from rest.   Determine the maximum velocity if the drive is in the rear and if both front and rear wheels are driven.

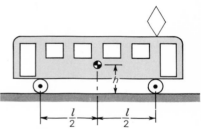

Fig. P 4.4-5

4.4-6   A car driven through the rear wheels is moving forward with acceleration a (see Fig. P 4.4-6).   Determine the forces on the front and rear wheels, neglecting air and rolling resistance.

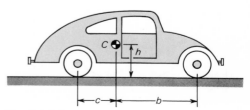

Fig. P 4.4-6

4.4-7   Brakes are applied to the four wheels of the car in Prob. 4.4-6, producing a deceleration of a. If the coefficient of friction between the tires and pavement is μ, determine the braking force in the front and rear wheels.

4.4-8   The locomotive shown in Fig. P 4.4-8 is driven by the two front wheels and is accelerating with acceleration a. Each of the front and rear wheel carriages is free to rotate about its center c. Determine the reaction under each wheel, neglecting air and rolling resistance.

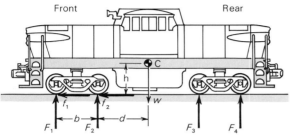

Fig. P 4.4-8

4.4-9   A log of weight w and length l is tied to the end of a truck at height h by a rope of length b (see Fig. P 4.4-9). Determine the acceleration of the truck that causes ABC to lie in a straight line.

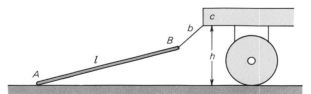

Fig. P 4.4-9

4.4-10   A uniform bar of weight w and length $\sqrt{2}\,R$ rests inside of a smooth half cylinder of radius R (see Fig. P 4.4-10). When the cylinder is given a horizontal accelera-

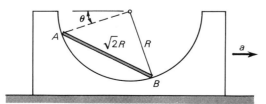

Fig. P 4.4-10

tion a, the equilibrium position of the bar is indicated by the angle θ. Determine the acceleration corresponding to $\theta = 30°$. Determine the reactions R_A and R_B acting on the bar.

4.4-11 A 10-ft uniform rod AB weighing 16.1 lb rests on a rough floor ($\mu = 0.40$) and pushes against a smooth ceiling ($\mu = 0$), because of a horizontally applied force F, as shown in Fig. P 4.4-11. Draw a free-body diagram of the bar, and determine all forces and the resulting acceleration if $F = 20$ lb.

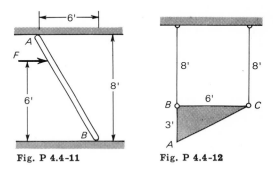

Fig. P 4.4-11   **Fig. P 4.4-12**

4.4-12 The velocity of point A at the instant shown in Fig. P 4.4-12 is 5.4 ft/sec. Determine the tensions in the massless 8-ft rods when m is the mass of the triangle ABC.

4.4-13 A horizontal force $F = kt^2$ acts on a block resting on a floor with coefficient of friction μ (see Fig. P 4.4-13). Determine the equation for the time at which the block overturns on its leading edge.

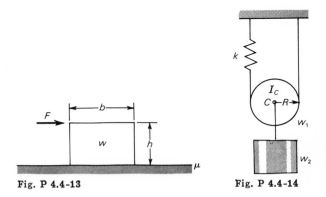

Fig. P 4.4-13   **Fig. P 4.4-14**

4.4-14 Determine the equation of motion for the system shown in Fig. P 4.4-14, and find its natural frequency of small vertical oscillations.

4.4-15   A uniform thin bar of mass m_1 and length l is riveted to a cylinder of mass m_2 and radius r that rolls without slipping on another cylinder of larger radius R (see Fig. P 4.4-15).   Determine the equation of motion and the natural frequency of small oscillations.

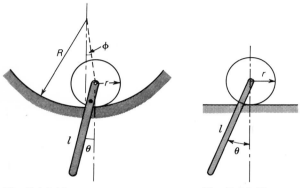

Fig. P 4.4-15   Fig. P 4.4-16

4.4-16   A bar of length l and weight w_2 is pinned to the center of a cylinder of radius r and weight w_1 (see Fig. P 4.4-16).   Determine the equation of motion and the period of small oscillations of the system.

4.4-17   If the bar in Prob. 4.4-16 is rigidly attached to the cylinder, determine the equation of motion and the period of small oscillations.

4.4-18   Determine the natural frequencies of the system shown in Fig. P 4.4-18 and the corresponding modes of vibration.

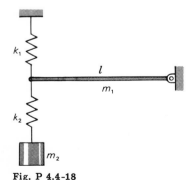

Fig. P 4.4-18

4.4-19   A circular cylinder of mass m and radius r rolls without slipping in a semicircular guide of radius R and mass M, resting on a smooth horizontal plane and attached to a spring of stiffness k (see Fig. P 4.4-19). Determine the equations of motion, and then simplify them for small amplitudes and determine the two natural frequencies.

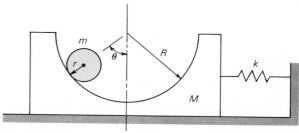

Fig. P 4.4-19

4.4-20 Two circular plates of equal thickness and density are riveted together, as shown in Fig. P 4.4-20. The face of the large plate rests on a smooth horizontal plane and is acted on by a couple $2FR$. What is the angular acceleration, and about what point does it rotate?

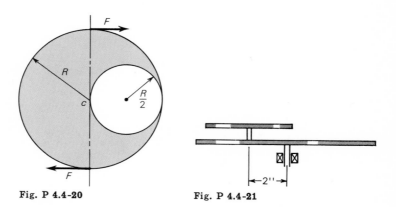

Fig. P 4.4-20   **Fig. P 4.4-21**

4.4-21 A small turntable, driven by a motor, is mounted eccentrically on a larger turntable, as shown in Fig. P 4.4-21. The weight and the radius of gyration of the small turntable are 3 lb and 1.5 in., and the large turntable weighs 10 lb and has a radius of gyration of 4 in. With the large table at rest, the small table is rotating at a speed of 1,200 rpm. What is the angular speed of the large table after the small table is brought to rest relative to the large table by means of a friction brake between the two disks?

4.4-22 Find the moment of inertia of a cam about an axis OO (see Fig. P 4.4-22). A weight w descends 10 ft from rest in 5 sec (friction is negligible).

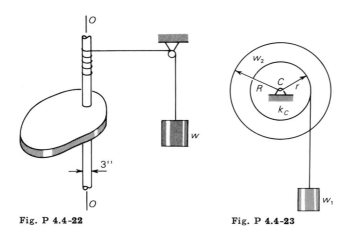

Fig. P **4.4-22**   Fig. P **4.4-23**

4.4-23 A weight w_1 unwinds off a small cylinder that is fastened to a larger one (see Fig. P 4.4-23). If the combined weight of the two cylinders is w_2 and its radius of gyration about its center is k_C, determine the acceleration of w_1.

4.4-24 When the temporary support shown in Fig. P 4.4-24 is removed, what is the angular acceleration of the homogeneous disk and the linear acceleration of the weights?

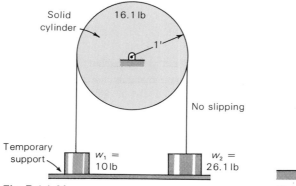

Fig. P **4.4-24**   Fig. P **4.4-25**

4.4-25 A hoop of radius R with a half-circle solid section is released on a rough horizontal plane from the position shown in Fig. P 4.4-25. Determine the initial angular acceleration. Neglect the mass of the hoop.

4.4-26   In the position shown in Fig. P 4.4-26, the center O of a wheel has a velocity of 6 ft/sec to the right.   The wheel weighs 20 lb, with center of mass at C, and has a radius of gyration about C of $\frac{2}{3}$ ft.   At the instant shown, determine the linear momentum of the wheel and its angular acceleration if the wheel rolls without slipping.

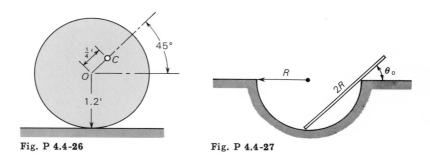

Fig. P 4.4-26   Fig. P 4.4-27

4.4-27   A uniform thin bar of length $2R$ is held at an angle θ_0 with the edge of a cylinder of radius R (see Fig. P 4.4-27).   Assuming all surfaces to be smooth, determine the initial angular acceleration of the bar as a function of θ_0 after the bar is released.

4.4-28   The combined wheel of weight w_2 has a radius of gyration of k_0 about its center (see Fig. P 4.4-28).   It rolls without slipping on a horizontal track because of weight w_1.   Determine its angular acceleration.

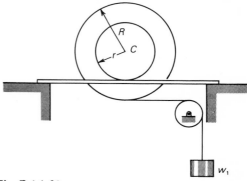

Fig. P 4.4-28

4.4-29   Determine the acceleration of a weight w_1 connected to a wheel of weight w_2 with a radius of gyration k_C about its center (see Fig. P 4.4-29) if the cylinder rolls without slipping.

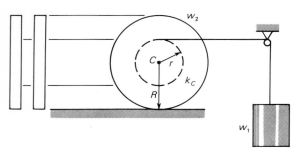

Fig. P 4.4-29

4.4-30   If in Prob. 4.4-29 the string is wound in the counterclockwise direction, which direction does the cylinder move in, and what is the acceleration of w_1?

4.4-31   A weight w_1 is attached to a uniform cylinder of weight w_2 and radius R as shown in Fig. P 4.4-31.   If friction between cylinder and floor is sufficient to prevent sliding, determine the acceleration of w_1 in terms of the two weights.

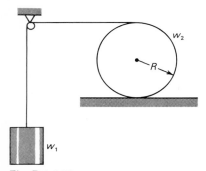

Fig. P 4.4-31

4.4-32   A uniform slender bar 10 ft long and weighing 12 lb is hinged at one end and supported by a cord passing over a pulley to a weight at the other end, as shown

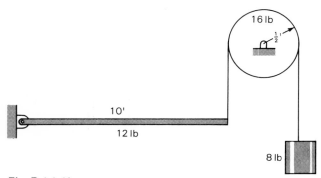

Fig. P 4.4-32

in Fig. P 4.4-32. The pulley is a cylinder of radius $\frac{1}{2}$ ft and weight 16 lb, and the attached weight weighs 8 lb. Determine the initial angular acceleration of the bar if released from the horizontal position.

4.4-33 A uniform cylinder of weight w_2 whose center is constrained to move in a frictionless vertical slot is connected by a cord to w_1, as shown in Fig. P 4.4-33. Determine the acceleration of w_1 and w_2 when released.

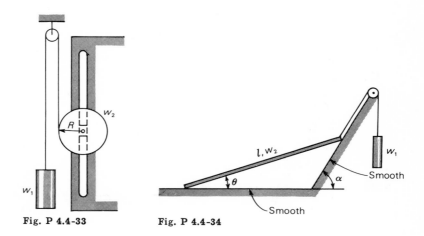

Fig. P 4.4-33   Fig. P 4.4-34

4.4-34 A uniform thin bar of length l and weight w_2 is supported by a weight w_1 at one end and a smooth floor at the other (see Fig. P 4.4-34). If released from the position θ, determine the initial acceleration of w_1. HINT: Since the bar is initially at rest, the instantaneous centers of velocity and acceleration coincide initially.

4.4-35 A cylindrical pulley 6 in. in diameter rests on a stationary belt conveyor with its axis at right angles to the direction of travel of the conveyor, as shown in Fig. P 4.4-35. If the conveyor starts with an acceleration of 2 ft/sec², how rapidly is the center of the pulley accelerated if no slipping occurs? The weight of the pulley is 16.1 lb, and the radius of gyration with respect to the center C is 2.5 in.

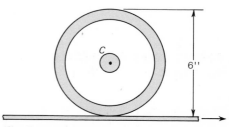

Fig. P 4.4-35

4.4-36   A slender bar AB is rigidly fastened to a cylindrical drum that rotates about a fixed axle O because of a weight w_1 (see Fig. P 4.4-36). The combined weight of the drum and bar is w_2 with radius of gyration k_0 and center of mass a distance d from O. Neglecting axle friction, find (a) the angular velocity $\dot\theta$ if the system starts from rest when $\theta = 0$, (b) the angular acceleration, (c) the cord tension when $\theta = 90°$ (given $\dot\theta = \%$ rad/sec, $\ddot\theta = 1\%$ rad/sec² clockwise, $w_1 = 180$ lb, and $R = 15$ in.).

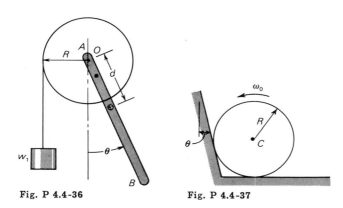

Fig. P 4.4-36   Fig. P 4.4-37

4.4-37   A uniform cylinder of radius R is placed in a corner with the wall making an angle θ with the vertical (see Fig. P 4.4-37). If the initial angular velocity of the cylinder is ω_0 counterclockwise, determine its angular acceleration. Assume μ between all surfaces.

4.4-38   A solid cylinder of mass m and radius R rests on a flat car of mass M (see Fig. P 4.4-38). Determine the acceleration of the center of the cylinder relative to the car when a horizontal force P is applied to the car. Assume the friction between m and M to be sufficient to preclude sliding.

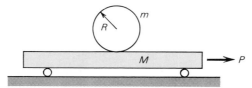

Fig. P 4.4-38

4.4-39   A cylinder of weight w_1 rolls without slipping down a wedge of angle α that rests on a smooth horizontal floor (see Fig. P 4.4-39). Show that the acceleration of the wedge is

$$\frac{gw_1 \sin 2\alpha}{3(w_1 + w_2) - 2w_1 \cos^2 \alpha}$$

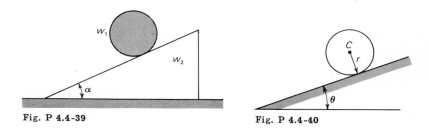

Fig. P 4.4-39   Fig. P 4.4-40

4.4-40   A cylinder of radius r, mass M, and radius of gyration k_C about its center axis is placed on an inclined plane of angle θ and released (see Fig. P 4.4-40). Determine the minimum coefficient of friction for no sliding.

4.4-41   A slender uniform bar 6 ft long weighing 64.4 lb is made to slide along a circular frictionless track of 5-ft radius in a horizontal plane (see Fig. P 4.4-41). Guides at A and B keep the ends on the track. The bar is propelled by a force F that is applied to it at A in the direction tangent to the track. At a certain instant end A has a velocity of 5 ft/sec that is increasing at the rate of 10 ft/sec². Determine, for this instant, the force F and the forces exerted by the track on the bar at A and B.

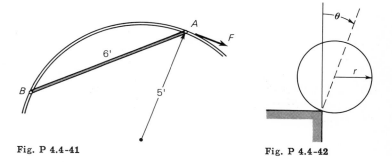

Fig. P 4.4-41   Fig. P 4.4-42

4.4-42   A uniform cylinder starting with zero velocity rolls off the corner of a table (see Fig. P 4.4-42). If slipping of the cylinder over the corner starts at $\theta = 30°$, determine the coefficient of friction μ.

4.4-43   A uniform slender bar of length l is held vertically on a rough horizontal floor and released. If the bottom end slides when the angle of the bar is θ_1 with the vertical, determine the coefficient of friction μ.

4.4-44   A uniform bar of length l is held in a horizontal position with its center of mass a distance c from the vertical edge of the table (see Fig. 4.4-44). If the bar slides relative to the table edge when the angle of the bar exceeds θ_0 with the horizontal, determine the coefficient of friction μ.

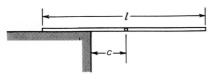

Fig. P 4.4-44

4.4-45   A uniform cylinder of radius R rotating about its axis of symmetry with angular velocity ω_0 is placed on a horizontal floor of coefficient of friction μ. How far does its center travel before slipping ceases and pure rolling begins?

4.4-46   A 4-ft cylinder is supported by a 3-ft cylinder that runs on tracks, one on each side. A constant force $P = 40$ lb is applied horizontally by a cord wrapped around the large cylinder, as shown in Fig. P 4.4-46. The total weight of the cylinders w is 128.8 lb, and the radius of gyration k_C is 1.0 ft. If no slippage occurs, what is the acceleration of the center? What is the frictional force? In what direction does the cylinder move?

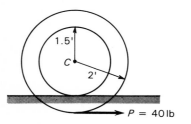

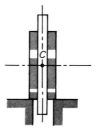

Fig. P 4.4-46

4.4-47   The drum-and-wheel assembly shown in Fig. P 4.4-47 weighs 96.6 lb and has a radius of gyration k_C of 2 ft. It rolls without slipping along a track BC under the action of a 60-lb force at an angle of 30° above the horizontal. Determine the acceleration of the center of the drum and the friction force exerted on it by the track.

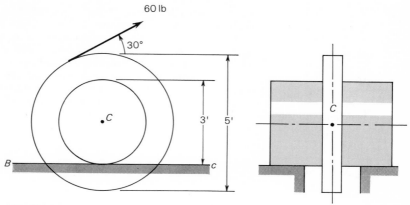

Fig. P 4.4-47

4.4-48   A steam roller of weight w_1 and radius r connected to a block of weight w_2 is released on a hill of angle θ (see Fig. P 4.4-48).   If the coefficient of sliding friction is μ, determine the acceleration and the force in the connecting bar (indicate compression or tension).

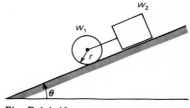

Fig. P 4.4-48

4.4-49   The block and cylinder shown in Fig. P 4.4-49 are equal in weight.   The cylinder has a radius of gyration about its center axis, k_C, of 1.5 ft, and rolls on an axle of

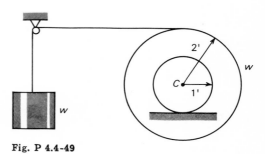

Fig. P 4.4-49

1-ft radius.   The coefficient of friction between the cylinder and track is $\mu = 0.20$.
Set up the necessary equations for the determination of the acceleration of the
block.   After checking the equations for correctness, evaluate the acceleration
and the friction force, and verify whether the cylinder slides or rolls.

4.4-50   A uniform bar of length 6 ft and weight 32.2 lb is pinned at A and connected by a
cord CO to the center of a horizontal table.   At a given instant the angular
velocity and acceleration are those given in Fig. P 4.4-50.   Determine the tension in the cord CO and the components of the force at the pin A parallel and perpendicular to the bar.

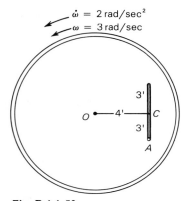

Fig. P 4.4-50

4.4-51   A horizontal turntable is rotating about a vertical axis through its center (see
Fig. P 4.4-51).   A slender uniform beam 6 ft long and weighing 10 lb is pinned
to the table at A and held in position by a smooth peg B.   Determine all forces
acting on the beam when the angular velocity and acceleration of the table are
$\omega = 2$ rad/sec and $\dot{\omega} = 3$ rad/sec².

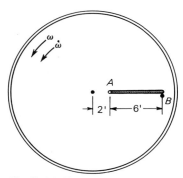

Fig. P 4.4-51

4.4-52 A thin uniform plate in the form of a 3-ft equilateral triangle weighing 100 lb is pinned to the center of a smooth horizontal turntable (see Fig. P 4.4-52). At B the plate pushes against a smooth pin fixed in the table. Determine the forces exerted on the plate by the pins at the instant when the table is rotating about a vertical axis through O with an angular velocity of 3 rad/sec and an angular acceleration of 5 rad/sec², both counterclockwise.

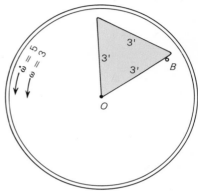

Fig. P **4.4-52**

4.4-53 A uniform bar of weight w and length $\sqrt{2}\,R$ is pinned at A, the other end B being free to push against the rim of a wheel when rotating (see Fig. P 4.4-53). The wheel rotates in a horizontal plane about its center O. At a given instant, $\omega = 3$ rad/sec and $\dot{\omega} = 6$ rad/sec². Determine, for this instant, the force B (assumed to be acting in the radial direction) and the tangential and radial components of the pin reaction at A.

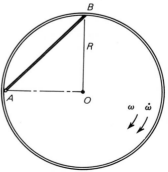

Fig. P **4.4-53**

4.4-54   The wheel shown in Fig. P 4.4-54 is in the horizontal plane and rotates about a vertical axis through its center.   A uniform bar 6 ft long and weighing 10 lb is pinned to the wheel at A, the other end B resting against the outer rim.   Assuming that the reaction of the rim on the bar is radial, determine its value and the radial and tangential components of the pin reaction at A at the instant when $\omega = 2$ rad/sec and $\dot{\omega} = 3$ rad/sec².

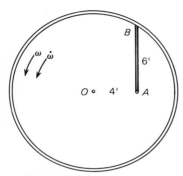

Fig. P 4.4-54

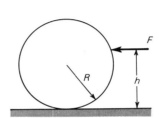

Fig. P 4.4-55

4.4-55   At what height h should a horizontal force F be applied to a uniform circular cylinder of radius R (see Fig. P 4.4-55) such that the reaction of the floor has no horizontal component?

4.4-56   At what point x above its center must a billiard ball be struck horizontally to result in zero friction force between it and the table?   What kind of motion does the ball have under such impact?

4.4-57   A uniform slender bar of length l is supported on a knife-edge at a distance a from one end, which is tied to the floor to hold the bar in the horizontal position (see Fig. P 4.4-57).   If the string is suddenly cut, determine the force on the knife-edge at the initial instant.

Fig. P 4.4-57

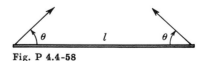

Fig. P 4.4-58

4.4-58   A uniform slender bar of length l is supported by strings tied to the ends at angle θ (see Fig. P 4.4-58).   If one side breaks, determine the tension on the other.

4.4-59   A uniform slender bar is supported in the horizontal position by a knife-edge and string, as shown (see Fig. P 4.4-59).   If the string is cut, determine the force of the knife-edge at the initial instant.

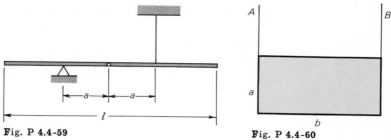

Fig. P 4.4-59   Fig. P 4.4-60

4.4-60   A uniform plate of weight w and dimensions a and b is being hoisted by two ropes, as shown (see Fig. P 4.4-60).   If rope B breaks, determine the force on rope A at the initial instant.

4.4-61   A bar AB of weight w and length l, with its center of mass at a distance b from A and radius of gyration k_C, is suspended in the horizontal position by two cords at A and B.   Determine the tension on B the instant after A is burned off.

4.4-62   Two uniform slender bars, of mass m and length l each, are hinged at B and lie in a straight line on a smooth horizontal floor (see Fig. P 4.4-62).   If an impulse $\hat{F}$ normal to the bar is applied at a point a distance b from the end, determine the angular velocity of each bar immediately after the impulse.

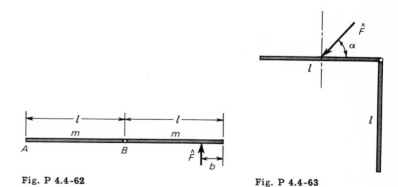

Fig. P 4.4-62   Fig. P 4.4-63

4.4-63   Two uniform slender bars, of length l each, are hinged at right angles and lie on a smooth horizontal floor.   A force impulse $\hat{F}$ is applied to the midpoint of one of the bars at an angle $\alpha = 45°$, as shown in Fig. P 4.4-63.   Determine the initial angular velocity of each bar.

4.4-64   In Prob. 4.4-63 determine the angle α for which both bars have equal angular velocity.   Determine the instantaneous center of rotation.

4.4-65   Two equal slender bars, each of mass m and length l, are hinged at O with only sufficient hinge moment M_O to keep them in a straight line when released from the horizontal position (see Fig. P 4.4-65). When vertical, the upper bar strikes a rigid obstacle and its velocity is suddenly reduced to zero. Determine the angular velocity ω of the bar OB immediately after impact, and find the angle through which it rotates before coming to a stop.

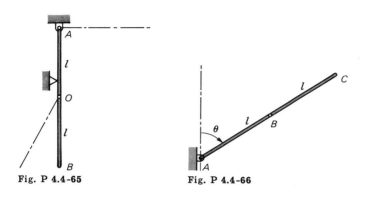

Fig. P 4.4-65   Fig. P 4.4-66

4.4-66   Two equal slender bars, each of mass m and length l, are tightly hinged at B and free to rotate in a vertical plane about A, as shown in Fig. P 4.4-66. If started from the vertical or horizontal position, how much moment M_B must the hinge at B offer against rotation in order for the two bars to remain in the same straight line throughout the motion?

4.4-67   A uniform L-shaped slender bar is pinned at A and released from the position shown in Fig. P 4.4-67. Determine the bending moment at B when released.

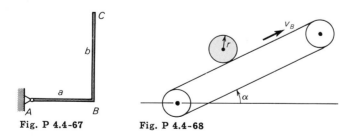

Fig. P 4.4-67   Fig. P 4.4-68

4.4-68   A thin cylinder of radius r and weight w is placed on a conveyor belt running with velocity v_B on an incline of angle α with the horizontal (see Fig. P 4.4-68). If no slipping occurs, determine the distance traveled by the cylinder in time t.

4.4-69   In Prob. 4.4-68 what is the distance traveled by the cylinder if the belt is suddenly accelerated from v_B with constant acceleration a_B for t sec?

4.4-70   A cylindrical drum of radius R is made to rotate at constant angular velocity ω about its horizontal axis (see Fig. P 4.4-70).   A mass m inside the drum remains at a position $\tan \theta = \mu$, where μ is the coefficient of friction between it and the drum.   If the mass m is disturbed from this position by a small angle ϕ, show that its differential equation of motion is

$$\ddot{\phi} + \frac{g}{R} \sqrt{1 + \mu^2}\, \phi = 0$$

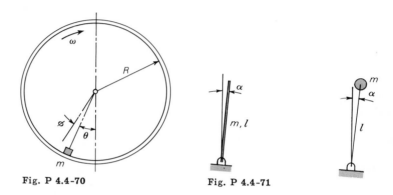

Fig. P 4.4-70   Fig. P 4.4-71

4.4-71   Two different bodies, a uniform slender bar and a mass on a rigid weightless arm, are hinged at the bottom and released from zero velocity in a slightly inclined position (angle α with vertical)—see Fig. P 4.4-71.   Which body reaches the horizontal position first?

4.4-72   Inside a horizontal tube of length l and mass m_1 there is a solid rod of the same length and mass m_2 (see Fig. P 4.4-72).   With the rod completely inside the tube, the tube is given an angular velocity ω about a vertical axis through its fixed center O.   Because of a slight disturbance the solid rod slides out without friction.   Determine the angular velocity ω' of the tube as the rod leaves the tube.

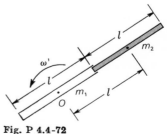

Fig. P 4.4-72

4.5 WORK AND ENERGY THEOREMS IN PLANE MOTION

We consider a "plane" rigid body in plane motion.   The velocity of the mass element dm is—see Eq. (4.2-2)—

$$\mathbf{v} = \dot{\mathbf{r}} = \mathbf{v}_C + \boldsymbol{\omega} \times \boldsymbol{\varrho}_C$$

where $\mathbf{v}_C$ is the velocity of the center of mass of the body in an inertial frame of reference and $\boldsymbol{\omega} \times \boldsymbol{\varrho}_C$ is the velocity of dm relative to C (see Fig. 4.5-1).

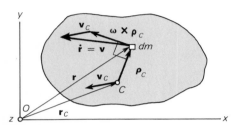

Fig. 4.5-1

The square of the velocity is found from its dot product:

$$v^2 = \mathbf{v} \cdot \mathbf{v} = v_C{}^2 + 2\mathbf{v}_C \cdot (\boldsymbol{\omega} \times \boldsymbol{\varrho}_C) + \omega^2 \rho_C{}^2$$

and substituting this into the equation for the kinetic energy, we obtain, by analogy with the expression found for a system of particles—see Eq. (3.4-4)—

$$T = \tfrac{1}{2} \int_m v^2 \, dm = \tfrac{1}{2}mv_C{}^2 + \mathbf{v}_C \cdot \int_m (\boldsymbol{\omega} \times \boldsymbol{\varrho}_C) \, dm + \tfrac{1}{2}\omega^2 \int_m \rho_C{}^2 \, dm$$

Since ω is not a variable regarding the integration with respect to m and since $\int_m \boldsymbol{\varrho}_C \, dm = \mathbf{0}$, the second term drops out and the equation above becomes

$$T = \tfrac{1}{2}mv_C{}^2 + \tfrac{1}{2}I_C\omega^2 \qquad \blacktriangleleft \quad (4.5\text{-}1)$$

Thus the kinetic energy of a rigid body in plane motion is found to consist of two terms:

(1) $$T_{\text{trans}} = \tfrac{1}{2}mv_C{}^2 \qquad \blacktriangleleft \quad (4.5\text{-}2)$$

which expresses the kinetic energy that the body has in the case of pure translation with the velocity $\mathbf{v}_C$ of the center of mass, and

(2) $$T_{\text{rot}} = \tfrac{1}{2}I_C\omega^2 \qquad \blacktriangleleft \quad (4.5\text{-}3)$$

which expresses the kinetic energy due solely to rotation of the rigid body about an axis through C normal to the plane of motion.

The expression for the kinetic energy of a rigid body in plane motion as given in Eq. (4.5-1) may be simplified by employing the concept of the instantaneous center.   From Eq. (4.2-5) we have

$$\mathbf{v}_C = \boldsymbol{\omega} \times \boldsymbol{\varrho}_{QC}$$

where $\boldsymbol{\varrho}_{QC}$ is the body-fixed position vector from the instantaneous center Q to the center of mass C, and thus, since $\boldsymbol{\omega}$ is normal to $\boldsymbol{\varrho}_{QC}$,

$$v_C{}^2 = \omega^2 \rho_{QC}{}^2$$

Hence Eq. (4.5-1) may be rewritten

$$T = \tfrac{1}{2}m\omega^2\rho_{QC}{}^2 + \tfrac{1}{2}I_C\omega^2 = \tfrac{1}{2}(I_C + m\rho_{QC}{}^2)\omega^2$$

In view of the parallel-axes theorem of Eq. (4.3-6) we have

$$I_C + m\rho_{QC}{}^2 = I_Q$$

and therefore
$$T = \tfrac{1}{2}I_Q\omega^2 \qquad \blacktriangleleft \quad (4.5\text{-}4)$$

Equation (4.5-4) expresses the total kinetic energy of a rigid body moving parallel to its plane of symmetry as rotatory kinetic energy, employing the axis through the instantaneous center as reference axis.

Kinetic energy can also be expressed in terms of the momentum and the moment of momentum of the body.   Since $m\mathbf{v}_C = \mathbf{G}$ and $I_C\boldsymbol{\omega} = \mathbf{h}_C$, we may write, for the kinetic energy—see Eq. (4.5-1)—

$$2T = \mathbf{v}_C \cdot \mathbf{G} + \boldsymbol{\omega} \cdot \mathbf{h}_C \qquad \blacktriangleleft \quad (4.5\text{-}5)$$

Equation (4.5-5) represents an expression for the kinetic energy that is valid even for the most general type of motion of a rigid body.

In considering the relationship between a rigid body's kinetic energy and the work done by external forces $\mathbf{F}_j$ and couples $\mathbf{M}_i$ acting on it in plane motion, we refer to Eqs. (3.4-5) and (3.4-6).   Hence we have, with $\mathbf{F} = \sum_{j=1}^{n} \mathbf{F}_j$, from Eq. (3.4-5),

$$\int_{t_1}^{t_2} \mathbf{F} \cdot \mathbf{v}_C \, dt = \tfrac{1}{2}m(\mathbf{v}_{C2}{}^2 - \mathbf{v}_{C1}{}^2) = T_{2,\text{trans}} - T_{1,\text{trans}} \qquad \blacktriangleleft \quad (4.5\text{-}6)$$

With regard to Eq. (3.4-6), we consider first that we may ignore the internal forces $\mathbf{F}_{jl}$ in a rigid body (see Sec. 4.1) and second that

$$\mathbf{v}_{Cj} = \boldsymbol{\omega} \times \boldsymbol{\varrho}_{Cj} \qquad (4.5\text{-}7)$$

Hence we may write for the left side of Eq. (3.4-6)

$$\int_{t_1}^{t_2} \sum_{j=1}^{n} \mathbf{F}_j \cdot (\boldsymbol{\omega} \times \boldsymbol{\varrho}_{Cj}) \, dt = \int_{t_1}^{t_2} \left(\sum_{j=1}^{n} \boldsymbol{\varrho}_{Cj} \times \mathbf{F}_j \right) \cdot \boldsymbol{\omega} \, dt$$

Thus with $\mathbf{M}_C = \sum_{j=1}^{n} \boldsymbol{\varrho}_{cj} \times \mathbf{F}_j$ the left side of Eq. (3.4-6) is written

$$\int_{t_1}^{t_2} \mathbf{M}_C \cdot \boldsymbol{\omega} \, dt$$

Turning to the right side of Eq. (3.4-6), we readily see, in view of Eq. (4.5-7), that it represents the change in the rotatory kinetic energy. Thus, employing Eq. (4.5-3), we may write for Eq. (3.4-6)

$$\int_{t_1}^{t_2} \mathbf{M}_C \cdot \boldsymbol{\omega} \, dt = \tfrac{1}{2} I_C(\omega_2{}^2 - \omega_1{}^2) = T_{2,\text{rot}} - T_{1,\text{rot}} \quad \blacktriangleleft \quad (4.5\text{-}8)$$

We have thus demonstrated that the work done by the resultant of all external forces acting on the center of mass brings about a change in the translatory kinetic energy, and that done by the sum of the moments of all external forces about the center of mass, and by the sum of all force couples,[1] leads to a change in the rotatory kinetic energy of a rigid body.

If the forces and force moments acting on a rigid body are conservative, then their work is equal to the negative of the change in their potentials, and the sum of the potential and kinetic energies remains constant:

$$U_2 + T_2 = U_1 + T_1 \qquad \blacktriangleleft \quad (4.5\text{-}9)$$

or

$$U + T = E = \text{const} \qquad \blacktriangleleft \quad (4.5\text{-}10)$$

ILLUSTRATIVE EXAMPLE 4.5-1

A useful setup for the experimental determination of the moment of inertia of a disk or wheel is shown in Fig. 4.5-2. Practical dimensions are, for example, $l = 80$ in. for r

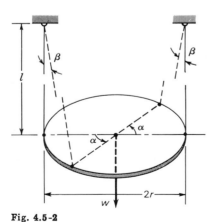

Fig. 4.5-2

between 4 and 8 in. If the disk is turned through an angle $\alpha = \alpha_0$ from its equilibrium position, then, on release, it carries out oscillations about its vertical axis with the angular

[1] Then, of course, we have $\mathbf{M}_C = \sum_{j} \boldsymbol{\varrho}_{cj} \times \mathbf{F}_j + \sum_{i} \mathbf{M}_i$.

amplitude α_0. Show how the period of oscillation τ is related to the moment of inertia I_C of the disk about the vertical axis through the center of mass C. The weight of the disk is w.

SOLUTION: We use the energy theorem, since we assume that in the type of motion discussed here any dissipative forces may be neglected. Furthermore we assume that the wires are so stiff that they do not change their length during the oscillation.

The disk is in its lowest position when α is zero. Taking this position as the reference level for the potential energy, the maximum potential energy is reached for $\alpha = \alpha_0$ when momentarily the kinetic energy becomes zero, because then the oscillation changes its direction. In order to calculate $U_{\max}$, we have to determine the height h through which the disk is lifted because of its turn through the angle α_0 (see Fig. 4.5-2):

$$h = l(1 - \cos \beta_0)$$

or for small angles

$$h = \frac{l\beta_0^2}{2}$$

With $\beta_0 = \alpha_0 r/l$ we then have

$$U_{\max} = wh = w \frac{r^2}{2l} \alpha_0^2 \tag{a}$$

We now consider that small oscillations under gravity or elastic forces are always harmonic with the circular frequency p (see Illustrative Example 2.2-2). Thus we have

$$\alpha = \alpha_0 \cos pt$$

and for the angular velocity of the oscillating disk

$$\dot{\alpha} = -\alpha_0 p \sin pt$$

Hence we see that for $t = i\pi/p$ $(i = 0, 1, 2, \ldots)$ we have $\dot{\alpha} = 0$ and $|\alpha| = \alpha_0$ $(U = U_{\max}$ and $T = 0)$, and for $t = (\pi/2p)(1 + 2i)$ we have $|\dot{\alpha}| = \alpha_0 p$ and $\alpha = 0$ $(T = T_{\max}$ and $U = 0)$. The maximum kinetic energy $T_{\max}$ is—see Eq. (4.5-3)[1]—with $\omega = \dot{\alpha}_{\max} = \alpha_0 p$,

$$T_{\max} = \tfrac{1}{2}\alpha_0^2 p^2 I_C$$

Since $p = 2\pi/\tau$, we may also write

$$T_{\max} = \tfrac{1}{2}\alpha_0^2 \frac{(2\pi)^2}{\tau^2} I_C \tag{b}$$

Since when $T = T_{\max}$, we have $U = 0$, and when $U = U_{\max}$, we have $T = 0$, then because of the conservation of energy we may state

$$U_{\max} = T_{\max}$$

and thus from Eqs. (a) and (b)

$$I_C = \frac{r^2 w}{l(2\pi)^2} \tau^2 \tag{c}$$

which is the wanted relation between I_C and the period of oscillation τ. This experimental method is, for practical purposes, sufficiently accurate, since τ can be measured quite exactly, especially when the time is taken for a large number of oscillation periods.

ILLUSTRATIVE EXAMPLE 4.5-2

In the Pioneer III lunar probe a despinning device, consisting of two diametrically opposed masses m on the ends of two light inextensible cords wrapped around the sym-

[1] T_{trans} is zero here.

metrical satellite (see Fig. 4.5-3), was used to reduce the spin of the spin-stabilized satellite by allowing the cord to unwind completely from the body and subsequently releasing the masses so that they would fly away. Determine the length l of the cords necessary to reduce the angular velocity of the satellite to zero. The moment of inertia of the satellite about its axis of symmetry is I_C.

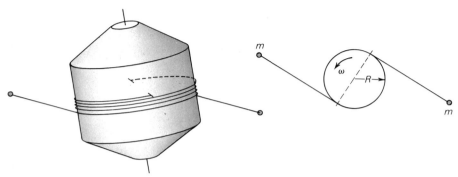

Fig. 4.5-3

SOLUTION: Because of the symmetry of the arrangement, gravitational forces can influence neither the moment of momentum of the system about the symmetry axis nor the rotational portion T_rot of the kinetic energy. Other external forces being absent in space and considering that the unwinding of the cords entails practically no energy dissipation, we may conclude that both

$$\mathbf{h}_C = \text{const} \qquad\qquad (a)$$

and
$$T_\text{rot} = \text{const} \qquad\qquad (b)$$

Referring to Fig. 4.5-4, $\mathbf{h}_C$ and T_rot are easily determined. The angular momentum and the kinetic energy of the satellite alone are simply $I_C\omega$ and $\tfrac{1}{2}I_C\omega^2$, respectively, where ω is the variable angular velocity of the satellite.

In order to determine the corresponding quantities for the two despinning masses m, we need their velocity $\mathbf{v}$ with respect to an inertial frame of reference. We consider the reference frame translating relative to the earth with the velocity of the center of mass C to be an inertial reference frame. Then $\mathbf{v}$ may be determined in the following two steps:

1   We take the cords (see Fig. 4.5-4) to be rigidly fixed to the spinning satellite. Then each mass has the velocity $\mathbf{v}_1$ of magnitude

$$|\mathbf{v}_1| = |\omega|R\sqrt{1 + \phi^2}$$

because, denoting the angle through which the cord has been unwound relative to the satellite by ϕ, the length of the cord extending beyond the instantaneous tangent point Q is $R\phi$. Thus the distance of m from C is $R\sqrt{1 + \phi^2}$.

2   Relative to the reference frame, fixed in the satellite, the angular velocity of the taut cord is $\dot\phi$. Thus with respect to this reference frame the velocity $\mathbf{v}_2$ of m is of magni-

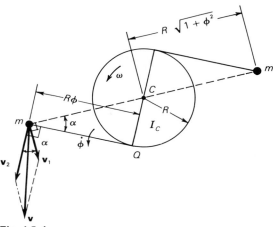

Fig. 4.5-4

tude (see Fig. 4.5-4)

$$|\mathbf{v}_2| = |\dot\phi|R|\phi|$$

Hence the velocity $\mathbf{v}$ of each mass m with respect to the inertial reference frame defined above is obtained as (see Fig. 4.5-4) $\mathbf{v} = \mathbf{v}_1 + \mathbf{v}_2$.

Considering that $\mathbf{v}_1$ is directed normal to the radial line connecting point C and the mass and that $\mathbf{v}_2$ is parallel to the radial line CQ, we readily obtain, for the magnitude of the moment of momentum of the two masses about C,

$$2m[\omega R^2(1 + \phi^2) + \dot\phi R^2\phi^2] = 2mR^2[\omega + \phi^2(\omega + \dot\phi)] \tag{c}$$

Furthermore, since we have by inspection of Fig. 4.5-4

$$v^2 = |\mathbf{v}_1 + \mathbf{v}_2|^2 = v_1{}^2 + v_2{}^2 + 2v_1v_2\cos\alpha$$

or with $\cos\alpha = R\phi/(R\sqrt{1 + \phi^2})$ (see Fig. 4.5-4)

$$v^2 = R^2[\omega^2(1 + \phi^2) + \dot\phi^2\phi^2 + 2\omega\phi\dot\phi^2] = R^2[\omega^2 + \phi^2(\omega + \dot\phi)^2]$$

we find for T_{rot} of the two masses

$$\tfrac{1}{2}2mR^2[\omega^2 + \phi^2(\omega + \dot\phi)^2] \tag{d}$$

Hence, the total moment of momentum of the system is of magnitude—see Eq. (c)—

$$h_C = I_C\omega + 2mR^2[\omega + \phi^2(\omega + \dot\phi)] \tag{e}$$

and the total rotational kinetic energy—see Eq. (d)—is

$$T_{\text{rot}} = \tfrac{1}{2}\{I_C\omega^2 + 2mR^2[\omega^2 + \phi^2(\omega + \dot\phi)^2]\} \tag{f}$$

Assuming that initially ($\phi = 0$) the angular velocity of the satellite was ω_0, we may now write for Eqs. (a) and (b), respectively,

$$I_C\omega + 2mR^2[\omega + \phi^2(\omega + \dot\phi)] = (I_C + 2mR^2)\omega_0 \tag{g}$$
$$I_C\omega^2 + 2mR^2[\omega^2 + \phi^2(\omega + \dot\phi)^2] = (I_C + 2mR^2)\omega_0{}^2 \tag{h}$$

Since our problem is to find the cord length $l = R\phi_e$ (ϕ_e being the wrapping angle of the entire cord) for which ω becomes zero, we may write, instead of Eqs. (g) and (h), with $\omega_e = 0$,

$$2mR^2\dot{\phi}_e\phi_e^2 = (I_C + 2mR^2)\omega_0 \qquad (i)$$
$$2mR^2\dot{\phi}_e^2\phi_e^2 = (I_C + 2mR^2)\omega_0^2 \qquad (j)$$

Division of these equations immediately yields

$$\dot{\phi}_e = \omega_0 \qquad (k)$$

and thus we find, after substitution of Eq. (k) in Eq. (i),

$$\phi_e = \sqrt{\frac{I_C + 2mR^2}{2mR^2}}$$

and hence

$$l = R\phi_e = \sqrt{R^2 + \frac{I_C}{2m}} \qquad (l)$$

Therefore we see that it is possible to despin a satellite completely by choosing such a yo-yo device with a cord length as given by Eq. (l). Note that l is independent of the initial spin velocity ω_0.

ILLUSTRATIVE EXAMPLE 4.5-3
A uniform block of length $2l$ and thickness $2b$ rests in a horizontal position on a rough cylinder of radius r. Show that, if the block is disturbed ($\theta_{\max}$ is a small angle), as shown in Fig. 4.5-5, it oscillates with a period

$$\tau = 2\pi \sqrt{\frac{l^2 + 4b^2}{3g(r - b)}}$$

Prove that the system is stable provided $r > b$.

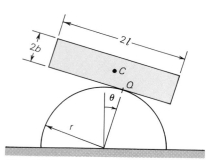

Fig. 4.5-5

SOLUTION: Since the only external force is due to gravity and since there is no energy dissipation on account of friction, the system is conservative and the sum of the kinetic and potential energy of the block is a constant. Hence we can establish the differential equation for the motion of the block by using the expression

$$\frac{d}{dt}(T + U) = 0 \qquad \text{See Eq. (4.5-10)}[1] \tag{a}$$

For small angles θ $(r\theta \ll b)$ the kinetic energy is—see Eq. (4.5-1)—

$$T(\theta) = \tfrac{1}{2}mb^2\theta^2 + \tfrac{1}{2}m\frac{l^2 + b^2}{3}\theta^2 = \tfrac{1}{2}m\frac{l^2 + 4b^2}{3}\theta^2 \tag{b}$$

and the potential energy with respect to the center of mass C for $\theta = 0$ is

$$U(\theta) = mg[(r + b)(\cos\theta - 1) + r\theta\sin\theta] \approx mg\left[-(r + b)\frac{\theta^2}{2} + r\theta^2\right]$$

$$= \frac{mg}{2}(r - b)\theta^2 \tag{c}$$

Substituting the relations (b) and (c) for T and U in Eq. (a), we obtain the equation of motion for small angular displacements θ:

$$m\frac{l^2 + 4b^2}{3}\dot\theta\ddot\theta + mg(r - b)\theta\dot\theta = 0$$

or

$$\ddot\theta + \frac{3g(r - b)}{l^2 + 4b^2}\theta = 0 \tag{d}$$

Thus the differential equation above has a harmonic solution (see Illustrative Example 2.2-2) provided $r > b$. The period of this oscillation is

$$\tau = 2\pi\sqrt{\frac{l^2 + 4b^2}{3g(r - b)}} \qquad r > b \tag{e}$$

From Eq. (d) one easily recognizes that, for $b > r$, Eq. (d) is of the type

$$\ddot\theta - c^2\theta = 0 \tag{f}$$

where c is a constant. Then the solution

$$\theta = A\cosh ct + B\sinh ct \tag{g}$$

satisfies Eq. (f), and we realize that the angle θ increases with t beyond all bounds; that is, the system is unstable for $b > r$.

The question of the static stability of the block's equilibrium for $\theta = 0$ could have been decided before by checking whether the second derivation of U with respect to θ was positive for $\theta = 0$ or not (see Dirichlet's theorem in "Statics"):

$$\frac{\partial^2 U}{\partial\theta^2} = -mg(b - r) > 0$$

which shows that the system is statically stable only for $r > b$.

PROBLEMS

4.5-1   An outer disk of radius r, weight w_1, and centroidal radius of gyration k_C rolls on a stationary disk A of radius R without slipping (see Fig. P 4.5-1). The weight

[1] See the remarks at the end of Sec. 2.6.

of the connecting link is w_2, and it may be treated as a uniform slender rod.   If started from the top with zero velocity, what is the angular velocity θ of the connecting link at the lowest point?

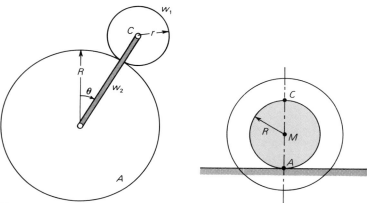

Fig. P 4.5-1   Fig. P 4.5-2

4.5-2   The eccentric wheel shown in Fig. P 4.5-2 rolls without slipping along a horizontal track. C is the center of mass, M the geometric center, and A a point of contact with the track.   The weight of the body is w, and the moment of inertia about M is I_M.   If the velocity of the geometric center is v_M, determine the kinetic energy of the body at the instant indicated.

4.5-3   A bar swings from the horizontal position and strikes a spring when in vertical position, coming to rest after compressing the spring $\frac{1}{2}$ in. (see Fig. P 4.5-3). Determine the spring constant k.

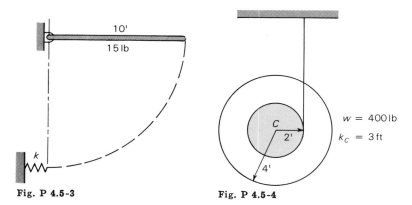

Fig. P 4.5-3   Fig. P 4.5-4

4.5-4   The wheel shown in Fig. P 4.5-4 starts from rest.   Determine the velocity of its center when it has moved 20 ft.

4.5-5   A uniform T-shaped bar of weight w slides on a smooth horizontal plane with constant velocity v parallel to one of the legs (see Fig. P 4.5-5).   The end A strikes a peg P in the table, causing the bar to rotate about it.   Determine the loss in kinetic energy due to the impact (assume that A remains in contact with P).

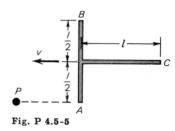

Fig. P 4.5-5

4.5-6   The end A of a log (uniform slender bar) of weight w is pulled with force F (see Fig. P 4.5-6).   If a rope at A breaks, determine the velocity of B at B'.   Assume the floor to be smooth.

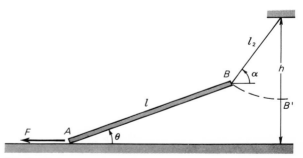

Fig. P 4.5-6

4.5-7   Two equal slender bars of length l and weight w_2 are hinged at B and tied to a weight w_1, as shown (see Fig. P 4.5-7).   Determine the velocity of w_1 as a function of θ.

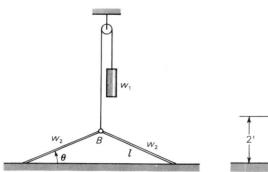

Fig. P 4.5-7

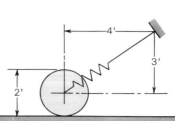

Fig. P 4.5-8

4.5-8   A solid homogeneous cylinder weighing 322 lb rolls on a horizontal plane without slipping. The cylinder is momentarily at rest in the position shown in Fig. P 4.5-8. The modulus of the spring is 50 lb/ft, and its unstretched length is 3.0 ft. Determine the angular velocity of the cylinder when its mass center is directly under the spring support.

4.5-9   A weight m_0 slides along a thin hoop of mass m hinged at O (see Fig. P 4.5-9). Determine the angular position of the diameter as a function of θ. The initial velocity of m_0 at $\theta = 0$ is v_0.

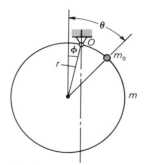

Fig. P 4.5-9

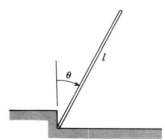

Fig. P 4.5-10

4.5-10   A uniform slender bar of length l is held vertically on a floor with its lower end against a step, as shown in Fig. P 4.5-10. If released from this position, determine the angle θ at which the lower end starts to move away from the step.

4.5-11   The system shown in Fig. P 4.5-11 is released from the position $\theta = 0$. Determine the largest angle θ_m through which the bar swings (no friction). The center of mass of w_1 is r_1 from O.

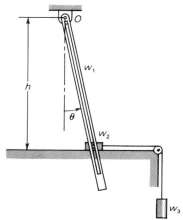

Fig. P 4.5-11

4.5-12   A large wheel A of moment of inertia I is coupled to a shaft D of torsional stiffness k through gears B and C with n_B and n_C teeth respectively (see Fig. P 4.5-12). Determine the natural frequency of oscillation with the right end of the shaft fixed.

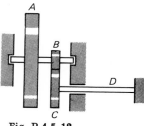

Fig. P 4.5-12

4.5-13   A cable joining two springs goes around a drum of radius r_1 and drives it without slipping; $r_1 = 3$ in., $I_O = 1.5$ lb ft²/g, $k = 5$ lb/in. (see Fig. P 4.5-13).   Find the natural period of oscillation of the system.

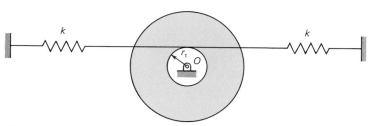

Fig. P 4.5-13

4.5-14   Determine the natural frequency of a torsional system (see Fig. P 4.5-14) consisting of a disk of moment of inertia I about its shaft of three different torsional
stiffnesses.

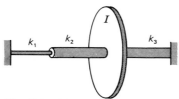

Fig. P 4.5-14

4.5-15   To reduce the natural frequency of a vibratory system k, m, k, a wheel of mass M
and radius of gyration k_C is attached to one of two rollers (see Fig. P 4.5-15).
Determine the frequency of vibration.   Assume that the mass of the rollers of
radius r is negligible.

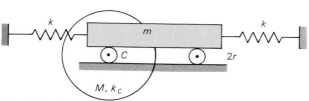

Fig. P 4.5-15

4.5-16   In the system shown in Fig. P 4.5-16, friction is sufficient to ensure pure rolling
of the cylinder.   Determine the equation of motion and the period of oscillation.

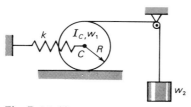

Fig. P 4.5-16

4.5-17   A uniform slender bar of weight w and length 15 ft is held in a spherical socket at
its lower end A; its upper end is held by cables CB and DB, each 15 ft long also

(see Fig. P 4.5-17). Support points C and D are such that plane CDB is horizontal. If cable DB breaks, determine the velocity of end B as it strikes wall ADC.

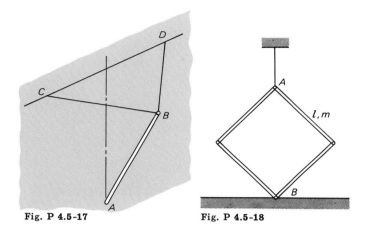

Fig. P 4.5-17   Fig. P 4.5-18

4.5-18   Four uniform slender bars each of length l are supported by a string at A and a fixed hinge at B, such that they represent a square (see Fig. P 4.5-18). If the string at A is cut, determine the velocity with which A strikes B and the angular velocity of the bars.

4 5-19   Pulleys of radius r and R are keyed together and have a moment of inertia of I_C about their center (see Fig. P 4.5-19). Wound around the small pulley is a cord connected to a plate p of negligible weight that can push against the spring of stiffness k, whereas the cord attached to a weight w is wound around the large pulley. When the weight is released with p a distance h below the spring, determine the maximum compression of the spring.

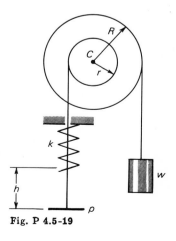

Fig. P 4.5-19

4.5-20   An angle iron ABC is pinned at the corner B (see Fig. P 4.5-20).   Determine θ for equilibrium.   If held in the position $\theta = 0$ and released, what maximum angle θ does BC reach?

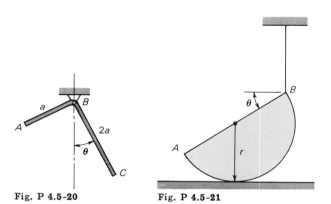

Fig. P 4.5-20   Fig. P 4.5-21

4.5-21   A half-solid cylinder of radius r is held in the position shown in Fig. P 4.5-21 by a string tied to point B.   If the string is suddenly cut, determine the reaction of the floor at $t = 0$ and the velocity of B when AB is horizontal, assuming that there is no slipping.

4.5-22   A uniform bar of length l is held in the position shown in Fig. P 4.5-22 by a smooth peg P, the smooth floor, and the tension of the string.   If the string suddenly breaks, determine its angular velocity and acceleration as a function of θ.

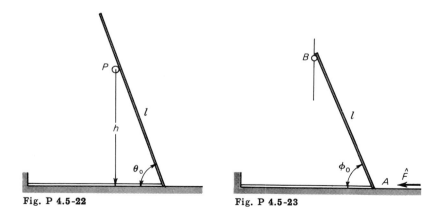

Fig. P 4.5-22   Fig. P 4.5-23

4.5-23   A uniform slender bar of length l is held in the position shown in Fig. P 4.5-23 by a cord at A and a peg at B.   What impulse $\hat{F}$ applied at A causes it barely to reach $\phi = 90°$.

4.5-24   A bar of length l and weight w_1 is hinged to a base block of weight w_2 that is free
to move horizontally (see Fig. P 4.5-24).   If the bar is allowed to fall from the
vertical position, how does it fall, compared with the case in which the hinge
point is fixed in inertial space?

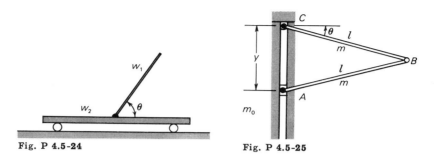

Fig. P 4.5-24   Fig. P 4.5-25

4.5-25   Bars AB and BC, each of mass m, are hinged, with C fixed and A attached to a
slider of mass m_0 (see Fig. P 4.5-25).   When released with A against C ($\theta_0 = 0$),
determine the velocity $\dot{y}$, the angular velocity $\dot{\theta}$, and the angular acceleration
$\ddot{\theta}$ as functions of y.

4.5-26   Show that in the absence of energy dissipation the despinning device discussed
in Illustrative Example 4.5-2 is capable of reversing the direction of the satellite's
initial spin, provided the cord is long enough.

4.5-27   Referring to Prob. 4.5-26, demonstrate, by simple energy considerations, that
$\omega_0 > \omega > -\omega_0$ for $0 < t < \infty$.

4.5-28   What time is taken by the despinning device in Illustrative Example 4.5-2 to
reduce the spin velocity to zero?   Does it depend on the amount of the initial
spin?

4.5-29   A uniform circular cylinder rests in unstable equilibrium at the edge of a table.
When disturbed, it rolls off the table, as shown in Fig. P 4.5-29.   If this takes
place without slipping, determine the angle θ at which the cylinder leaves the
table.

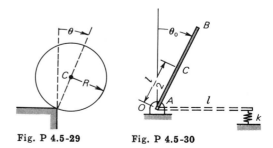

Fig. P 4.5-29   Fig. P 4.5-30

4.5-30   A uniform bar AB of length l and mass m is pinned at O.   When allowed to fall,
the end B strikes a spring of stiffness k in the horizontal position.   Determine the
maximum deflection δ of the spring.

**4.6 MISCELLANEOUS EXAMPLES OF LAGRANGE'S EQUATIONS IN THE
PLANE MOTION OF BODIES**

Lagrange's equations, as derived in Sec. 3.7 for a system of particles, are, of
course, also valid for any system of extended bodies, deformable or rigid,
since any extended body can be viewed as an assembly of particles.   The
rigid bodies considered here are, then, a special case of a system of particles
in which the distance between any two individual mass elements never
changes.   For this reason we repeat the following version of Lagrange's
equations:

$$\frac{d}{dt}\left(\frac{\partial T}{\partial \dot{q}_i}\right) - \frac{\partial T}{\partial q_i} + \frac{\partial U}{\partial q_i} = Q_i \qquad i = 1, 2, \ldots, N \quad \blacktriangleleft \quad (3.7\text{-}12)$$

where q_i is one of the N generalized coordinates, T the kinetic energy, U the
potential energy, and Q_i one of the N generalized forces not already covered
by the term $\partial U/\partial q_i$.   The simplest way to determine Q_i is to subject the
system to a virtual displacement δq_i.   Then all external forces do virtual
work equal to that done by the generalized force, that is, equal to $Q_i\,\delta q_i$
(see Illustrative Example 3.7-1).

ILLUSTRATIVE EXAMPLE 4.6-1

A rotor is placed on a homogeneous rigid table so that its axis is in a vertical plane of
symmetry with the table (see Fig. 4.6-1a).   We consider that the horizontal motion of

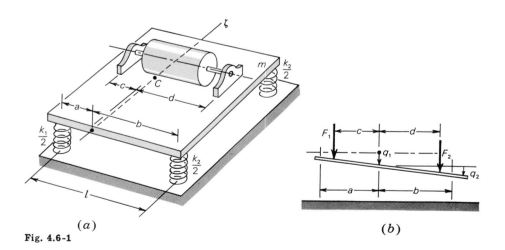

(a)

(b)

Fig. 4.6-1

the table is somehow prevented and that we have to determine its vertical motion.
Because of symmetry this is a plane motion caused by the vertical components $F_1(t)$

and $F_2(t)$ of the forces transmitted from the rotor to the table through the rotor's bearing pedestals. Establish the differential equations for the plane motion of the structure, calculating the deflection q_1 of the center of mass and the slope q_2 from the equilibrium position (see Fig. 4.6-1b). The moment of inertia of the table about the ζ axis through its center of mass C is I_C, the total mass of the table m, and the combined spring constant of the two left (right) struts k_1 (k_2).

SOLUTION: Since q_1 and q_2 are calculated from the equilibrium position, the influence of gravity can be disregarded, and we have to consider only the potential energy stored in the elastic struts,

$$U = \tfrac{1}{2}[k_1(q_1 - aq_2)^2 + k_2(q_1 + bq_2)^2]$$

The kinetic energy is, neglecting the mass of the struts,

$$T = \tfrac{1}{2}(m\dot{q}_1{}^2 + I_C\dot{q}_2{}^2)$$

The generalized forces Q_1 and Q_2 are found by subjecting the system to the virtual displacements δq_1 and δq_2 respectively:

$$Q_1\,\delta q_1 = (F_1 + F_2)\,\delta q_1$$
or
$$Q_1 = F_1 + F_2$$
and
$$Q_2\,\delta q_2 = -F_1 c\,\delta q_2 + F_2 d\,\delta q_2$$
or
$$Q_2 = -F_1 c + F_2 d$$

Substituting these expressions in Lagrange's equations (3.7-12), we obtain

$$m\ddot{q}_1 + (k_1 + k_2)q_1 + (-k_1 a + k_2 b)q_2 = F_1 + F_2$$
$$I_C\ddot{q}_2 + (k_1 a^2 + k_2 b^2)q_2 + (-k_1 a + k_2 b)q_1 = -F_1 c + F_2 d$$

ILLUSTRATIVE EXAMPLE 4.6-2

A mass m slides on a smooth uniform rod of length l and mass M that moves against a smooth vertical wall and horizontal floor (see Fig. 4.6-2). Use Lagrange's equations to establish the equations of motion.

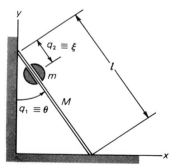

Fig. 4.6-2

SOLUTION: The assembly has two degrees of freedom. Thus we employ the coordinates θ and ξ shown in Fig. 4.6-2 as the two generalized coordinates q_1 and q_2. Using the floor level as reference, the potential energy of the system is

$$U = Mg\frac{l}{2}\cos\theta + mg(l - \xi)\cos\theta$$

For the determination of the kinetic energy, we need the velocities of m and the center of mass M expressed in terms of θ and ξ. The coordinates of m and the center of mass M are

$$x_m = \xi\sin\theta \qquad\qquad x_M = \frac{l}{2}\sin\theta$$

$$y_m = (l - \xi)\cos\theta \qquad y_M = \frac{l}{2}\cos\theta$$

Differentiating, the corresponding velocities are

$$\dot{x}_m = \dot\xi\sin\theta + \xi\dot\theta\cos\theta \qquad\qquad \dot{x}_M = \frac{l}{2}\dot\theta\cos\theta$$

$$\dot{y}_m = -\dot\xi\cos\theta - (l - \xi)\dot\theta\sin\theta \qquad \dot{y}_M = -\frac{l}{2}\dot\theta\sin\theta$$

Thus the kinetic energy of the system is

$$T = \tfrac{1}{2}m\{(\dot\xi\sin\theta + \xi\dot\theta\cos\theta)^2 + [-\dot\xi\cos\theta - (l - \xi)\dot\theta\sin\theta]^2\}$$
$$+ \frac{1}{2}M\left[\left(\frac{l}{2}\dot\theta\cos\theta\right)^2 + \left(-\frac{l}{2}\dot\theta\sin\theta\right)^2\right] + \tfrac{1}{2}M\frac{l^2}{12}\dot\theta^2$$

where the last term is the kinetic energy of rotation of the bar about its center of mass. The equations of motion are then established by substitution into Lagrange's equations (3.7-8), noting that only potential forces are involved:

$$\frac{d}{dt}\left(\frac{\partial T}{\partial \dot{q}_i}\right) - \frac{\partial T}{\partial q_i} + \frac{\partial U}{\partial q_i} = 0 \qquad i = 1, 2$$

where $q_i = \theta$ and ξ respectively. Hence we obtain, as the two differential equations of motion,

$$\ddot\theta\left[\xi^2 + l(l - 2\xi)\sin^2\theta + \frac{M}{m}\frac{l^2}{3}\right] + \ddot\xi l\sin\theta\cos\theta + \dot\theta^2 l(l - 2\xi)\sin\theta\cos\theta$$

$$+ 2\dot\theta\dot\xi(\xi - l\sin^2\theta) = g\sin\theta\left(\frac{M}{m}\frac{l}{2} + l - \xi\right) \quad (a)$$

$$\ddot\theta l\sin\theta\cos\theta + \ddot\xi + \dot\theta^2(l\cos^2\theta - \xi) = g\cos\theta \quad (b)$$

As an exercise the reader should verify Eqs. (a) and (b) without the use of Lagrange's equations.

Since a closed solution of these two nonlinear differential equations cannot be expected, they should be solved on a computer.

ILLUSTRATIVE EXAMPLE 4.6-3
Establish the equations of motion for the system shown in Fig. 4.6-3. It can rotate freely on a horizontal plane about a point O. Both slender bars are homogeneous. The torsional spring constant is k. The generalized coordinate q_1 (angle) is measured from a fixed line in the horizontal plane, q_2 (angle) from the normal to bar 1 (for $q_2 = 0$ the spring is unstressed).

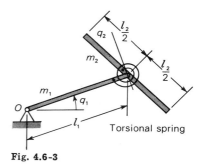

Fig. 4.6-3

SOLUTION: Since the motion takes place in a horizontal plane, there is no effect of gravity. Thus the total potential energy is entirely due to the torsional spring:

$$U = \tfrac{1}{2}kq_2{}^2 \qquad\qquad (a)$$

The kinetic energy is easily found to be

$$T = \frac{1}{2}\left[\left(\frac{m_1 l_1{}^2}{3} + m_2 l_1{}^2\right)\dot{q}_1{}^2 + \frac{m_2 l_2{}^2}{12}(\dot{q}_1 + \dot{q}_2)^2\right] \qquad\qquad (b)$$

Hence Eqs. (3.7-8) yield the following equations of motion:

$$\left(\frac{m_1 l_1{}^2}{3} + m_2 l_1{}^2 + \frac{m_2 l_2{}^2}{12}\right)\ddot{q}_1 + \frac{m_2 l_2{}^2}{12}\ddot{q}_2 = 0$$

$$\frac{m_2 l_2{}^2}{12}\ddot{q}_1 + \frac{m_2 l_2{}^2}{12}\ddot{q}_2 + kq_2 = 0$$

The solution of these two linear ordinary differential equations with constant coefficients is easily found. When the initial conditions at time $t = 0$ are $q_{10} = q_{20} = 0$ and $\dot{q}_1(0) = \dot{q}_{10}, \dot{q}_2(0) = \dot{q}_{20}$, we obtain

$$q_1 = -\frac{\alpha \dot{q}_{20}}{\omega}\sin \omega t + (\dot{q}_{10} + \alpha \dot{q}_{20})t$$

with $\quad \alpha = \dfrac{m_2 l_2{}^2/12}{m_1 l_1{}^2/3 + m_2 l_1{}^2 + m_2 l_2{}^2/12} \quad$ and $\quad \omega = \sqrt{k/\alpha(m_1 l_1{}^2/3 + m_2 l_1{}^2)}$

and

$$q_2 = \frac{\dot{q}_{20}}{\omega}\sin \omega t$$

Note that bar 1 is rotating about O with a superimposed oscillation of circular frequency ω.

PROBLEMS
4.6-1 to 4.6-8 Consider Probs. 1, 6, 8, 13, 15, 16, 22, 24 of Sec. 4.5 again. Instead of answering the questions asked there, establish the equations of motion, using Lagrange's equation, by choosing suitable generalized coordinates.

4.6-9   A cylindrical drum whose center of mass is at a radius r rolls without slipping
down an inclined plane (see Fig. P 4.6-9). The mass m and the moment of
inertia I_C of the drum are given. Establish the equation of motion.

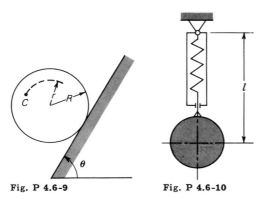

Fig. P 4.6-9   Fig. P 4.6-10

4.6-10 A uniform circular disk of mass m and radius r and a spring with spring constant
k are the elements of a physical pendulum (see Fig. P 4.6-10). In equilibrium
position the length of the pendulum is l. The suspending parts are considered
massless. Derive the equations for plane motions.

4.6-11 A hollow half cylinder (radius R_1, mass m_1, moment of inertia about center I_1,
wall thickness $\delta \ll R_1$) and a homogeneous solid drum (radius R_2, mass m_2), as
shown in Fig. P 4.6-11, constitute a system equivalent to a double pendulum.
Assuming that there is no rolling friction in the system, find the equations of
motion.

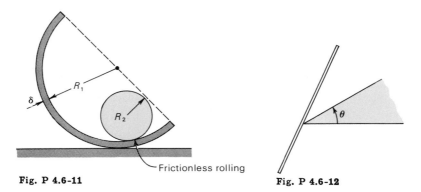

Fig. P 4.6-11   Fig. P 4.6-12

4.6-12   A uniform slender rod of length l and mass per unit length μ slides down a smooth inclined plane of angle θ.   Finally it turns over the edge, as shown in Fig. P 4.6-12.   For some time it is still in contact with the edge.   Establish the equations of motion for this time, and specify the initial conditions.   Assume that initially the lower end of the rod and the apex of the wedge coincide.

4.6-13   A uniform slender bar (mass m, length l_2, density γ_2) is suspended by a massless string of length l_1 (see Fig. P 4.6-13).   The point of suspension is at a height h $(l_1 + l_2 > h > l_1)$ above the surface of a liquid of density γ_1.   Determine the position of equilibrium and the equations of plane motion, neglecting drag forces.   Consider only the case in which the bar is partially submerged.

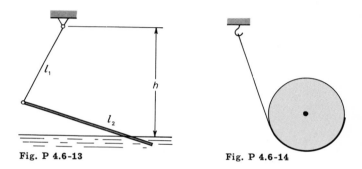

Fig. P 4.6-13   Fig. P 4.6-14

4.6-14   A massless inextensible string is wound around a homogeneous disk of radius R and mass m (see Fig. P 4.6-14).   One end of the string is attached to a hook. Starting in a position where the string is not vertical, the disk is released, so that because of its weight it descends in plane motion, always keeping the unwound end of the string taut.   Establish the equations of motion.

4.6-15   A smooth uniform bar of length l and mass per unit length μ is suspended at its left end and initially held in a horizontal position, and a point mass m is located at x_0 (see Fig. P 4.6-15).   Write the equations of motion that takes place after the system is released.   There is no friction in the system.

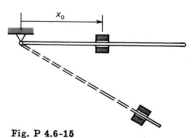

Fig. P 4.6-15

4.7 COLLISION OF TWO BODIES (PLANE CASE)

In this section we treat the problem of impact from a more general point of view than in Sec. 3.5, which the reader is advised to review. Of the basic assumptions made there, the first three are dropped, so that only the following two remain:

4   The two bodies are considered rigid before and after their collision, but not during the impact period. However, their mass distribution is not changed by the impact.

5   The impact duration is considered infinitely short, so that the positions of the bodies immediately before and immediately after the collision are identical.

Figure 4.7-1a depicts the two bodies at the instant of collision. The yz plane is chosen to coincide with the common tangential plane in the point of

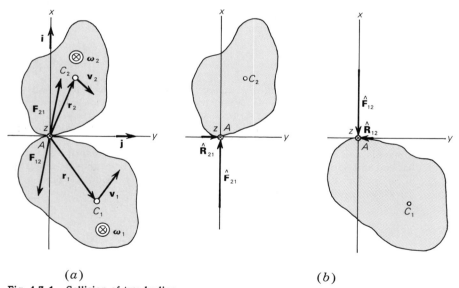

(a) (b)

Fig. 4.7-1   Collision of two bodies.

contact A. In order to avoid writing too many subscripts, we drop the subscript C for all quantities referring to the center of mass. Hence, in particular, the velocities v_1, v_2, c_1, and c_2 are those of the centers of mass of the two colliding bodies immediately before and after the collision, respectively.

GENERAL CONSIDERATIONS

The total momentum of the two bodies is not changed by the collision. Thus we have

$$m_1\mathbf{v}_1 + m_2\mathbf{v}_2 = m_1\mathbf{c}_1 + m_2\mathbf{c}_2 \qquad (4.7\text{-}1)$$

Nor is the total moment of momentum. And the moment of momentum of each body with respect to the space-fixed point coinciding with the body point of contact A is not changed by the moment of the impact force, for the moment of $\mathbf{F}_{12}$ or $\mathbf{F}_{21}$ with respect to point A, which according to assumption 5 in Sec. 3.5 is not displaced during the impact period, is identically zero. Thus we may write the following two moment-of-momentum equations with respect to the space-fixed point coinciding with A during the impact period:

$$\boldsymbol{\omega}_1 I_1 + \mathbf{r}_1 \times m_1\mathbf{v}_1 = \boldsymbol{\Omega}_1 I_1 + \mathbf{r}_1 \times m_1\mathbf{c}_1 \qquad (4.7\text{-}2)$$
$$\boldsymbol{\omega}_2 I_2 + \mathbf{r}_2 \times m_2\mathbf{v}_2 = \boldsymbol{\Omega}_2 I_2 + \mathbf{r}_2 \times m_2\mathbf{c}_2 \qquad (4.7\text{-}3)$$

where I_1 and I_2 denote the moments of inertia of the two bodies referred to their respective centers of mass and $\boldsymbol{\Omega}_1$ and $\boldsymbol{\Omega}_2$ the angular velocities of body 1 and 2, respectively, after the collision.

It is convenient to write the preceding three vector equations in cartesian coordinates:

$$m_1 v_{1x} + m_2 v_{2x} = m_1 c_{1x} + m_2 c_{2x} \qquad \blacktriangleleft \quad (4.7\text{-}4)$$
$$m_1 v_{1y} + m_2 v_{2y} = m_1 c_{1y} + m_2 c_{2y} \qquad \blacktriangleleft \quad (4.7\text{-}5)$$
$$\omega_{1z} I_1 + m_1(x_1 v_{1y} - y_1 v_{1x}) = \Omega_{1z} I_1 + m_1(x_1 c_{1y} - y_1 c_{1x}) \qquad \blacktriangleleft \quad (4.7\text{-}6)$$
$$\omega_{2z} I_2 + m_2(x_2 v_{2y} - y_2 v_{2x}) = \Omega_{2z} I_2 + m_2(x_2 c_{2y} - y_2 c_{2x}) \qquad \blacktriangleleft \quad (4.7\text{-}7)$$

where x_1, y_1 and x_2, y_2 are the coordinates of the centers of mass of body 1 and body 2, respectively.

These four equations are not sufficient to determine the six unknowns c_{1x}, c_{1y}, Ω_1; c_{2x}, c_{2y}, Ω_2. One of the two missing equations is given by Newton's hypothesis as stated by Eq. (3.5-10): the relative velocities of the two bodies in the x direction (direction of the impact normal), measured at their points of contact immediately after and before the collision, are related by the coefficient of restitution, that is,

$$\frac{c_{Rx}}{v_{Rx}} = \frac{\mathbf{c}_R \cdot \mathbf{i}}{\mathbf{v}_R \cdot \mathbf{i}} = \frac{[(\mathbf{c}_1 - \boldsymbol{\Omega}_1 \times \mathbf{r}_1) - (\mathbf{c}_2 - \boldsymbol{\Omega}_2 \times \mathbf{r}_2)] \cdot \mathbf{i}}{[(\mathbf{v}_1 - \boldsymbol{\omega}_1 \times \mathbf{r}_1) - (\mathbf{v}_2 - \boldsymbol{\omega}_2 \times \mathbf{r}_2)] \cdot \mathbf{i}} = -e$$

or

$$\frac{c_{Rx}}{v_{Rx}} = \frac{c_{1x} - c_{2x} + \Omega_{1z} y_1 - \Omega_{2z} y_2}{v_{1x} - v_{2x} + \omega_{1z} y_1 - \omega_{2z} y_2} = -e \qquad \blacktriangleleft \quad (4.7\text{-}8)$$

The sixth equation can then be found only by making assumptions regarding the forces acting during the impact period in the tangential plane at the point of contact. To investigate the actual nature of these forces would pose a far too complex problem. Even the assumption of proportionality between the forces in the y and x directions[1] leads to quite complicated considerations. Hence we confine our treatment to two limiting cases:

1   Absence of tangential forces, which might be an acceptable approximation when the deformation of the colliding bodies at the point of contact is very small and when the surfaces of the colliding bodies are quite smooth, for example, as in the case of billiard balls.

2   The tangential force during impact is such that the relative velocity c_{Ry} of the two bodies at the point of contact becomes zero as soon as the bodies collide. This case could serve, for example, as a crude approximation of the conditions occurring during a severe crash of two automobiles.

TWO SPECIAL CASES

In the absence of tangential forces in the y direction, the momentum component in the y direction of each body is not changed by the collision. Therefore Eq. (4.7-5) is replaced by the two equations

$$m_1 c_{1y} - m_1 v_{1y} = 0 \qquad \blacktriangleleft \quad (4.7\text{-}9)$$
$$m_2 c_{2y} - m_2 v_{2y} = 0 \qquad \blacktriangleleft \quad (4.7\text{-}10)$$

which, together with Eqs. (4.7-4) and (4.7-6) to (4.7-8), suffice to determine the six unknowns.

When the tangential force between the colliding bodies is such that their relative velocity component in the y direction is zero immediately after the impact, we have, as our sixth equation, in addition to Eqs. (4.7-4) to (4.7-8),

$$c_{Ry} = \mathbf{c}_R \cdot \mathbf{j} = c_{1y} - c_{2y} - x_1 \Omega_{1z} + x_2 \Omega_{2z} = 0 \qquad \blacktriangleleft \quad (4.7\text{-}11)$$

A further specialization of this case often occurs in technical problems when instant fixation takes place between two bodies at their point of contact, so that $\mathbf{c}_{Rx}$ also becomes zero.

ILLUSTRATIVE EXAMPLE 4.7-1

Consider the impact of a smooth ball of radius r and mass $m_1 = m$ on a smooth ($\mu = 0$) wall (see Fig. 4.7-2). The ball is in plane motion; that is, only v_{1x}, v_{1y}, and ω_{1z} are not zero. Determine the state of motion of the ball immediately after the impact.
SOLUTION: In the absence of forces in the y direction the problem is, in general, governed by Eqs. (4.7-4) to (4.7-10). Considering that the wall remains at rest, that is, $\mathbf{v}_2 = \mathbf{c}_2 = 0$, $\boldsymbol{\omega}_2 = \boldsymbol{\Omega}_2 = 0$, and that m_2 is infinite, we use only Eqs. (4.7-6), (4.7-8), and (4.7-9) for the determination of the three unknowns c_{1x}, c_{1y}, and Ω_{1z}. Equation (4.7-9) immediately yields

$$c_{1y} = v_{1y} \qquad (a)$$

Furthermore from Eq. (4.7-6) we have, in view of Eq. (a) and $y_1 = 0$,

$$\Omega_{1z} = \omega_{1z} \qquad (b)$$

---

[1] This assumption has induced many authors to speak here of the application of Coulomb's law of dry friction. The nature of the forces in the tangential plane during impact, however, differs greatly from what is customarily, and vaguely, understood as friction, because of the enormous deformation of the bodies in the vicinity of the contact point.

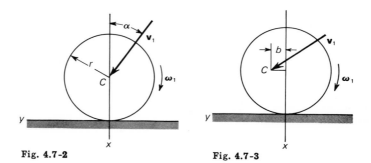

Fig. 4.7-2   Fig. 4.7-3

Hence the angular velocity, as well as the y component of the center-of-mass velocity, is not changed by the impact. On the other hand we obtain from Eq. (4.7-8)

$$c_{1x} = -ev_{1x} \qquad (c)$$

The situation is somewhat more difficult if the center of mass is displaced from the geometric center of the ball, as shown in Fig. 4.7-3. Now we have from Eq. (4.7-6), with $y_1 = b$ and $I_1 = mk_C^2$, in view of Eq. (a),

$$\omega_{1z}k_C^2 - bv_{1x} = \Omega_{1z}k_C^2 - bc_{1x} \qquad (d)$$

Besides, Eq. (4.7-8) yields

$$c_{1x} - \Omega_{1z}b = -e(v_{1x} - \omega_{1z}b) \qquad (e)$$

Hence we obtain from Eqs. (d) and (e)

$$c_{1x} = \frac{b^2 + ek_C^2}{b^2 - k_C^2} v_{1x} - (1 + e) \frac{bk_C^2}{b^2 - k_C^2} \omega_{1z} \qquad (f)$$

$$\Omega_{1z} = \omega_{1z} - (1 + e) \frac{b^2}{b^2 - k_C^2} \left(\frac{v_{1x}}{b} - \omega_{1z} \right) \qquad (g)$$

Equation (g) shows that even in the absence of tangential forces the angular velocity is changed. If eccentricity b of the center of mass is zero, Eqs. (f) and (g) reduce to Eqs. (c) and (b).

ILLUSTRATIVE EXAMPLE 4.7-2
A particle of mass m_1 attaches itself to a homogeneous rod of length l and mass m_2, as shown in Fig. 4.7-4. The rod is at rest before impact ($\mathbf{v}_2 = 0$, $\omega_2 = 0$), and the impact

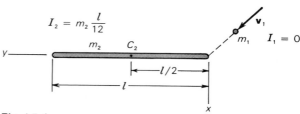

Fig. 4.7-4

velocity of mass m_1 is $\mathbf{v}_1$, and $\boldsymbol{\omega}_1$ is, of course, zero. Determine the motion of the rod immediately after impact.

SOLUTION: In this simple problem of plastic impact the tangential plane in the point of impact does not govern the choice of coordinates. On the other hand, it is advantageous to choose the x, y coordinates as shown in Fig. 4.7-4. With the information given we may then write the following equations:

$$m_1 v_{1x} = m_1 c_{1x} + m_2 c_{2x} \qquad \text{See Eq. (4.7-4)} \tag{a}$$
$$m_1 v_{1y} = m_1 c_{1y} + m_2 c_{2y} \qquad \text{See Eq. (4.7-5)} \tag{b}$$

Equation (4.7-6) drops out, since $x_1 = y_1 = 0$ and $I_1 = 0$. Furthermore

$$\Omega_{2z} \frac{m_2 l^2}{12} - m_2 \frac{l}{2} c_{2x} = 0 \qquad \text{See Eq. (4.7-7)}$$

or
$$c_{2x} = \frac{l}{6} \Omega_{2z} \tag{c}$$

Since there is no rebound, $e = 0$.   Thus with $v_{Rx} \neq 0$, Eq. (4.7-8) yields

$$c_{1x} - c_{2x} - \Omega_{2z} \frac{l}{2} = 0 \tag{d}$$

aad finally we obtain from Eq. (4.7-11)

$$c_{1y} = c_{2y} \tag{e}$$

Equations (e) and (b) immediately give

$$c_{1y} = c_{2y} = \frac{m_1}{m_1 + m_2} v_{1y} \tag{f}$$

Substituting Eqs. (c) and (d) in Eq. (a), we find

$$\Omega_{2z} = \frac{v_{1x}}{l} \frac{6m_1}{4m_1 + m_2} \tag{g}$$

and then we obtain from Eqs. (c) and (d)

$$c_{2x} = \frac{m_1}{4m_1 + m_2} v_{1x} \tag{h}$$

and
$$c_{1x} = \frac{4m_1}{4m_1 + m_2} v_{1x} \tag{i}$$

If $v_{1y} = 0$, an instantaneous center can be located on the rod immediately after impact. From Eq. (f) we see then that the y component remains zero even after impact and the x component is zero at the point $(0,y)$ on the rod where y is found from the relation

$$c_{1x} - \Omega_{2z} y = 0 \qquad \text{or} \qquad y = \frac{c_{1x}}{\Omega_{2z}}$$

which yields with Eqs. (g) and (i)

$$y = \tfrac{2}{3} l$$

IMPACT IN THE PRESENCE OF CONSTRAINTS

A special case of great practical importance is encountered when one or both colliding bodies are constrained by a hinge.   We discuss the case shown in

Fig. 4.7-5, where only body 2 is held in a hinge at point O and friction is neglected. The great difference between this problem and the collision cases above is that during the impact period a reaction force is exerted by

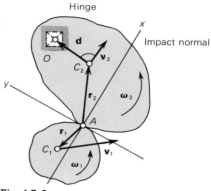

Fig. **4.7-5**

the hinged support O on body 2 whose time integral is the unknown impulse $\mathbf{\hat{F}}_R$. Therefore Eqs. (4.7-1) and (4.7-3) are now

$$m_1\mathbf{v}_1 + m_2\mathbf{v}_2 + \mathbf{\hat{F}}_R = m_1\mathbf{c}_1 + m_2\mathbf{c}_2 \qquad (4.7\text{-}12)$$

$$\omega_2 I_2 + \mathbf{r}_2 \times m_2\mathbf{v}_2 + (\mathbf{r}_2 + \mathbf{d}) \times \mathbf{\hat{F}}_R = \Omega_2 I_2 + \mathbf{r}_2 \times m_2\mathbf{c}_2 \qquad (4.7\text{-}13)$$

but Eq. (4.7-2) remains unchanged, because there is no external impulse exerted on body 1. The unwelcome fact that we have now one more unknown quantity, the impulse $\mathbf{\hat{F}}_R$, is made up by the new kinematic relation representing the "hinge condition":

$$\mathbf{c}_2 = -\mathbf{\Omega}_2 \times \mathbf{d} \qquad (4.7\text{-}14)$$

Before establishing all necessary equations in x, y coordinates, we consider that because of the impulse $\mathbf{\hat{F}}_R$ the hinge is exposed to a force of extremely high intensity. It is possible, however (see Illustrative Example 4.7-3), to find a location for the hinge where $\mathbf{\hat{F}}_R$ vanishes and thus avoid damage to the bearing. This is of great practical importance, and therefore we first limit our considerations to finding this location. Hence we concentrate our attention on body 2, and body 1 is considered only so far as its impulse $\hat{F}$ on body 2 in the x direction is concerned. With the choice of the x, y coordinates, as shown in Fig. 4.7-5, $\hat{F}$ is, of course, positive. If we now drop the subscript 2, the moment-of-momentum equation for body 2 with respect to the hinge point O is

$$m(k_C{}^2 + d^2)(\Omega_z - \omega_z) = y_O\hat{F} = (y_C + d_y)\hat{F} \qquad (4.7\text{-}15)$$

where $mk_C{}^2$ denotes the moment of inertia of body 2 with respect to its center of mass C_2. The change of momentum of body 2 in the x direction is

$$m(c_x - v_x) = md_y(\Omega_z - \omega_z) = \hat{F}_{R_x} + \hat{F} \qquad (4.7\text{-}16)$$

and in the y direction

$$m(c_y - v_y) = -md_x(\Omega_z - \omega_z) = \hat{F}_{R_y} \qquad (4.7\text{-}17)$$

Now, if we want $\hat{\mathbf{F}}_R = \hat{F}_{R_x}\mathbf{i} + \hat{F}_{R_y}\mathbf{j}$ to be zero, we immediately obtain from Eq. (4.7-17)

$$d_x = 0 \qquad \blacktriangleleft \qquad (4.7\text{-}18)$$

Hence we see that the point where the reaction impulse is zero is located on the line through the center of mass perpendicular to the impact normal.

Then we have $d^2 = d_y{}^2$, and requiring $\hat{F}_{R_x} = 0$, the division of Eqs. (4.7-15) and (4.7-16) yields

$$\frac{k_C{}^2 + d_y{}^2}{d_y} = y_C + d_y$$

or

$$d_y = \frac{k_C{}^2}{y_C} \qquad \blacktriangleleft \qquad (4.7\text{-}19)$$

Thus with the coordinate system as used in Fig. 4.7-5 the coordinates of the so-called center of percussion[1] are

$$x_O = x_C \qquad \text{and} \qquad y_O = \frac{y_C{}^2 + k_C{}^2}{y_C} \qquad \blacktriangleleft \qquad (4.7\text{-}20)$$

The center of percussion is of great importance for the design of machine parts and tools that are subjected to impact, for example, the hammer, and, of course, for the "design" of baseball bats and golf clubs also, although one may be sure that their early designers never heard of it. The second Eq. (4.7-20) shows that the handle of hitting instruments must be longer, the closer the impact point is to the center of mass. Think of the long handle of a golf club, and remember you feel the blow in your hand when you hold a hammer too close to the head.

On the other hand, when the geometric locations of the hinge O and the impact normal are given, Eqs. (4.7-15) to (4.7-17) may serve to determine c_x and c_y as well as Ω_z for body 2, depending, however, on the yet unknown internal impulse $\hat{F}$. In order to find $\hat{F}$, we also have to consider the unknowns c_{1x}, c_{1y}, and Ω_{1z} of body 1, so that we need four more equations in all. One is given by Newton's hypothesis in Eq. (4.7-8). In the absence of tangential impact forces, Eq. (4.7-9) also holds. Furthermore the

[1] Its importance was already recognized by Descartes (1596–1650), who is also responsible for the name *centrum percussionis*. Huygens (1629–1695) also used this concept extensively in his work on the theory and practice of the pendulum.

change of momentum of body 1 in the x direction is

$$m_1(c_{1z} - v_{1z}) = -\hat{F} \qquad (4.7\text{-}21)$$

and the change of its moment of momentum referred to its center of mass C_1 is

$$I_1(\Omega_{1z} - \omega_{1z}) = -y_1\hat{F} \qquad (4.7\text{-}22)$$

ILLUSTRATIVE EXAMPLE 4.7-3

A bullet of mass m_1 hits a box of mass m_2 (filled with homogeneous material) that is suspended by a massless rod on a fixed frictionless hinge O (see Fig. 4.7-6). After impact

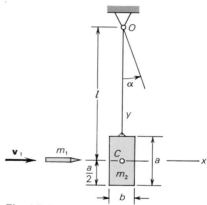

Fig. 4.7-6

the bullet is trapped in the box, which then swings out by an angle α. This device is known as the ballistic pendulum. Determine the speed v_1 of the bullet and the reaction impulse $\hat{F}_R$ exerted by the hinge O on the rod if the center of mass of the box is on the path of the bullet, as shown in Fig. 4.7-6.

SOLUTION: After impact the total mechanical energy remains unchanged:

$$U + T = \text{const}$$

and we can compute the speed $c_1 = c_2$ of the box and bullet from this equation. Taking the position of the undeflected pendulum as zero level for the potential energy, we immediately have, after impact, the kinetic energy

$$\tfrac{1}{2}\left[(m_1 + m_2)c_2^2 + m_2 \frac{a^2 + b^2}{12}\left(\frac{c_2}{l}\right)^2 \right] \qquad (a)$$

After the pendulum has swung out, its kinetic energy has been transformed into the potential energy

$$(m_1 + m_2)gl(1 - \cos\alpha) \qquad (b)$$

since the total weight has been lifted by $l(1 - \cos \alpha)$. Thus we find from Eqs. (a) and (b)

$$c_2 = \left[2gl(1 - \cos \alpha) \frac{m_1 + m_2}{m_1 + m_2 + m_2(a^2 + b^2)/12l^2} \right]^{1/2} \qquad (c)$$

or if $(a^2 + b^2)/12l^2 \ll 1$, we have approximately

$$c_2 = \sqrt{2gl(1 - \cos \alpha)} \qquad (c')$$

Thus we also know the angular velocity of the box:

$$\Omega_{2z} = \frac{c_2}{l} \qquad (d)$$

Next we use the condition that the moment of momentum of the box and bullet about the point O is also conserved; that is, the external reaction impulse of the hinge exerts no moment about O, because of the assumption of zero frictional force in the bearings. Neglecting the moment of inertia of the box about its center of mass C or, in other words, putting $(a^2 + b^2)/12l^2$ equal to zero, we obtain

$$m_1 v_1 l = (m_1 + m_2)c_2 l = (m_1 + m_2) \sqrt{2gl(1 - \cos \alpha)}\, l \qquad (e)$$

or
$$v_1 = \frac{m_1 + m_2}{m_1} \sqrt{2gl(1 - \cos \alpha)} \qquad (f)$$

The reaction impulse $\hat{F}_R$ is easily obtained by equating it to the change of the total momentum in the horizontal direction (positive to the right):

$$\hat{F}_R = (m_1 + m_2)c_2 - m_1 v_1 \qquad (g)$$

Now with Eqs. (c') and (e), where the box is idealized as a particle of mass m_2, we see that $\hat{F}_R = 0$. This, however, is not the case when $(a^2 + b^2)/12l^2$ is not neglected. If we use instead of Eq. (e)

$$m_1 v_1 l = (m_1 + m_2)c_2 l + m_2 \frac{a^2 + b^2}{12} \frac{c_2}{l} \qquad (h)$$

which includes the moment of momentum of the box about its center, we find from Eq. (g)

$$\hat{F}_R = -m_2 \frac{a^2 + b^2}{12l^2} c_2 \qquad (i)$$

In order that $\hat{F}_R = 0$, we realize from Eq. (4.7-19) that the bullet should hit the box (consider that $d_y = l$)

$$y_C = \frac{a^2 + b^2}{12l}$$

below its center of mass.

LAGRANGE'S EQUATIONS IN IMPACT PROBLEMS

When systems of several degrees of freedom are subjected to impact, it is advantageous to use Lagrange's equations. For this purpose we integrate Lagrange's equations

$$\frac{d}{dt}\left(\frac{\partial T}{\partial \dot{q}_i}\right) - \frac{\partial T}{\partial q_i} + \frac{\partial U}{\partial q_i} = Q_i \qquad i = 1, 2, \ldots, N \qquad (3.7\text{-}12)$$

with respect to time over the impact period $\Delta t = t_2 - t_1$ and then carry out the limiting process $\Delta t \to 0$:

$$\left(\frac{\partial T}{\partial \dot q_i}\right)_2 - \left(\frac{\partial T}{\partial \dot q_i}\right)_1 - \lim_{\Delta t \to 0} \int_{t_1}^{t_2} \left(\frac{\partial T}{\partial q_i} - \frac{\partial U}{\partial q_i}\right) dt = \lim_{\Delta t \to 0} \int_{t_1}^{t_2} Q_i \, dt$$

Since $\partial T/\partial q_i$ and $\partial U/\partial q_i$ remain finite during the impact period, the integral on the left side vanishes. On the other hand the integral

$$\hat Q_i = \lim_{\Delta t \to 0} \int_{t_1}^{t_2} Q_i \, dt$$

is the generalized impulse $\hat Q_i$ belonging to the generalized impact force Q_i. Hence Lagrange's equations in the case of impact are

$$\left(\frac{\partial T}{\partial \dot q_i}\right)_2 - \left(\frac{\partial T}{\partial \dot q_i}\right)_1 = \hat Q_i \qquad i = 1, 2, \ldots, N \qquad (4.7\text{-}23)$$

These equations are no longer differential equations, but difference equations, involving the generalized velocities of the system before and after impact.

ILLUSTRATIVE EXAMPLE 4.7-4
Consider the system consisting of a slider of mass m and two homogeneous rods, each of mass m also, connected by frictionless hinges, as shown in Fig. 4.7-7. Before the impulse $\hat{\mathbf{F}}$ of infinitesimally short duration is applied, the system is at rest. What is its motion immediately after impact?

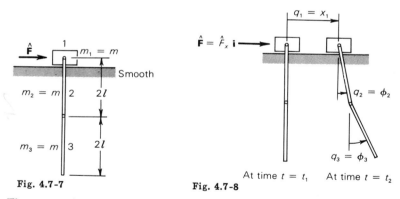

Fig. 4.7-7   Fig. 4.7-8

SOLUTION: The system has three degrees of freedom. To describe its configuration, we use the three generalized coordinates depicted in Fig. 4.7-8. For the application of Lagrange's equations (4.7-23) we first determine the expressions for the kinetic energy.

The kinetic energy at time $t = t_1$ is zero, and so $(\partial T/\partial \dot q_i)_1 = 0$. At time $t = t_2$, the kinetic energy T_2 of the system is

$$T_2 = \frac{m}{2}(\dot x_1{}^2 + v_{C2}{}^2 + v_{C3}{}^2) + \frac{I_C}{2}(\dot\phi_2{}^2 + \dot\phi_3{}^2)$$

or with $I_C = ml^2/3$ and

$$v_{C2} = \dot x_1 + l\dot\phi_2 \qquad \text{and} \qquad v_{C3} = \dot x_1 + 2l\dot\phi_2 + l\dot\phi_3$$

$$T_2 = \frac{ml^2}{6}\left[3\left(\frac{\dot x_1}{l}\right)^2 + 3\left(\frac{\dot x_1}{l} + \dot\phi_2\right)^2 + 3\left(\frac{\dot x_1}{l} + 2\dot\phi_2 + \dot\phi_3\right)^2 + \dot\phi_2{}^2 + \dot\phi_3{}^2\right]$$

Corresponding to Eq. (3.7-11), we obtain the generalized impulses

$$\hat{F}_x \, dx_1 = \hat{F}_1 \, dq_1 + \hat{F}_2 \, dq_2 + \hat{F}_3 \, dq_3$$

Since $dx_1 \equiv dq_1$, we have, therefore, simply

$$\hat{F}_1 = \hat{F}_x \qquad \text{and} \qquad \hat{F}_2 = \hat{F}_3 = 0$$

Thus Eqs. (4.7-23) yield the following three equations for the velocities $\dot{x}_1$, $\dot{\phi}_2$, and $\dot{\phi}_3$ immediately after impact:

$$3\frac{\dot{x}_1}{l} + 3\dot{\phi}_2 + \dot{\phi}_3 = \frac{\hat{F}_x}{ml}$$

$$9\frac{\dot{x}_1}{l} + 16\dot{\phi}_2 + 6\dot{\phi}_3 = 0$$

$$3\frac{\dot{x}_1}{l} + 6\dot{\phi}_2 + 4\dot{\phi}_3 = 0$$

Hence we obtain, for the velocities of the system immediately after impact,

$$\dot{x}_1 = \frac{7}{9}\frac{\hat{F}_x}{m} \qquad \dot{\phi}_2 = -\frac{\hat{F}_x}{2ml} \qquad \dot{\phi}_3 = \frac{\hat{F}_x}{6ml}$$

PROBLEMS

4.7-1   A uniform bar of length l translates with velocity v on a smooth floor and encounters a fixed peg A of coefficient of restitution e (see Fig. P 4.7-1). Determine the velocity of its mass center and its angular velocity immediately after impact. If A is placed at $b = l/4$ and the center of mass comes to rest after impact, determine e.

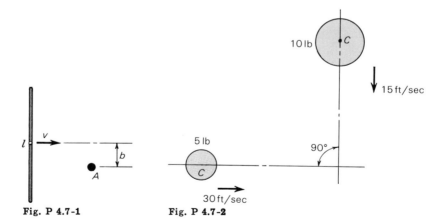

Fig. P 4.7-1   Fig. P 4.7-2

4.7-2   A 5-lb sphere having a speed of 30 ft/sec and a 10-lb sphere having a speed of 15 ft/sec move along lines that intersect at right angles when they collide, so that the line through their centers when they are in contact makes the angle $\tan^{-1} 0.75$ with the direction in which the 5-lb sphere moves before the collision (see Fig. P 4.7-2). The spheres are smooth, and the coefficient of restitution for the impact is 0.5. Find the speed and direction of motion of each sphere

after the collision.   Refer these directions to the line through the centers during
contact.

4.7-3   A smooth sphere of mass m_1 with velocity v_1 in direction shown in Fig. P 4.7-3
strikes a stationary smooth sphere of mass m_2.   Determine the velocities of the
spheres after impact (coefficient of restitution e) and the loss in kinetic energy.

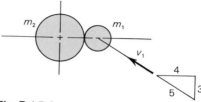

Fig. P 4.7-3

4.7-4   Two equal spheres of radius r approach each other with velocity v along parallel
lines separated by $r/2$ (see Fig. P 4.7-4).   Determine the angle of rebound.
Assume zero coefficient of friction and $e = 1$.

Fig. P 4.7-4   **Fig. P 4.7-5**

4.7-5   Two equal smooth elastic spheres have the velocities shown in Fig. P 4.7-5 on
impact.   Determine the velocities after impact (coefficient of restitution e).

4.7-6   A uniform slender bar AB of length l is dropped through a height h on a smooth
horizontal floor (see Fig. P 4.7-6).   What is the angular velocity of the bar
immediately before point B strikes the floor if the bar falls with $\theta = \text{const}$
$(e = 0)$?

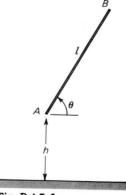

Fig. P 4.7-6

4.7-7   The rectangular block shown in Fig. P 4.7-7 slides along a smooth horizontal floor with velocity v and strikes a small step at O. What angular velocity does it have immediately after impact ($e = 0$)? What is the greatest velocity that it can have and still not turn over?

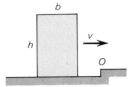

Fig. P 4.7-7

4.7-8   A sphere of radius r spinning about a horizontal axis with angular velocity ω_0 is dropped on a rough horizontal floor with velocity v_0 (see Fig. P 4.7-8). The coefficient of restitution is e, and the friction force is assumed to be such that no slipping takes place. Show that the sphere bounces to a point

$$x = \frac{4e}{7} r \frac{\omega_0 v_0}{g}$$

from the point of impact.

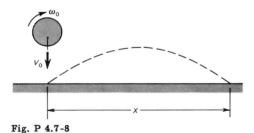

Fig. P 4.7-8

4.7-9   A sphere of radius R spinning about a horizontal diameter is dropped on a perfectly rough horizontal plane with coefficient of restitution e. If it rebounds at an angle ϕ with the normal, determine the ratio of the rotational to the translational kinetic energy before impact in terms of e and ϕ (I_{dia} of a sphere $= \frac{2}{5}mR^2$).

4.7-10   A particle of mass m strikes the end of a uniform bar of mass M and length l in the normal direction with velocity v (see Fig. P 4.7-10). Assuming a coefficient of restitution of e, determine the angular velocity of the bar immediately after impact and the velocity of m. What velocity v causes the bar to rotate through 90°? What e makes the velocity of m equal to zero after impact?

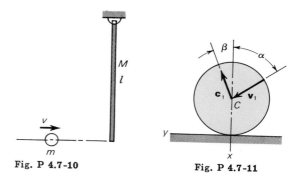

Fig. P 4.7-10   Fig. P 4.7-11

4.7-11   Reconsider Illustrative Example 4.7-1, now, however, with a tangential impact force large enough to make the y component of the velocity of the ball's contact point zero during the impact period. Under what angle β does the center of mass rebound?

RELATIVE
MOTION

As stated in Sec. 1.1, it may often be very convenient to describe the motion of a body by means of a coordinate system that moves relative to the reference frame chosen for the definition of the body's kinematic properties of interest. In most dynamics problems the reference frame is a newtonian or inertial reference body K, that is, a frame in which Newton's laws are valid.

Besides, in the field of dynamics we might find it advantageous, in certain types of problems, to set up the equations of motion in a nonnewtonian reference frame L, that is, in a reference frame L that is in accelerated motion relative to an inertial reference body K. From a kinematic point of view our problem in this case is identical to that arising in connection with the moving coordinate system mentioned above if we consider its coordinate axes fixed in a reference body L. For then, also, our first task consists in defining the motion of the reference body L with respect to the reference body K.

Before turning to this problem in Sec. 5.1, we should like to point out that the title of the present chapter stems from the somewhat unfortunate usage of defining the motion of a particle with respect to a nonnewtonian moving reference body L as "relative motion." In contrast, the motion of a particle with respect to a newtonian or inertial reference body is often referred to as "absolute" motion, following Newton's erroneous notion of the existence of an "absolute" reference frame.

5.1 BASIC KINEMATIC RELATIONSHIPS BETWEEN TWO DIFFERENT REFERENCE BODIES

We consider two reference bodies K and L, shown in Fig. 5.1-1, and we define the motion of body L with respect to body K. First we choose arbitrary reference points O and A, fixed in bodies K and L, respectively. In order to define the position of L with respect to K completely, we have to choose two[1] more points 1 and 2, fixed in L, such that A, 1, and 2 are not in a straight line. Then point O in K is related to the body points A, 1, and 2 in L by the position vectors $\mathbf{r}_A$, $\mathbf{r}_1$, and $\mathbf{r}_2$, respectively. Referring to Fig. 5.1-1, we define the position of the body points 1 and 2 with respect to the body point A by ϱ_{A1} and ϱ_{A2}, respectively, and thus we may express $\mathbf{r}_1$ and $\mathbf{r}_2$ as follows:

$$\mathbf{r}_1 = \mathbf{r}_A + \varrho_{A1}$$
$$\mathbf{r}_2 = \mathbf{r}_A + \varrho_{A2} \tag{5.1-1}$$

[1] The reader can easily convince himself that one more body point in L is not sufficient for this purpose.

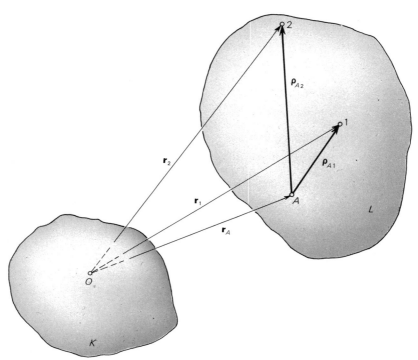

Fig. 5.1-1

Now we turn to Fig. 5.1-2, where body L is shown in its position at time t, as well as at time $t + dt$. During the time interval dt the three body points A, 1, and 2 suffer, with respect to reference body K, the infinitesimal displacements $d\mathbf{r}_A$, $d\mathbf{r}_1$, and $d\mathbf{r}_2$, respectively (see Fig. 5.1-2, where only $d\mathbf{r}_A$ and $d\mathbf{r}_1$ are displayed). For example (see Fig. 5.1-2), if body point A coincides at time t with point a in the reference frame K, then at time $t + dt$ the body point A is at point a' in K; that is, $\overrightarrow{aa'} = d\mathbf{r}_A$. Corresponding to Eqs. (5.1-1), we split the infinitesimal displacements $d\mathbf{r}_1$ and $d\mathbf{r}_2$:

$$dr_1 = dr_A + d\varrho_{A1}$$
$$dr_2 = dr_A + d\varrho_{A2} \tag{5.1-2}$$

where $d\varrho_{A1}$ and $d\varrho_{A2}$ are the infinitesimal displacements of points 1 and 2, respectively, relative to point A. Since the magnitudes of ϱ_{A1} and ϱ_{A2} are constants, $d\varrho_{A1}$ and $d\varrho_{A2}$ must be normal to ϱ_{A1} and ϱ_{A2}, respectively; for with $\varrho_{A1} \cdot \varrho_{A1} = \text{const}$, we have, by differentiation,

$$\varrho_{A1} \cdot d\varrho_{A1} = 0$$

In order to interpret the displacements $d\varrho_{A1}$, and $d\varrho_{A2}$, we erect planes normal to $d\varrho_{A1}$ and $d\varrho_{A2}$, respectively, both containing point A. These planes intersect in a straight line through A (see Fig. 5.1-3).

It is now easy to show that all points on this line of intersection suffer the same infinitesimal displacement as the reference point A, and so we may take any body point P on the line of intersection. Since the body is rigid, the distance AP cannot change. Hence, the infinitesimal displacement vector $d\varrho_{AP}$, if it were not zero, would have to lie in the plane through P normal to $\overrightarrow{AP}$. Equally, because of the body's rigidity, the distance between points 1 and P cannot change. Now the infinitesimal displacement of point 1, $d\varrho_{A1}$, is normal to the line $\overrightarrow{1P}$. Thus the displacement vector $d\varrho_{AP}$ would also have to lie in the plane through P normal to $\overrightarrow{1P}$. And with the same

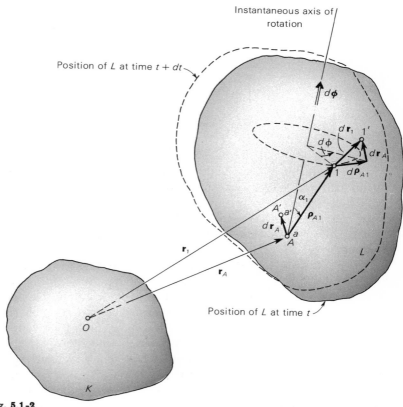

Fig. 5.1-2

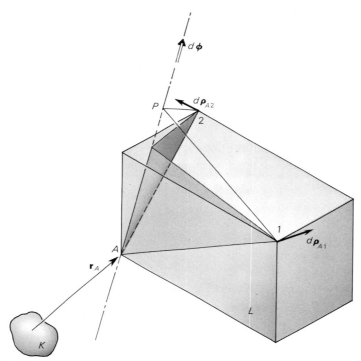

Fig. 5.1-3

reasoning, $d\boldsymbol{\varrho}_{AP}$ would also have to lie on the plane through P normal to $\overrightarrow{2P}$. Since the point of intersection of these three planes coincides with point P, we immediately deduce that $d\boldsymbol{\varrho}_{AP} = \mathbf{0}$, or considering the complete infinitesimal displacement of body L, we have $d\mathbf{r}_P = d\mathbf{r}_A$. This reasoning holds for all points on the line AP, and therefore we may consider this line an instantaneous axis of rotation by which the displacements $d\boldsymbol{\varrho}_{A1}$ and $d\boldsymbol{\varrho}_{A2}$ are produced.

This leads us to conceive the infinitesimal displacement of body L—see Eqs. (5.1-2)—with respect to body K as having been achieved in two steps: (1) translation, such that every point in body L suffers the same displacement $d\mathbf{r}_A$, (2) rotation about an instantaneous axis through the reference point A, such that the points 1 and 2 move, in addition, through the infinitesimal displacements $d\boldsymbol{\varrho}_{A1}$ and $d\boldsymbol{\varrho}_{A2}$, respectively.

This interpretation of the infinitesimal displacements $d\boldsymbol{\varrho}_{A1}$ and $d\boldsymbol{\varrho}_{A2}$ opens the way to the following mathematical description. For this purpose we introduce the representation of the infinitesimal rotation of body L with respect to body K by means of a vector $d\boldsymbol{\phi}$ whose sense of direction along the instantaneous axis is defined by the right-hand rule (see Fig. 5.1-2). Then the vector algebraic operation in the following:

$$d\varrho_{A1} = d\phi \times \varrho_{A1}$$
$$d\varrho_{A2} = d\phi \times \varrho_{A2}$$

(5.1-3)

yields the infinitesimal displacement vectors $d\varrho_{A1}$ and $d\varrho_{A2}$, respectively, compatible with our reasoning above. They are:

1   Normal to both ϱ_{A1} and ϱ_{A2}, respectively, as well as to the instantaneous axis of rotation whose direction coincides with that of $d\phi$.

2   Their magnitude is in accordance with our concept of the infinitesimal rotation, since, referring to Fig. 5.1-2, we readily see that

$$|d\varrho_{A1}| = |d\phi||\varrho_{A1}||\sin \alpha_1|$$

In view of Eqs. (5.1-2) and (5.1-3) we may therefore express the total infinitesimal displacements of the body points 1 and 2 as

$$d\mathbf{r}_1 = d\mathbf{r}_A + d\phi \times \varrho_{A1}$$
$$d\mathbf{r}_2 = d\mathbf{r}_A + d\phi \times \varrho_{A2}$$

(5.1-4)

Dividing these equations by dt, we obtain the differential quotients defining the instantaneous velocities[1] of the body points A, 1, and 2 with respect to body K:

$$\frac{d\mathbf{r}_1}{dt} = \frac{d\mathbf{r}_A}{dt} + \frac{d\phi}{dt} \times \varrho_{A1}$$

or

$$\mathbf{v}_1 = \mathbf{v}_A + \omega \times \varrho_{A1}$$

and

$$\mathbf{v}_2 = \mathbf{v}_A + \omega \times \varrho_{A2}$$

(5.1-5)

where $d\phi/dt = \omega$ is the vectorial representation of the instantaneous angular velocity of body L with respect to body K, such that not only the angular speed but also the direction of the instantaneous axis and the sense of rotation are defined. By its definition ω, as well as $d\phi$, is an axial vector like the moment and therefore is graphically represented as a double-shafted arrow. Hence, the motion of the reference body L with respect to the reference body K is completely defined by the velocity $\mathbf{v}_A$ of an arbitrary point A in body L and the angular velocity ω of the body L, both taken with respect to body K.

At this stage we believe that the critical reader still wants to satisfy himself that the representation of the infinitesimal angle $d\phi$, and thus also the angular velocity ω, as vectors is warranted. The simplest test is to check whether the parallelogram law holds for these quantities. This means here that it must be possible to carry out the same infinitesimal displacement

---

[1] Assuming that $\mathbf{r}_A$, $\mathbf{r}_1$, . . . , as well as ϕ, are continuous functions of t.

of a body point P fixed in L relative to the body point A, which was executed above by one infinitesimal rotation, by the vector sum of several infinitesimal rotations, say of two such rotations. This is indeed the case. Referring to Eqs. (5.1-3), we may describe the infinitesimal displacement[1] $\vec{pp'}$ of an arbitrary body point P relative to the reference point A, also body-fixed, (see Fig. 5.1-4) by

$$\vec{pp'} = d\phi \times \varrho$$

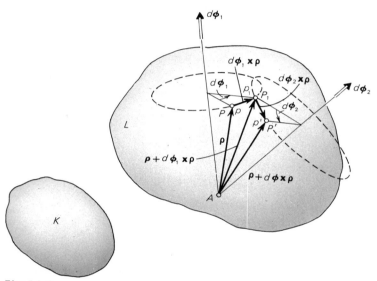

Fig. 5.1-4

Let us now achieve the same infinitesimal displacement in two steps. First we displace body point P by carrying out an infinitesimal rotation $d\phi_1$ of body L about an axis through A different from the instantaneous axis defined by $d\phi$. Thereby body point P moves from p to p_1:

$$\vec{pp_1} = d\phi_1 \times \varrho$$

Next we wish to move body point P from position p_1 to the "final" position p' by a rotation $d\phi_2$ of body L about another instantaneous axis containing the reference point A. Here we have to consider that with respect to the

---

[1] Remember that all displacements, velocities, and the like, are measured with respect to the reference body K. In our case, initially body point P coincides with point p in K, and finally it is at p' in K.

reference body K the body point P is now at point p_1, which is located by the vector

$$\vec{ap_1} = \varrho_1 = \varrho + d\phi_1 \times \varrho$$

so that the relationship between the displacement $\vec{pp'}$ and the infinitesimal rotation $d\phi_2$ is

$$\begin{aligned}
\vec{p_1p'} &= d\phi_2 \times \varrho_1 \\
&= d\phi_2 \times (\varrho + d\phi_1 \times \varrho) \\
&= d\phi_2 \times \varrho + d\phi_2 \times (d\phi_1 \times \varrho)
\end{aligned}$$

or neglecting second-order terms,

$$\vec{p_1p'} = d\phi_2 \times \varrho$$

Now since

$$\vec{pp'} = \vec{pp_1} + \vec{p_1p'}$$

or

$$d\phi \times \varrho = d\phi_1 \times \varrho + d\phi_2 \times \varrho$$

we may conclude that

$$d\phi = d\phi_1 + d\phi_2 \qquad (5.1\text{-}6)$$

The sequence of addition is immaterial also, because the derivation above admits immediately the conclusion that

$$d\phi = d\phi_2 + d\phi_1$$

Thus we may state that infinitesimal rotations may be added like vectors and therefore are truly vectorial quantities. Hence, dividing Eq. (5.1-6) by dt, we also have that the angular velocities are truly vectors, such that (see Fig. 5.1-5)

$$\omega = \omega_1 + \omega_2 = \omega_2 + \omega_1 \qquad (5.1\text{-}7)$$

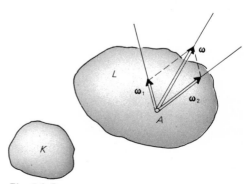

Fig. 5.1-5

Therefore a body L that is simultaneously subjected to two angular velocities ω_1 and ω_2 (see Fig. 5.1-6) with respect to a reference body K can be considered to rotate with the angular velocity $\omega = \omega_1 + \omega_2$.

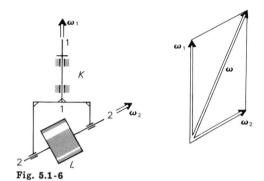

Fig. 5.1-6

An immediate consequence of the vectorial character of the angular velocity is its representation in cartesian coordinates fixed in body K:

$$\omega = \omega_x \mathbf{i} + \omega_y \mathbf{j} + \omega_z \mathbf{k} \tag{5.1-8}$$

However, although ω defines the angular velocity of body L with respect to the reference frame K, it is usually more useful to represent ω in the cartesian coordinates ξ, η, ζ fixed in body L (see Fig. 5.1-7):

$$\omega = \omega_\xi \mathbf{1}_\xi + \omega_\eta \mathbf{1}_\eta + \omega_\zeta \mathbf{1}_\zeta \tag{5.1-9}$$

We now show that the angular velocity ω is a property of the motion of body L with respect to body K and is independent of the choice of the point A in body L (see Sec. 4.2). Taking a different body-fixed reference point B (see Fig. 5.1-8), the position of an arbitrary body point P is defined by

$$\mathbf{r} = \mathbf{r}_B + \varrho_{BP}$$

and thus in view of Eqs. (5.1-5) its velocity with respect to body K is

$$\dot{\mathbf{r}} = \mathbf{v} = \mathbf{v}_B + \mathbf{\Omega} \times \varrho_{BP} \tag{5.1-10}$$

where $\mathbf{v}_B$ is the velocity of the new reference point B and the vector defining the angular velocity of body L about the instantaneous axis through B is assumed to be $\mathbf{\Omega}$, in contrast to ω, which defines the angular velocity of L about the instantaneous axis through the original reference point A. We now prove that $\mathbf{\Omega} = \omega$. Since

$$\mathbf{r}_B = \mathbf{r}_A + \varrho_{AB}$$

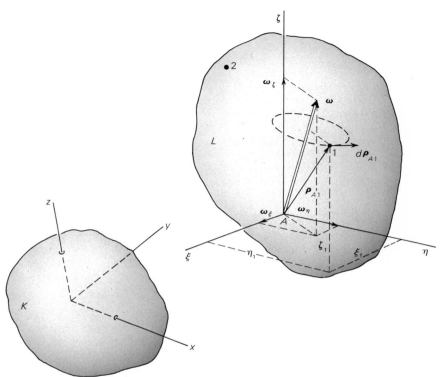

Fig. 5.1-7

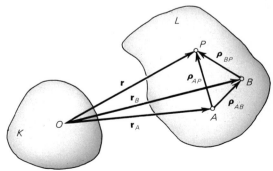

Fig. 5.1-8

the velocity of point B is

$$\mathbf{r}_B = \mathbf{v}_B = \mathbf{v}_A + \boldsymbol{\omega} \times \boldsymbol{\varrho}_{AB} \tag{5.1-11}$$

Hence for the velocity of point P we can write

$$\mathbf{v} = \mathbf{v}_A + \boldsymbol{\omega} \times \boldsymbol{\varrho}_{AB} + \boldsymbol{\Omega} \times \boldsymbol{\varrho}_{BP} \tag{5.1-12}$$

On the other hand we have from Eqs. (5.1-5)

$$\mathbf{v} = \mathbf{v}_A + \boldsymbol{\omega} \times \boldsymbol{\varrho}_{AP}$$

and since $\boldsymbol{\varrho}_{AP} = \boldsymbol{\varrho}_{AB} + \boldsymbol{\varrho}_{BP}$, Eqs. (5.1-5) may be written

$$\mathbf{v} = \mathbf{v}_A + \boldsymbol{\omega} \times \boldsymbol{\varrho}_{AB} + \boldsymbol{\omega} \times \boldsymbol{\varrho}_{BP} \tag{5.1-13}$$

Comparison of Eqs. (5.1-12) and (5.1-13) proves that $\boldsymbol{\Omega} = \boldsymbol{\omega}$. From this result we may also draw the conclusion that the angular velocity is a free axial vector, like the moment vector of a force couple, that may be translated to any point in the moving body L. Note, however, that the velocity of the reference point depends on the choice of the latter—see Eq. (5.1-11).

We now demonstrate how the angular velocity $\boldsymbol{\omega}$ of body L with respect to body K may be determined once the velocities $\mathbf{v}_1 - \mathbf{v}_A$ and $\mathbf{v}_2 - \mathbf{v}_A$ of points 1 and 2, respectively, relative to point A are known.[1] Consider that

$$\mathbf{v}_1 - \mathbf{v}_A = \boldsymbol{\omega} \times \boldsymbol{\varrho}_{A1}$$

and

$$\mathbf{v}_2 - \mathbf{v}_A = \boldsymbol{\omega} \times \boldsymbol{\varrho}_{A2}$$

Hence

$$(\mathbf{v}_1 - \mathbf{v}_A) \times (\mathbf{v}_2 - \mathbf{v}_A) = (\boldsymbol{\omega} \times \boldsymbol{\varrho}_{A1}) \times (\boldsymbol{\omega} \times \boldsymbol{\varrho}_{A2})$$

Treating $\boldsymbol{\omega} \times \boldsymbol{\varrho}_{A1}$ as $\mathbf{a}$, $\boldsymbol{\omega}$ as $\mathbf{b}$, and $\boldsymbol{\varrho}_{A2}$ as $\mathbf{c}$, use of the identity

$$\mathbf{a} \times (\mathbf{b} \times \mathbf{c}) = \mathbf{a} \cdot \mathbf{c}\,\mathbf{b} - \mathbf{a} \cdot \mathbf{b}\,\mathbf{c}$$

gives

$$(\mathbf{v}_1 - \mathbf{v}_A) \times (\mathbf{v}_2 - \mathbf{v}_A) = [(\boldsymbol{\omega} \times \boldsymbol{\varrho}_{A1}) \cdot \boldsymbol{\varrho}_{A2}]\boldsymbol{\omega} - [(\boldsymbol{\omega} \times \boldsymbol{\varrho}_{A1}) \cdot \boldsymbol{\omega}]\boldsymbol{\varrho}_{A2}$$

In the first term on the right, we replace $\boldsymbol{\omega} \times \boldsymbol{\varrho}_{A1}$ by $\mathbf{v}_1 - \mathbf{v}_A$. The second term is zero, because $(\boldsymbol{\omega} \times \boldsymbol{\varrho}_{A1}) \cdot \boldsymbol{\omega} = 0$. Thus we have

$$(\mathbf{v}_1 - \mathbf{v}_A) \times (\mathbf{v}_2 - \mathbf{v}_A) = [(\mathbf{v}_1 - \mathbf{v}_A) \cdot \boldsymbol{\varrho}_{A2}]\boldsymbol{\omega}$$

Hence for $\boldsymbol{\omega}$ we obtain

$$\boldsymbol{\omega} = \frac{(\mathbf{v}_1 - \mathbf{v}_A) \times (\mathbf{v}_2 - \mathbf{v}_A)}{(\mathbf{v}_1 - \mathbf{v}_A) \cdot \boldsymbol{\varrho}_{A2}} \tag{5.1-14}$$

It is obvious that we also have

$$\boldsymbol{\omega} = \frac{(\mathbf{v}_2 - \mathbf{v}_A) \times (\mathbf{v}_1 - \mathbf{v}_A)}{(\mathbf{v}_2 - \mathbf{v}_A) \cdot \boldsymbol{\varrho}_{A1}} \tag{5.1-15}$$

---

[1] The velocity differences $\mathbf{v}_1 - \mathbf{v}_A$ and $\mathbf{v}_2 - \mathbf{v}_A$ are measured by an observer fixed in the reference frame K.

From Eqs. (5.1-14) and (5.1-15) we conclude that ϱ_{A1}, ϱ_{A2} and the velocities are not independent of each other but must satisfy the following relationship:

$$(\mathbf{v}_1 - \mathbf{v}_A) \cdot \varrho_{A2} = -(\mathbf{v}_2 - \mathbf{v}_A) \cdot \varrho_{A1} \qquad (5.1\text{-}16)$$

In our considerations above we showed that infinitesimal angular displacements are vectorial quantities. In order to counteract the possibility that the beginner might be induced to consider finite angular displacements as vectorial quantities also, we subject a brick-shaped body successively to two different 90° rotations (see Figs. 5.1-9 and 5.1-10). We immediately

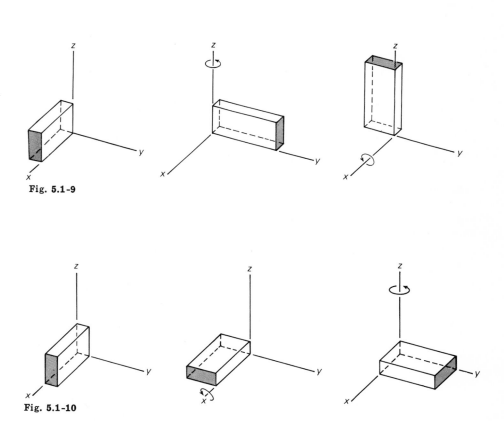

Fig. 5.1-9

Fig. 5.1-10

see that the reversal of the sequence produces completely different final positions of the brick.

If we described each finite angular displacement by means of a vector, as we did successfully for the infinitesimal angular displacement, then the resultant angular-displacement vector would be the same for the two cases of Figs. 5.1-9 and 5.1-10, as shown in Fig. 5.1-11.   This, however, contra-

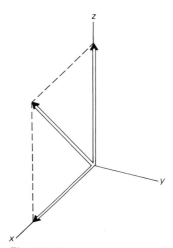

Fig. 5.1-11

dicts the experimental evidence.   Hence we conclude that vectors are not suited to the mathematical description[1] of finite angular displacements.

Let us finally do the same thing for rotations of 15° instead of 90°.   Then the respective final positions of the body differ only very little; that is, they are influenced by the sequence of the two rotations only to a slight extent (see Figs. 5.1-12 and 5.1-13).   What conclusions do you draw from these experiments?

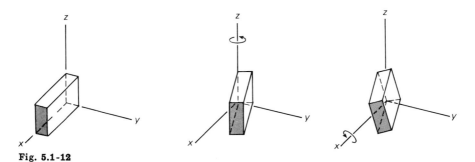

Fig. 5.1-12

[1] For an extensive mathematical treatment of finite rotations the reader is referred to J. S. Beggs, "Advanced Mechanism," chap. 2, The Macmillan Company, New York, 1966.

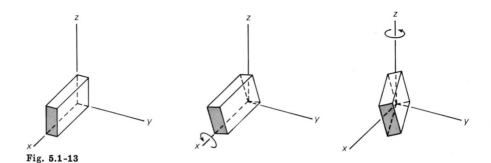

Fig. 5.1-13

ILLUSTRATIVE EXAMPLE 5.1-1

The motion of a rigid body L at a specified instant is given by the position and velocity vectors for three noncollinear points on the body measured with respect to the frame K as follows:

$$r_1 = 7i + 10j + 3k$$
$$v_1 = 5i + 6j - 2k$$
$$r_2 = 4i + 16j + 8k$$
$$v_2 = -2i + 4j - 3.80k$$
$$r_3 = 5i + 4j + 5k$$
$$v_3 = 8i + 4.65j - 3.03k$$

Using point 1 as origin of the moving coordinates tied to body L, determine the angular velocity ω of the body, and check whether the given velocities are consistent or not.

SOLUTION: The position vectors of points 2 and 3 with respect to point 1 are (see Fig. 5.1-14)

$$\varrho_{12} = r_2 - r_1 = -3i + 6j + 5k$$
$$\varrho_{13} = r_3 - r_1 = -2i - 6j + 2k$$

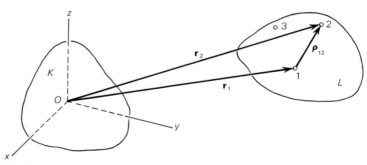

Fig. 5.1-14

The corresponding velocities are

$$v_2 - v_1 = -7i - 2j - 1.80k$$
$$v_3 - v_1 = 3i - 1.35j - 1.03k$$

We then find ω, using Eq. (5.1-14), as follows:

$$\omega = \frac{(\mathbf{v}_2 - \mathbf{v}_1) \times (\mathbf{v}_3 - \mathbf{v}_1)}{(\mathbf{v}_2 - \mathbf{v}_1) \cdot \boldsymbol{\varrho}_{13}}$$

The solution of this equation yields the components of the instantaneous angular velocity vector:

$$\omega_x = -0.0165 \qquad \omega_y = -0.563 \qquad \omega_z = 0.688$$

PROBLEMS

5.1-1   Check the results of Illustrative Example 5.1-1 by using point 2 as the reference point in body L.

5.1-2   The position of a rigid body at a given instant is defined by the position vectors

$$\mathbf{r}_1 = 8\mathbf{i} + 4\mathbf{j} + 3\mathbf{k}$$
$$\mathbf{r}_2 = 3\mathbf{i} + 2\mathbf{j} - 4\mathbf{k}$$
$$\mathbf{r}_3 = 5\mathbf{i} + 3\mathbf{j} + 6\mathbf{k}$$

measured with respect to the reference frame K.   If the velocity of point 1 and the angular velocity of the body for this instant are

$$\mathbf{v}_1 = 2\mathbf{i} + 6\mathbf{j} + 4\mathbf{k}$$
$$\omega = -0.5\mathbf{i} - 1\mathbf{j} + 2\mathbf{k}$$

determine $\mathbf{v}_2$ and $\mathbf{v}_3$.

5.1-3   The position of a rigid body at a given instant is defined by the position vectors

$$\mathbf{r}_1 = 5\mathbf{i} + 7\mathbf{j} + 2\mathbf{k}$$
$$\mathbf{r}_2 = -2\mathbf{i} + 4\mathbf{j} + 6\mathbf{k}$$
$$\mathbf{r}_3 = 3\mathbf{i} - 6\mathbf{j} - 2\mathbf{k}$$

The corresponding velocities with respect to the x, y, z frame of reference at this same instant are to be measured.   However, the available pickups permit only the following six velocity components to be measured:

$$v_{1x} = 2 \qquad v_{1y} = 3 \qquad v_{1z} = 1$$
$$v_{2x} = 4 \qquad\qquad\qquad v_{2z} = 1$$
$$v_{3x} = 0$$

Determine the missing components.

5.1-4   Three points of a rigid body L are located in body-fixed coordinates as follows:

$$\xi_1 = \eta_1 = \zeta_1 = 0$$
$$\xi_2 = 5 \text{ ft} \qquad \eta_2 = 0 \qquad \zeta_2 = 0$$
$$\xi_3 = 0 \qquad \eta_3 = 0 \qquad \zeta_3 = -2 \text{ ft}$$

Taking the x, y, z axes to coincide with the ξ, η, ζ axes at this instant, determine the x, y, z coordinates of these three points after $\frac{1}{1,000}$ sec if $\mathbf{v}_1 = 3\mathbf{i} + 2\mathbf{j} - 4\mathbf{k}$ ft/sec and $\omega = 2\mathbf{i} - 4\mathbf{j} + 3\mathbf{k}$ sec^{-1}.   Consider both $\mathbf{v}_1$ and ω constants.

5.2   KINEMATICS OF RELATIVE MOTION

We now turn to step 2 (see Sec. 1.1), that is, describing the motion of a point with respect to a reference frame K in terms of coordinates tied to another reference body L.† The motion of L with respect to K (see Sec. 5.1) is defined by the vectors $\mathbf{v}_A$ and $\boldsymbol{\omega}$, denoting the velocity of the reference point A in L and the angular velocity of L, respectively. Figure 5.2-1 shows that

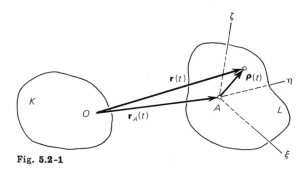

Fig. 5.2-1

the location of the moving point with respect to the reference point A, defined by the position vector $\boldsymbol{\varrho}$, and the location of the same moving point with respect to the reference point O, defined by the position vector $\mathbf{r}$, are related as follows:

$$\mathbf{r}(t) = \mathbf{r}_A(t) + \boldsymbol{\varrho}(t) \tag{5.2-1}$$

The position vector $\mathbf{r}$ is split in this fashion, because we wish to describe the motion of the moving point in terms of coordinates tied to the reference body L. For this purpose we fix the ξ, η, ζ coordinate axes in body L with point A as their origin, and therefore we may write

$$\boldsymbol{\varrho} = \xi \mathbf{1}_\xi + \eta \mathbf{1}_\eta + \zeta \mathbf{1}_\zeta \tag{5.2-2}$$

where $\mathbf{1}_\xi$, $\mathbf{1}_\eta$, $\mathbf{1}_\zeta$ denote unit vectors defining the positive direction of the ξ, η, ζ axes, respectively. In order to obtain the velocity $\mathbf{v}$ of the moving point with respect to the reference frame K, we take the time derivative of Eq. (5.2-1):

$$\dot{\mathbf{r}} = \mathbf{v} = \dot{\mathbf{r}}_A + \dot{\boldsymbol{\varrho}} \tag{5.2-3}$$

On the right side of Eq. (5.2-3) $\dot{\mathbf{r}}_A$ is the velocity $\mathbf{v}_A$ of the point A, fixed in L, with respect to the reference frame K. Now, $\dot{\boldsymbol{\varrho}}$, being the time rate of change of $\boldsymbol{\varrho}$ in the reference frame K, is most easily determined by differentiating Eq. (5.2-2), observing that the unit vectors $\mathbf{1}_\xi$, $\mathbf{1}_\eta$, $\mathbf{1}_\zeta$ change their direction with respect to K:

$$\dot{\boldsymbol{\varrho}} = \dot{\xi} \mathbf{1}_\xi + \dot{\eta} \mathbf{1}_\eta + \dot{\zeta} \mathbf{1}_\zeta + \xi \dot{\mathbf{1}}_\xi + \eta \dot{\mathbf{1}}_\eta + \zeta \dot{\mathbf{1}}_\zeta \tag{5.2-4}$$

† This problem arises not only in dealing with kinematics but also frequently in the treatment of the dynamics of rigid bodies.

The first three terms on the right side of Eq. (5.2-4) are readily interpreted. Just as $\dot{\mathbf{r}} = \dot{x}\mathbf{i} + \dot{y}\mathbf{j} + \dot{z}\mathbf{k}$ is defined as the velocity of a moving point with respect to the reference body in which the x, y, z coordinates are fixed, the vectorial time derivative

$$\overset{\frown}{\dot{\boldsymbol{\varrho}}} = \dot{\xi}\mathbf{1}_{\xi} + \dot{\eta}\mathbf{1}_{\eta} + \dot{\zeta}\mathbf{1}_{\zeta} \tag{5.2-5}$$

defines the velocity of a moving point with respect to the reference body L in which the ξ, η, ζ coordinates are fixed. The curved arrow above $\dot{\boldsymbol{\varrho}}$ indicates that the time derivative of the vector is taken in the reference frame L that is moving with respect to the reference body K.

It has become common usage to call the velocity $\overset{\frown}{\dot{\boldsymbol{\varrho}}}$ the "relative" velocity $\mathbf{v}_{\mathrm{rel}}$, because it is the velocity of the moving point defined relative to the moving reference frame L, and thus we may write

$$\mathbf{v}_{\mathrm{rel}} = \overset{\frown}{\dot{\boldsymbol{\varrho}}} = \dot{\xi}\mathbf{1}_{\xi} + \dot{\eta}\mathbf{1}_{\eta} + \dot{\zeta}\mathbf{1}_{\zeta} \qquad \blacktriangleleft \tag{5.2-6}$$

This usage is also responsible for the title of the present section.[1]

Now we turn to a discussion of the second part of the three terms on the right side of Eq. (5.2-4). Here we are faced with the interpretation of the time derivatives of the unit vectors $\mathbf{1}_{\xi}$, $\mathbf{1}_{\eta}$, $\mathbf{1}_{\zeta}$ that rotate with the reference body L. Their time rate of change is taken with respect to the reference body K. Since unit vectors are of constant magnitude (unity), their time rate of change can only be due to the change of their direction with respect to the reference frame K, which takes place with the angular velocity $\boldsymbol{\omega}$ of the reference body L. Now, taking a geometric point of view, we consider, for example, the unit vector $\mathbf{1}_{\xi}$ to be rotating with the reference body L, as shown in Fig. 5.2-2. Then the "velocity" of the arrowhead of $\mathbf{1}_{\xi}$, and thus

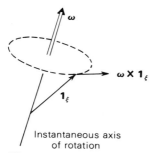

Fig. 5.2-2

---

[1] This usage is somewhat unfortunate, since any motion is meaningful only "relative" to a reference frame. It also has the even more unwelcome consequence of calling the motion relative to the reference body K "absolute."

the time rate of change of $\mathbf{1}_\xi$, with respect to the reference frame K is easily seen to be—see Eqs. (5.1-5)—

$$\dot{\mathbf{i}}_\xi = \boldsymbol{\omega} \times \mathbf{1}_\xi \qquad \blacktriangleleft \quad (5.2\text{-}7)$$

Thus we may write

$$\xi \dot{\mathbf{i}}_\xi + \eta \dot{\mathbf{i}}_\eta + \zeta \dot{\mathbf{i}}_\zeta = \boldsymbol{\omega} \times (\xi \mathbf{1}_\xi + \eta \mathbf{1}_\eta + \zeta \mathbf{1}_\zeta) = \boldsymbol{\omega} \times \boldsymbol{\varrho} \qquad (5.2\text{-}8)$$

Hence we have with Eqs. (5.2-5) and (5.2-8)

$$\dot{\boldsymbol{\varrho}} = \overset{\frown}{\dot{\boldsymbol{\varrho}}} + \boldsymbol{\omega} \times \boldsymbol{\varrho} \qquad (5.2\text{-}9)$$

or with Eq. (5.2-6)

$$\dot{\boldsymbol{\varrho}} = \mathbf{v}_{\mathrm{rel}} + \boldsymbol{\omega} \times \boldsymbol{\varrho} \qquad \blacktriangleleft \quad (5.2\text{-}10)$$

We now show Eq. (5.2-9) to be a general formula, yielding, for any vector quantity $\mathbf{Q}$, the time rate of change $\dot{\mathbf{Q}}$ with respect to a reference frame K when $\mathbf{Q}$ is described in coordinates tied to another reference body L that is rotating with respect to K with angular velocity $\boldsymbol{\omega}$. If

$$\mathbf{Q} = Q_\xi \mathbf{1}_\xi + Q_\eta \mathbf{1}_\eta + Q_\zeta \mathbf{1}_\zeta \qquad (5.2\text{-}11)$$

then the time rate of change of $\mathbf{Q}$ in the reference frame K is

$$\dot{\mathbf{Q}} = \dot{Q}_\xi \mathbf{1}_\xi + \dot{Q}_\eta \mathbf{1}_\eta + \dot{Q}_\zeta \mathbf{1}_\zeta + Q_\xi \dot{\mathbf{i}}_\xi + Q_\eta \dot{\mathbf{i}}_\eta + Q_\zeta \dot{\mathbf{i}}_\zeta$$

Now defining, in analogy to Eq. (5.2-5),

$$\overset{\frown}{\dot{\mathbf{Q}}} = \dot{Q}_\xi \mathbf{1}_\xi + \dot{Q}_\eta \mathbf{1}_\eta + \dot{Q}_\zeta \mathbf{1}_\zeta \qquad \blacktriangleleft \quad (5.2\text{-}12)$$

and using Eq. (5.2-7), we obtain

$$\dot{\mathbf{Q}} = \overset{\frown}{\dot{\mathbf{Q}}} + \boldsymbol{\omega} \times \mathbf{Q} \qquad \blacktriangleleft \quad (5.2\text{-}13)$$

Equation (5.2-13) is always useful when it is simpler to express $\mathbf{Q}$ in ξ, η, ζ coordinates than in the x, y, z coordinates tied to the reference body K. The case most encountered in the application of Eq. (5.2-13) concerns the moment of momentum $\mathbf{h}$ of a rotating body (see Chap. 6).

Returning now to our point of departure, that is, Eq. (5.2-3), we express the velocity $\mathbf{v}$ of the moving point with respect to K as follows—see Eq. (5.2-10):

$$\mathbf{v} = \mathbf{v}_A + \boldsymbol{\omega} \times \boldsymbol{\varrho} + \mathbf{v}_{\mathrm{rel}} \qquad \blacktriangleleft \quad (5.2\text{-}14)$$

Time differentiation of Eq. (5.2-14) then yields the acceleration $\mathbf{a}$ of the moving point:

$$\mathbf{a} = \dot{\mathbf{v}} = \dot{\mathbf{v}}_A + \dot{\boldsymbol{\omega}} \times \boldsymbol{\varrho} + \boldsymbol{\omega} \times \dot{\boldsymbol{\varrho}} + \dot{\mathbf{v}}_{\mathrm{rel}} \qquad (5.2\text{-}15)$$

In this equation we have

$$\dot{\mathbf{v}}_A = \mathbf{a}_A$$

the acceleration of the reference point A with respect to K. If $\mathbf{v}_A$ is stated in the rotating ξ, η, ζ coordinates, then we compute $\mathbf{a}_A = \overset{\frown}{\dot{\mathbf{v}}}_A + \boldsymbol{\omega} \times \mathbf{v}_A$ in accordance with Eq. (5.2-13).

$\dot{\boldsymbol{\omega}}$ is the time rate of change of the angular velocity, that is, the angular acceleration, of the reference body L, and thus of the ξ, η, ζ coordinates, with respect to K. Considering that $\boldsymbol{\omega}$ is multiplied by $\boldsymbol{\varrho}$, it should be stated in ξ, η, ζ coordinates. Thus we also compute $\dot{\boldsymbol{\omega}}$ according to Eq. (5.2-13), finding, however, because of $\boldsymbol{\omega} \times \boldsymbol{\omega} = \mathbf{0}$,

$$\dot{\boldsymbol{\omega}} = \overset{\frown}{\dot{\boldsymbol{\omega}}} \qquad \blacktriangleleft \quad (5.2\text{-}16a)$$

That is, the time derivatives of the ξ, η, ζ components of the angular velocity $\boldsymbol{\omega}$ yield the same angular-acceleration vector as the time derivatives of the x, y, z components of $\boldsymbol{\omega}$:

$$\dot{\omega}_x \mathbf{i} + \dot{\omega}_y \mathbf{j} + \dot{\omega}_z \mathbf{k} = \dot{\omega}_\xi \mathbf{1}_\xi + \dot{\omega}_\eta \mathbf{1}_\eta + \dot{\omega}_\zeta \mathbf{1}_\zeta \qquad (5.2\text{-}16b)$$

Furthermore

$$\dot{\boldsymbol{\varrho}} = \overset{\frown}{\dot{\boldsymbol{\varrho}}} + \boldsymbol{\omega} \times \boldsymbol{\varrho} = \mathbf{v}_{\text{rel}} + \boldsymbol{\omega} \times \boldsymbol{\varrho} \qquad \text{See Eq. (5.2-10)}$$

$\dot{\mathbf{v}}_{\text{rel}}$ is expressed in ξ, η, ζ coordinates and computed thus, using Eq. (5.2-13):

$$\dot{\mathbf{v}}_{\text{rel}} = \overset{\frown}{\dot{\mathbf{v}}}_{\text{rel}} + \boldsymbol{\omega} \times \mathbf{v}_{\text{rel}}$$

where $\overset{\frown}{\dot{\mathbf{v}}}_{\text{rel}} = \mathbf{a}_{\text{rel}}$ is the acceleration defined with respect to the reference frame L:

$$\mathbf{a}_{\text{rel}} = \ddot{\xi}\mathbf{1}_\xi + \ddot{\eta}\mathbf{1}_\eta + \ddot{\zeta}\mathbf{1}_\zeta$$

Hence we obtain for Eq. (5.2-15), describing the acceleration of the moving point with respect to the reference frame K in terms of quantities described in coordinates rotating in K with angular velocity $\boldsymbol{\omega}$,

$$\mathbf{a} = \mathbf{a}_A + \dot{\boldsymbol{\omega}} \times \boldsymbol{\varrho} + \boldsymbol{\omega} \times (\boldsymbol{\omega} \times \boldsymbol{\varrho}) + 2\boldsymbol{\omega} \times \mathbf{v}_{\text{rel}} + \mathbf{a}_{\text{rel}} \qquad \blacktriangleleft \quad (5.2\text{-}17)$$

Equations (5.2-14) and (5.2-17) may be rewritten using the concept of the coincident point. This is the point in the rotating frame L that coincides with the moving point at the instant considered. Then the velocity of the coincident point with respect to K is

$$\mathbf{v}_{\text{cp}} = \mathbf{v}_A + \boldsymbol{\omega} \times \boldsymbol{\varrho} \qquad (5.2\text{-}18)$$

so that we may rewrite Eq. (5.2-14),

$$\mathbf{v} = \mathbf{v}_{\text{cp}} + \mathbf{v}_{\text{rel}} \qquad (5.2\text{-}19)$$

The reader may find, on his own, that the acceleration of the coincident point with respect to K is

$$\mathbf{a}_{cp} = \mathbf{a}_A + \dot{\boldsymbol{\omega}} \times \boldsymbol{\varrho} + \boldsymbol{\omega} \times (\boldsymbol{\omega} \times \boldsymbol{\varrho}) \qquad (5.2\text{-}20)$$

so that we may rewrite Eq. (5.2-17),

$$\mathbf{a} = \mathbf{a}_{cp} + 2\boldsymbol{\omega} \times \mathbf{v}_{rel} + \mathbf{a}_{rel} \qquad (5.2\text{-}21)$$

Thus the acceleration $\mathbf{a}$ of the moving point with respect to K is not simply the sum of the acceleration $\mathbf{a}_{cp}$ of the coincident point and the "relative" acceleration $\mathbf{a}_{rel}$, as one might conclude from the corresponding equation for the velocity of the moving point—see Eq. (5.2-19)—but, in addition, we have the term $2\boldsymbol{\omega} \times \mathbf{v}_{rel}$, known as the Coriolis acceleration $\mathbf{a}_{Cor}$, named for the French scientist G. Coriolis[1] (1792–1843), who also attained fame by his treatise on the theory of billiards.

ILLUSTRATIVE EXAMPLE 5.2-1
An airplane flies horizontally west in a north wind of 30 mph at a ground speed of 500 mph.   What is its speed relative to the air?
SOLUTION: We let the reference frame, and thus the ξ, η, ζ coordinates, move with the wind, so that the ξ axis points south and the η axis west.   The x, y, z system tied to the ground (body K) is chosen so that the x and y axes coincide with the ξ and η axes respectively.   Therefore we have $\boldsymbol{\omega} = \mathbf{0}$.   Then we express the data as follows:

$$\dot{x}_A = -30 \text{ mph} \qquad \dot{y}_A = \dot{z}_A = 0$$
and
$$\dot{x} = 0 \qquad \dot{y} = 500 \text{ mph} \qquad \dot{z} = 0$$

Hence we have, as components of the airspeed, expanding the vector equation

$$\mathbf{v}_{rel} = \mathbf{v} - \mathbf{v}_A$$

—see Eq. (5.2-14), with $\boldsymbol{\omega} = \mathbf{0}$—

$$\dot{\xi} = 30 \text{ mph} \qquad \dot{\eta} = 500 \text{ mph} \qquad \dot{\zeta} = 0$$

and thus the airspeed is

$$v_{rel} = (30^2 + 500^2)^{1/2} = 500.9 \text{ mph}$$

ILLUSTRATIVE EXAMPLE 5.2-2
In Fig. 5.2-3 the arm AS, at a specified position θ, has a constant angular velocity θ in the counterclockwise direction.   Determine the velocity v_{rel} of the slider S relative to AS and the angular acceleration $\ddot{\phi}$ of the arm OS.
SOLUTION: In the solution of this problem we note that, on the one hand, point S moves on a circle of radius c around O and that, on the other, point S may be considered a point in relative motion on the arm rotating about the fixed point A.

With A as the origin of the rotating coordinate system we let $\mathbf{1}_\xi$ and $\mathbf{1}_\eta$ be unit vectors along AS and normal to it.   From Eq. (5.2-14) the velocity of S is

$$\mathbf{v}_S = \boldsymbol{\omega} \times \boldsymbol{\varrho} + \mathbf{v}_{rel}$$

which yields, with $\boldsymbol{\omega} = \theta \mathbf{1}_\zeta$ and $\boldsymbol{\varrho} = \xi \mathbf{1}_\xi$,

$$\mathbf{v}_S = \xi\theta\mathbf{1}_\eta + \dot{\xi}\mathbf{1}_\xi \qquad (a)$$

[1] Actually long before Coriolis, L. Euler (1707–1781) established this important term in linking the "absolute" and the "relative" acceleration of a moving point.

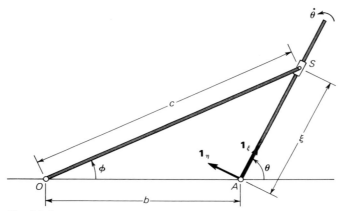

Fig. 5.2-3

To determine $\mathbf{v}_{\text{rel}} = \dot{\xi}\mathbf{1}_\xi$, we note that S, being a fixed part of the arm OS, moves in a circle of radius c about O, and therefore $\mathbf{v}_S$ is normal to OS. Equation (a) is then represented by the vector triangle in Fig. 5.2-4, from which the relative velocity of the slider S

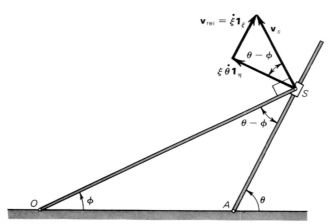

Fig. 5.2-4

is found to be

$$v_{\text{rel}} = \dot{\xi} = \xi\dot{\theta}\tan(\theta - \phi) \tag{b}$$

where $\theta - \phi = \arcsin[(b/c)\sin\theta]$.

For the determination of the angular acceleration $\ddot{\phi}$ we again consider that point S belongs to both arms OS and AS. If we take it to be the end point of arm OS, then its acceleration consists of two components: the centripetal acceleration $c\dot{\phi}^2 = v_S^2/c$ and the tangential acceleration $c\ddot{\phi}$. Of these we know the centripetal acceleration from Eqs.

(a) and (b). However, the tangential component is not known, $\ddot{\phi}$ being the quantity that we are looking for. Thus we know only that the arrowhead of the vector $\mathbf{a}_S$ must lie somewhere on the dashed line 1-1 normal to arm OS (see Fig. 5.2-5). On the other

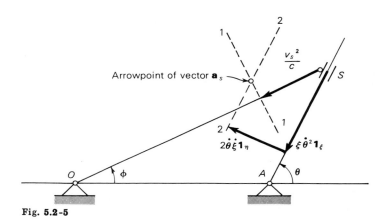

Fig. 5.2-5

hand, if we take point S to be a point sliding along the arm rotating about point A, then we find the acceleration $\mathbf{a}_S$ by making use of Eq. (5.2-17):

$$\mathbf{a}_S = \dot{\boldsymbol{\omega}} \times \boldsymbol{\varrho} + \boldsymbol{\omega} \times (\boldsymbol{\omega} \times \boldsymbol{\varrho}) + 2\boldsymbol{\omega} \times \mathbf{v}_{\text{rel}} + \mathbf{a}_{\text{rel}}$$

or in ξ, η, ζ components,

$$\mathbf{a}_S = \mathbf{O} - \xi\dot{\theta}^2\mathbf{1}_\xi + 2\dot{\theta}\dot{\xi}\mathbf{1}_\eta + \ddot{\xi}\mathbf{1}_\xi$$

Of the terms on the right side only $\mathbf{a}_{\text{rel}} = \ddot{\xi}\mathbf{1}_\xi$ is not known except that its direction is defined by the unit vector $\mathbf{1}_\xi$. Hence, if we draw, in Fig. 5.2-5, the vector polygon consisting of the three terms, we then know the arrowhead of $\mathbf{a}_S$ lies on the dashed line 2-2 parallel to arm AS (ξ direction), where it intersects the other dashed line, drawn before normal to arm OS. Thus we obtain the diagram shown in Fig. 5.2-6. From this vector

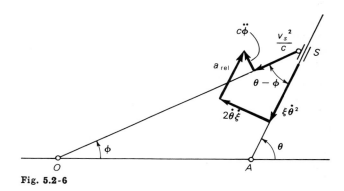

Fig. 5.2-6

diagram we can sum the components normal to $\mathbf{a}_{\text{rel}}$ to obtain

$$\frac{v_S{}^2}{c} \sin (\theta - \phi) + c\ddot{\phi} \cos (\theta - \phi) = 2\dot{\theta}\dot{\xi}$$

which may be solved for $\ddot{\phi}$. If one now wishes to compute the relative acceleration $\mathbf{a}_{\text{rel}}$ the components parallel to $\mathbf{a}_{\text{rel}}$ can be summed, since $\ddot{\phi}$ is now known.

ILLUSTRATIVE EXAMPLE 5.2-3

Determine the acceleration with respect to the earth (body K) of a boy running on a ship at $\varrho_{AP} = 30\,\mathbf{1}_\xi + 100\,\mathbf{1}_\eta$ ft, shown in Fig. 5.2-7, with constant relative velocity $\mathbf{v}_{\text{rel}} = 20\,\mathbf{1}_\eta$ ft/sec. The ship's constant speed is 40 ft/sec, and the constant radius of its course $R_0 = 2,000$ ft.

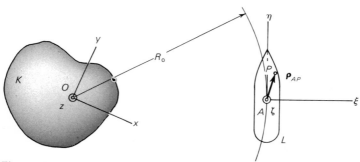

Fig. 5.2-7

SOLUTION: For this problem Eq. (5.2-17) applies. Since the ship's speed is constant, we have, for the base point A of the ξ, η, ζ coordinates (see Fig. 5.2-7), only the centripetal acceleration, that is,

$$a_{A\xi} = -\frac{|\mathbf{v}_A|^2}{R_0} = -\frac{1,600}{2,000} = -0.8 \text{ ft/sec}^2$$

and

$$a_{A\eta} = a_{A\zeta} = 0$$

For the same reason we have $\dot{\omega} = 0$ and $\omega_\zeta = 40/2,000 = 0.02$ rad/sec. Furthermore the data show that $\ddot{\xi} = \ddot{\eta} = \ddot{\zeta} = 0$ and $\dot{\xi} = \dot{\zeta} = 0$ and that $\dot{\eta} = 20$ ft/sec. Besides we are given $\xi = 30$ ft and $\eta = 0$. Thus Eq. (5.2-17) yields, on expansion, the following results:

$$a_\xi = -0.8 - 0.0004 \times 30 - 2 \times 0.02 \times 20 = -1.612 \text{ ft/sec}^2$$
$$a_\eta = a_\zeta = 0$$

Discuss the case $\dot{\eta} = -20$ ft/sec. Why, then, is $a_\xi \approx 0$, although the ship's speed is 40 ft/sec, that is, twice as much?

ILLUSTRATIVE EXAMPLE 5.2-4

The center of mass of a missile in flight follows a curve in a vertical plane. At a specified point on the curve, where the radius of curvature is R, the missile's forward speed is v

and its rate of roll is $\dot{\phi}$. Assuming all these quantities to be changing in time, determine the angular velocity and the angular acceleration of the missile in a coordinate system ξ, η, ζ with its origin at the center of mass of the missile, where ξ is in the direction of flight tangent to the flight path, η is normal to the vertical plane containing the flight path, and ζ completes the right-handed coordinate system.

SOLUTION: The angular velocity of the missile is

$$\omega = \dot{\phi}\mathbf{1}_\xi - \frac{v}{R}\mathbf{1}_\eta + 0\,\mathbf{1}_\zeta$$

Differentiating, we obtain

$$\dot{\omega} = \ddot{\phi}\mathbf{1}_\xi + \dot{\phi}\dot{\mathbf{1}}_\xi - \frac{R\dot{v} - v\dot{R}}{R^2}\mathbf{1}_\eta$$

where $\dot{\mathbf{1}}_\eta = 0$, since $\mathbf{1}_\eta$ remains normal to the vertical plane. Since

$$\dot{\mathbf{1}}_\xi = \omega \times \mathbf{1}_\xi = \frac{v}{R}\mathbf{1}_\zeta$$

the angular acceleration becomes

$$\dot{\omega} = \ddot{\phi}\mathbf{1}_\xi - \frac{R\dot{v} - v\dot{R}}{R^2}\mathbf{1}_\eta + \dot{\phi}\frac{v}{R}\mathbf{1}_\zeta$$

PROBLEMS

(A) TRANSLATION OF REFERENCE FRAMES

5.2-1   A small airplane capable of an airspeed of 160 mph has to travel north under a steady 40-mph wind that is coming from a direction 60° west of north. Determine the proper heading direction of the airplane and the ground speed attained.

5.2-2   An airport landing strip is in the east-west direction. On a calm day an airplane coming in for a landing from the east normally lands at 100 mph, so that its airspeed can also be said to be 100 mph. On a stormy day the same airplane encounters a head wind of 40 mph in the direction N60°E relative to the ground. What should be the heading of the airplane relative to the wind in order to come in parallel to the landing strip?

5.2-3   A man starts to swim at right angles to the bank of a river at a uniform rate of $1\frac{1}{4}$ mph. The current for part of the way is flowing uniformly at the rate of 1 mph and for the rest of the way at 2 mph. On reaching the other side, the man finds that he has drifted downstream a distance equal to the breadth of the river. At what point did the speed of the current change?

5.2-4   A tear-gas bomb is fired directly backward at an elevation θ_0 relative to the floor of a vehicle traveling with speed v. If the muzzle velocity of the bomb is $v_0 > v$, determine the range and the elevation angle for maximum range (muzzle height above the ground = h; air resistance is neglected).

5.2-5   A helicopter is attempting to land on an aircraft carrier traveling north at 30 knots (1 knot = 1.152 mph). A 20-knot wind is blowing in a direction perpendicular to the carrier's course. If, to the crew on the carrier, the helicopter appears to be descending vertically at 8 knots, determine its velocity (a) relative to the water, (b) relative to the air.

5.2-6   Two railroad tracks perpendicular to each other join at c by a quarter circle of 1 mile radius, as shown in Fig. P 5.2-6.   Train B, traveling at 40 mph, enters the curved section at the same time that train A, traveling at 60 mph, is sighted directly ahead.   Determine the velocity of train A as observed by a passenger on train B 1 min after entering the curved track.

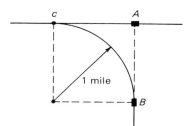

Fig. P 5.2-6

5.2-7   A target at $(x,y,0)$ is to be hit by a rocket shell launched horizontally from an airplane traveling at 500 mph at a constant altitude of $h = 8,000$ ft, as shown in Fig. P 5.2-7.   If the launching speed of the shell relative to the airplane is 400 ft/sec, determine the position y_0 and the heading angle θ of the shell relative to the direction of motion of the airplane.

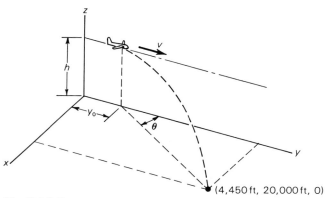

(4,450 ft, 20,000 ft, 0)

Fig. P 5.2-7

5.2-8   Rain coming down at an angle θ with the vertical is assumed to have a constant velocity of 20 ft/sec.   A man running against it with a speed of 15 ft/sec notices that relative to him the rain appears to be making an angle ϕ with the vertical. Determine the relationship between ϕ and θ.

5.2-9   A transparent plastic sheet moves with constant velocity v_0 across the front of a wheel rotating with angular velocity ω about its fixed center (see Fig. P 5.2-9). Determine the motion of a point on the rim of the wheel as traced out on the plastic sheet.

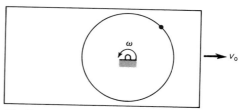

Fig. P 5.2-9

5.2-10   The wheel-and-arm arrangement shown in Fig. P 5.2-10 is kinematically connected so that the straight line OP remains parallel to itself as the arm CO rotates with angular velocity ω and angular acceleration $\dot{\omega}$. (a) Determine the magnitude and direction of the acceleration of P in the four positions A, B, C, D. (b) How does the acceleration of P depend on r?

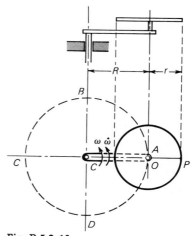

Fig. P 5.2-10

(B)   REFERENCE FRAME ROTATING ABOUT A FIXED AXIS

5.2-11   A wheel rotates about a vertical axis with a constant angular speed of 2 rad/sec. A slider m moves outward along a radial slot with a constant speed of 8 in./sec. Determine the acceleration of m when it is 16 in. from the center.

5.2-12   A small mass m slides along the spoke of a rotating wheel with a fixed center. In the position shown in Fig. P 5.2-12, $\rho = 3$ ft, $\theta = \tan^{-1} \frac{4}{3}$, $\dot\theta = 2$ rad/sec, and $\ddot\theta = 4$ rad/sec², both counterclockwise.   The velocity and acceleration of m relative to the spoke are 5 ft/sec toward O and 6 ft/sec² outward.   Determine the radial and transverse components of the acceleration of m.

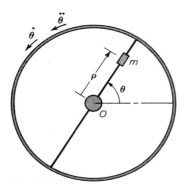

Fig. P 5.2-12

5.2-13   A particle P moves outward with speed $\dot\rho$ along a tube that makes an angle θ with the vertical axis AB rotating with constant speed ω (see Fig. P 5.2-13). If θ also changes at a constant rate $\dot\theta$, determine the velocity and acceleration of P in position ρ.

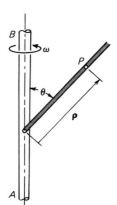

Fig. P 5.2-13

5.2-14   A horizontal turntable of a merry-go-round rotates at a constant speed ω.   Two boys at the opposite ends of the diameter D wish to throw a ball between them.

If the velocity with which they can throw the ball relative to the turntable is v_{rel}, indicate which direction they should throw the ball in.

5.2-15   For efficient operation, steam should enter the wheel of an impulse turbine in a direction equal to the entrance angle of the blades shown in Fig. P 5.2-15. Determine the proper nozzle angle θ when the steam velocity is 1,000 ft/sec, the blade speed 600 ft/sec, and the entrance angle of the blades 55°.

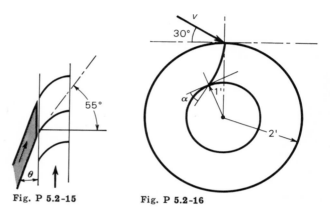

Fig. P 5.2-15   **Fig. P 5.2-16**

5.2-16   A radial-flow turbine has water entering at a velocity of 80 ft/sec at an angle of 30° with the tangent to the wheel (see Fig. P 5.2-16). The blade of the wheel at the inlet is 90° with the tangent. Find (a) the turbine speed that allows the water to enter in a direction tangent to the blade, (b) for this speed. the blade angle α that gives the water a radial direction at the exit.

5.2-17   In the centrifugal pump shown in Fig. P 5.2-17, water flows out at point P with a constant velocity of 100 ft/sec relative to the blade. With the following quantities given for the wheel: $\rho = 18$ in., $R = 24$ in., $\omega = 6\pi$ rad/sec, $\dot{\omega} = 0$, determine the absolute velocity and acceleration of the water at P.

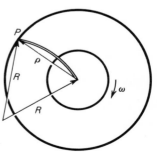

Fig. P 5.2-17

5.2-18   In Prob. 5.2-17 discuss the motion of the water immediately after it leaves the impeller from the standpoint of a rotating as well as of a fixed observer.

5.2-19   If the impeller in Prob. 5.2-17 is rotated counterclockwise with the same speed, determine the absolute velocity of the water as it leaves the impeller and the acceleration immediately before it does.

5.2-20   A particle moves along a curve s fixed in a plane that rotates about an axis O normal to the plane with angular velocity ω. Show that the component of the acceleration tangent to the curve is

$$v\,\frac{dv}{ds} + pv\,\frac{d\omega}{ds} - \omega^2 r\,\frac{dr}{ds}$$

where p is the perpendicular distance from O to the tangent, as shown in Fig. P 5.2-20.

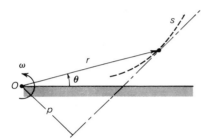

Fig. P 5.2-20

5.2-21   A particle moves outward along a radial line on a horizontal disk rotating with angular velocity ω about a fixed vertical axis. Show that half of the Coriolis acceleration comes from the change in direction of the radial velocity due to the rotation, and the other half from the rate of increase of the transverse velocity as the particle moves out.

5.2-22   An insect is located at a point P on a phonograph record that rotates with constant angular speed ω about its center O. If the insect moves so that the rate of its acceleration is parallel to OP, prove that

$$\ddot{r} - \frac{\omega^2}{3}\,r = 0 \qquad \text{where } r = OP$$

HINT: Use polar coordinates for the relative motion, and consider θ negligible compared with ω.

5.2-23   A rigid body rotates about an axis passing through the origin of the ξ, η, ζ system and the point $\varrho_1 = 3\,\mathbf{1}_\xi + 5\,\mathbf{1}_\eta + 2\,\mathbf{1}_\zeta$ with angular speed of 75 rpm. Determine the velocity of a point that is defined by the vector $\varrho_2 = 2\,\mathbf{1}_\xi + 3\,\mathbf{1}_\eta + \mathbf{1}_\zeta$.

5.2-24   The axis of rotation of a body through the origin of the ξ, η, ζ system is specified by the direction cosines $l = 0.707$, $m = 0.50$, $n = 0.50$. What is the velocity of a point in the body rotating with angular speed 20 rad/sec if its position is $\varrho = 2\,\mathbf{1}_\xi + 4\,\mathbf{1}_\eta + 3\,\mathbf{1}_\zeta$?

5.2-25 The rate gyro of an airplane coming in for a landing indicates that the airplane with the body-fixed coordinates shown in Fig. P 5.2-25 has an angular velocity of

$$\omega = 0.15 \ 1_\xi + 0.05 \ 1_\eta + 0.02 \ 1_\zeta$$

Determine the velocity of the right wing tip relative to its center of mass if its coordinates are

$$\varrho = 40 \ 1_\xi - 25 \ 1_\eta - 2 \ 1_\zeta$$

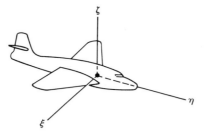

Fig. P 5.2-25

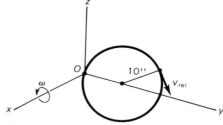

Fig. P 5.2-26

5.2-26 A circular ring 10 in. in radius is fixed in the yz plane and rotates about the x axis at a speed of $\omega = \pi$ rad/sec, as shown in Fig. P 5.2-26. A particle moves clockwise along the ring at a constant speed of 60 in./sec relative to it. Determine the velocity and acceleration of the particle when it makes an angle of 45° with the y axis.

5.2-27 At a given instant, a wire hoop of 6-in. radius rotates with angular acceleration and velocity of 2.00 rad/sec² and 1.50 rad/sec, respectively. At the same instant, when the hoop is in the xy plane, a bead sliding on the hoop with constant speed of 8.00 in./sec relative to it is in the position shown in Fig. P 5.2-27. Determine the acceleration of the bead relative to the fixed space when in this position.

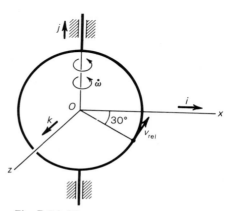

Fig. P 5.2-27

5.2-28   Assuming the earth to be a perfect sphere rotating about its polar axis with
angular velocity ω, show that the free-fall acceleration at latitude λ is equal to

$$g_\lambda = g_p \sin^2 \lambda + g_e \cos^2 \lambda$$

where g_p and g_e are the free-fall accelerations at the pole and the equator; that
is, $g_e = g_p - R\omega^2$. HINT: The component of g perpendicular to the radial line
toward the center of earth is negligible when computing the magnitude.

(C)   ROTATING REFERENCE FRAME WITH TRANSLATING AXIS OF ROTATION

5.2-29   A wheel of 2-ft radius rolls on a belt that moves to the right with a speed of
1 ft/sec (see Fig. P 5.2-29).   To an observer standing on the ground, the center
of the wheel appears to move to the left with a speed of 3 ft/sec.   Determine the
velocity and acceleration of point P.

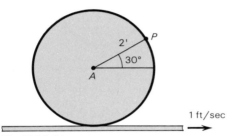

2'

P

30°

A

1 ft/sec

Fig. P 5.2-29

5.2-30   A particle moves out radially along a spoke of a wheel of radius R according to
the equation $\rho = k\theta$ (see Fig. P 5.2-30).   If the wheel rolls along the horizontal
with angular speed and acceleration θ and $\dot\theta$, determine the velocity and acceleration of the particle resolved along ρ and normal to ρ.

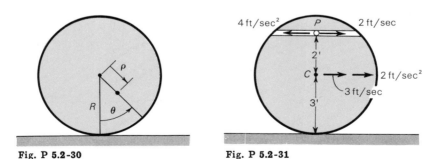

ρ

R θ

Fig. P 5.2-30

4 ft/sec²

P

2 ft/sec

2'

C

2 ft/sec²

3 ft/sec

3'

Fig. P 5.2-31

5.2-31   A vertical disk rolls without slipping on a horizontal track (see Fig. P 5.2-31).
At a given instant the velocity and acceleration of its center are 3 ft/sec and 2 ft/

sec² to the right. Also at this instant a slot in which P moves is horizontal, and P is directly above C with velocity and acceleration of 2 ft/sec and 4 ft/sec² relative to the slot. Determine the velocity and acceleration of P with respect to a fixed reference.

5.2-32 A helicopter hovering at constant height rotates about the vertical axis OO with angular velocity ω (see Fig. P 5.2-32). The vertical tail fan, causing the rotation, is spinning about its axis through point C with angular speed Ω. Determine the velocity and acceleration of a point P on the fan in the position θ. Indicate clearly the coordinates used.

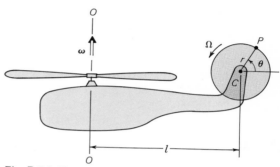

Fig. P 5.2-32

5.2-33 Determine the velocity and acceleration of point P of a grinder wheel rotating with constant angular speed Ω about an axis inclined from the vertical by ϕ when the vertical axis rotates with angular speed ω (see Fig. P 5.2-33).

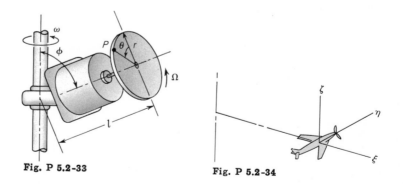

Fig. P 5.2-33   Fig. P 5.2-34

5.2-34 An airplane flying at 341 mph makes a 1.55g turn to the left in a horizontal plane. The propeller rotates at 100 rad/sec in a clockwise direction, as seen by the pilot. (a) What is the radius of the turn? (b) What is the velocity of the propeller tip, which, at this instant, has the coordinates (0, 10 ft, 3 ft) in the ξ, η, ζ system with origin at the center of mass of the airplane, as shown in Fig. P 5.2-34?   (c) Determine the acceleration of the propeller tip in (b).

5.2-35   An airplane flies south at 600 mph.   Determine the Coriolis acceleration at latitudes 60°N, 45°N, and 30°N.   Use $R = 3,960$ miles for the radius of the earth and $\omega = 0.729 \times 10^{-4}$ rad/sec for its rotational speed.

5.2-36   The speedway near Salt Lake City is approximately 40°N latitude.   If a racing car travels at a constant speed of 240 mph east, determine its acceleration along coordinates that are ξ = south, η = east, and ζ = radially outward from the center of the earth.

5.3 NEWTON'S SECOND LAW IN A NONNEWTONIAN REFERENCE FRAME

In Chap. 2 we assumed there was a reference frame in which Newton's second law was valid:

$$\mathbf{F} = m\mathbf{a} \qquad (2.1\text{-}2)$$

We now use a reference frame L that is in accelerated motion relative to a newtonian reference body K.   The path of the particle in L is then (see Fig. 5.3-1) described by

$$\varrho(t) = \mathbf{r}(t) - \mathbf{r}_A(t) \qquad (5.3\text{-}1)$$

and, according to Eq. (5.2-21), the acceleration $\mathbf{a}_{\text{rel}}$ relative to L is related

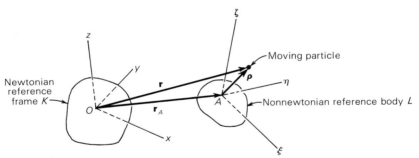

Fig. 5.3-1

to the acceleration $\mathbf{a}$ of the particle in K by

$$\mathbf{a}_{\text{rel}} = \mathbf{a} - \mathbf{a}_{\text{cp}} - 2\boldsymbol{\omega} \times \mathbf{v}_{\text{rel}} \qquad (5.3\text{-}2)$$

where $\boldsymbol{\omega}$ is the vector describing the angular velocity of the nonnewtonian reference frame L with respect to the newtonian reference body K, $\mathbf{v}_{\text{rel}}$ is the relative velocity of the particle in L, and—see Eq. (5.2-20)—

$$\mathbf{a}_{\text{cp}} = \mathbf{a}_A + \boldsymbol{\omega} \times (\boldsymbol{\omega} \times \varrho) + \dot{\boldsymbol{\omega}} \times \varrho$$

is the acceleration of the coincident point.   Multiplying all terms in Eq.

(5.3-2) by the mass m of the particle, we obtain

$$ma_{rel} = ma - ma_{cp} - m(2\omega \times v_{rel})$$

or

$$ma_{rel} = F + F_{cp} + F_{Cor} \qquad \blacktriangleleft \quad (5.3\text{-}3)$$

Here F is the force producing the acceleration a of the particle as measured in the newtonian frame of reference, and

$$F_{Cor} = -m(2\omega \times v_{rel}) \qquad \text{and} \qquad F_{cp} = -ma_{cp} \qquad (5.3\text{-}4)$$

are called kinetic body forces.[1] F_{cp} is proportional to the mass as well as to the coincident-point acceleration a_{cp}, and F_{Cor} is proportional to the mass as well as to the Coriolis acceleration a_{Cor} and thus bears the name Coriolis force. Among the terms making up the kinetic body force F_{cp}, the best known is the centrifugal force[2] $-m\omega \times (\omega \times \varrho)$. The velocity v_{rel} and the position ϱ of the particle relative to the nonnewtonian reference frame L are then found by integrating a_{rel} with due consideration to the initial values of v_{rel} and ϱ.

The observer in L experiences the kinetic body forces in the same way as he experiences, for example, the effect of gravity. Hence he considers them like all other external forces and states that Newton's second law—see Eq. (5.3-3)—also holds in his reference frame L. Yet there is still a decisive difference between L and the newtonian reference frame K in which the equation $F = ma$ holds. In order to clarify this point, we consider that the body forces F_b generally change to F_b^* when the frame of reference is changed —see Eq. (5.3-3):

$$F_b^* = F_b + F_{cp} + F_{Cor} \qquad (5.3\text{-}5)$$

We now assume there is a reference frame in which there are no kinetic body forces; that is, $F_{cp} + F_{Cor} = 0$. This would be a frame in which a body would be subjected only to surface forces and gravity or other field forces. If it were possible to carry out an experiment in such a reference frame whereby all forces are excluded, Newton's first axiom (Galilei's law of inertia) would be proved valid; however, the frame would not be an "absolute" reference frame at rest, as Newton postulated, because on the strength of his own first law it is impossible to decide whether the reference body is at rest or moving in translation with constant velocity. For in any reference frame that moves with respect to such a reference body with constant velocity v_{cp}, the acceleration components a_{cp} and a_{Cor} are zero, and consequently the kinetic body forces F_{cp} and F_{Cor} are also zero. Thus for such frames of reference the law of inertia as stated by Galilei and Newton would be valid. Consequently, such frames of references are called *inertial reference frames*, which is simply another term for newtonian reference

---

[1] These forces are often called inertia forces.

[2] To see this, we evaluate the expression for the special case in which ω, and thus the direction of the instantaneous axis of rotation, is normal to the position vector ϱ. We then obtain $-m\omega \times (\omega \times \varrho) = m\omega^2\varrho$, pointing in the direction ϱ away from the axis of rotation.

bodies. Hence we have used both names for the same concept of reference frame.

The transformation from one inertial frame to another is called a galileian transformation, in honor of Galileo Galilei (1564–1642).[1] It results in transferring from one newtonian reference frame to another that is translating with constant velocity relative to the former. By a galileian transformation of reference frames the body forces, as well as the surface forces, remain unaffected. On the other hand, a mathematically identical transformation from one nonnewtonian system to another produces, in general, a change of body forces, because, owing to the resulting change of v_{rel}, the Coriolis force is altered. Hence one may state that, in the sense of newtonian mechanics, the inertial frames of reference are essentially distinct from any reference frame that rotates with respect to an inertial frame.

The galileian transformation expresses the principle of relativity in classical mechanics, according to which it is impossible to determine, by a mechanics experiment, a frame of reference absolutely fixed in space. Of course, there is also no such thing as an exact inertial system. The reference body most nearly approaching this ideal is the sun, assuming it does not rotate with respect to the fixed stars of the Milky Way. In this frame of reference there are almost no kinetic body forces. We say "almost," because we know, from the observation of other galaxies, that accelerated motion must also be assumed for the Milky Way.

We now study briefly the limitations of the earth as far as its use as an inertial reference body is concerned. In the earth-sun system, shown in Fig. 5.3-2, the xz plane of the inertial coordinate system fixed in the sun (body K) is chosen so that it contains the elliptic (nearly circular) path of the earth.[2] The ξ, η, ζ coordinate system tied to the earth (body L) is ori-

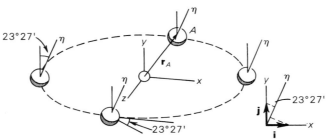

Fig. 5.3-2

[1] Note the somewhat symbolic coincidence of Galilei's death and Newton's birth.

[2] The Greek scientist Aristarchus of Samos (310–250 B.C.) and Copernicus (1473–1543) assumed the path of the planets around the sun to be circular. Only Kepler (1571–1630), evaluating the observations of his preceptor, Tycho Brahe (1546–1601), determined the geometry and kinematics of the planets with great accuracy and found their paths to be elliptic.

ented so that the η axis coincides with the pole axis of the earth. The η axis is inclined against the x, y, z system so that

$$\mathbf{1}_\eta = (\sin 23.5°)\mathbf{i} + (\cos 23.5°)\mathbf{j} \qquad (5.3\text{-}6)$$

The rotation of the earth, and hence of the ξ, η, ζ system, relative to the x, y, z system of the sun, takes place around the η axis:

$$\boldsymbol{\omega} = \omega \mathbf{1}_\eta = 7.2924 \times 10^{-5}\, \mathbf{1}_\eta \text{ rad/sec} \qquad (5.3\text{-}7)$$

The origin A of the ξ, η, ζ system is in the center of the earth. Its speed around the sun is nearly constant, and its average acceleration is

$$\ddot{\mathbf{r}}_A = \mathbf{a}_A = -0.0196\, \frac{\mathbf{r}_A}{r_A} \qquad \text{ft/sec}^2 \qquad (5.3\text{-}8)$$

The motion of the earth as described by Eqs. (5.3-7) and (5.3-8) causes kinetic body forces to be present when we consider the motion of bodies in the ξ, η, ζ frame. In a great many cases they may be neglected, so that the earth may be used as an inertial frame of reference. For example, the centrifugal force due to the acceleration $\boldsymbol{\omega} \times (\boldsymbol{\omega} \times \mathbf{R})$, where $\mathbf{R}$ is a vector drawn from the earth's center to its surface, is largest at the equator; however, it diminishes the gravity force there by only 0.35 percent. On the other hand, if a body moves in this frame of reference with high speed or if we consider the motion of a particle during a rather long time, like the motion of Foucault's pendulum, then we find it moves in a way quite different from the motion that one expects if the kinetic body forces are neglected.

Hence, when dealing with a new problem, it is wise to check first to what approximation the earth or any other reference system can be regarded as an inertial frame. It may be stated, however, that in most engineering problems of mechanics it is permissible to neglect the kinetic body forces when the earth is chosen as reference body. Then only those kinetic body forces have to be taken into account which are due to the accelerated motion of reference frames, not fixed to earth but to a moving machine part, vehicle, and the like.

ILLUSTRATIVE EXAMPLE 5.3-1

An elevator accelerates upward with constant acceleration a_0. A boy in the elevator throws a ball upward with velocity v_{rel_0} so that it just reaches the ceiling, which is h ft above the point where the ball is released. Determine the velocity v_{rel_0}.

SOLUTION: Using the elevator as the accelerating frame of reference, we have from Eq. (5.3-3)

$$\begin{aligned} ma_{rel} &= F - ma_0 \\ &= -mg - ma_0 \end{aligned} \qquad (a)$$

Integrating with initial relative velocity v_{rel_0},

$$v_{rel} = -(g + a_0)t + v_{rel_0} \qquad (b)$$

With $\eta = \int_0^t v_{\text{rel}}\, dt$ measured upward relative to the position where the ball is released, we have

$$\eta = -(g + a_0)\frac{t^2}{2} + v_{\text{rel}_0}t \qquad (c)$$

Since the ball just reaches the ceiling, $v_{\text{rel}} = 0$ when $\eta = h$ and $t = t^*$.   Thus t^* is found from Eq. (b) to be

$$t^* = \frac{v_{\text{rel}_0}}{g + a_0}$$

which, substituted into Eq. (c) with $\eta = h$, gives

$$k = \frac{1}{2}\frac{v_{\text{rel}_0}^2}{g + a_0}$$

Thus the required initial velocity of the ball relative to the elevator is

$$v_{\text{rel}_0} = \sqrt{2(g + a_0)h}$$

The reader should rework this problem using absolute coordinates and discuss the case in which $a_0 = -g$ (free-falling elevator).

ILLUSTRATIVE EXAMPLE 5.3-2

Figure 5.3-3 is a schematic representation of a vibratory rate gyroscope,[1] which may be used to detect the rate of turn (angular velocity) of vehicles on which it is mounted.   By the way, the device has been "anticipated" in the flight-control system of the housefly.

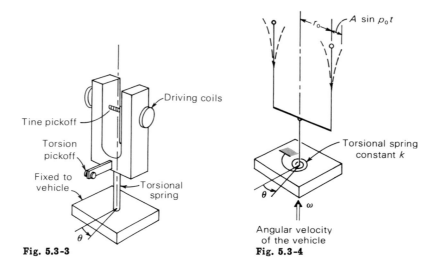

Fig. 5.3-3   Fig. 5.3-4

[1] It is actually not a gyroscopic device in the usual sense, since it has no gyro rotor.   Furthermore it is inferior to the conventional rate-of-turn indicator (see Sec. 6.5); however, it has the advantage of not having rotating parts, thereby virtually eliminating wear.

Essentially, it consists of a tuning fork whose tines are electromagnetically excited to vibrate in their common plane at constant frequency $p_0/2\pi$ with constant amplitude A. It may turn (angle θ) about its axis of symmetry restrained by a torsional spring K that is mounted on the vehicle whose rate of turn is to be measured. For the sake of simplicity, the mass of each tine is taken to be concentrated as a point mass, each of mass m (Fig. 5.3-4). Derive the equation of motion relating the angle θ and the rate of turn of the vehicle ω.

SOLUTION: In the reference frame tied to the vehicle, which turns with angular velocity ω, each mass m is subjected to a Coriolis force equal to $F_{\text{Cor}} = 2m\omega p_0 A \cos p_0 t$, as shown

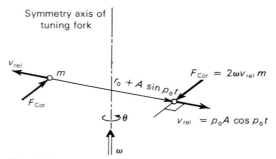

Fig. 5.3-5

in Fig. 5.3-5.   Considering that $A \ll r_0$, these Coriolis forces exert a moment $-4mr_0 A \omega p_0 \cos p_0 t$ in the negative θ direction about the symmetry axis of the tuning fork.   In the same negative direction we have the restoring moment of the torsional spring $-k\theta$, so that the equation of "relative" motion is

$$2mr_0^2 \ddot{\theta} = -k\theta - 4mr_0 A \omega p_0 \cos p_0 t$$

Substituting as solution for the steady state of the forced oscillation

$$\theta = \theta_0 \cos p_0 t$$

we obtain

$$-2mr_0^2 p_0^2 \theta_0 = -k\theta_0 - 4mr_0 A \omega p_0$$

$$\theta = -\omega \frac{4mr_0 A p_0}{k - 2mr_0^2 p_0^2} \cos p_0 t$$

We see that, in the absence of damping, the angle θ goes to infinity when the exciting frequency p_0 is equal to $\sqrt{k/2mr_0^2}$.   Of course, this device is not built without damping, so that it may be employed at its greatest sensitivity, that is, for $p_0 = \sqrt{k/2mr_0^2}$.

PROBLEMS

5.3-1   An 18,000-lb airplane descending with a velocity of 10 ft/sec meets the deck of a carrier that, at the time, moves downward with a speed of 2 ft/sec.   The airplane wheels are shock-supported by springs whose combined modulus is 50,000 lb/ft. Assuming the deck to continue downward with the above speed, determine the maximum compression of the springs. Assume lift and weight to be balanced during this motion.

5.3-2   A conveyor belt travels with a constant speed V. A small block of weight w is projected on the belt at an angle α and initial speed v_0, as shown in Fig. P 5.3-2. If the coefficient of friction between the block and the belt is μ, determine its motion.

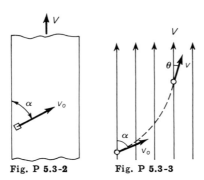

Fig. P 5.3-2   **Fig. P 5.3-3**

5.3-3   A Ping-Pong ball is projected into a stream of air at an angle α, as shown in Fig. P 5.3-3. If the initial velocity of the ball is v_0 and that of the air stream is V, and the force of the air on the ball is kv, where v is the relative velocity of the air against the ball, determine when the velocity of the ball becomes parallel to the air stream. How far normal to the air stream does it go?

5.3-4   The centrifugal governor shown in Fig. P 5.3-4 rotates at a constant speed of 90 rpm. Determine the spring force, and the pin force at O.

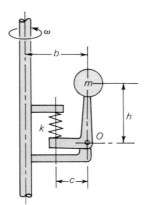

Fig. P 5.3-4

5.3-5   A block of wood rests on a rotating turntable at a distance r_0 from its center. If the turntable starts to rotate with an angular acceleration of $\dot{\omega}$, determine the speed at which the block starts to slide, assuming a coefficient of friction μ.

5.3-6 In Prob. 5.3-5 write the equation of motion relative to the turntable that applies to the block after it starts to slide.

5.3-7 A mass m, free to slide in a smooth slot in a wheel, is restrained in the position shown in Fig. P 5.3-7 by springs of total stiffness k. Determine the equation of motion and the natural frequency of oscillation when the wheel rotates with constant angular speed ω.

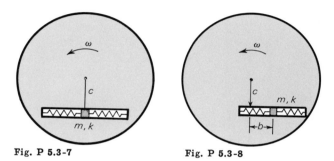

Fig. P 5.3-7   Fig. P 5.3-8

5.3-8 If the slot in the wheel is to the side, as shown in Fig. P 5.3-8, and the equilibrium position of m is (b,c) for $\omega = 0$, determine the equilibrium position and the frequency of free oscillation when the wheel rotates with constant speed ω. Does the direction of rotation have any effect?

5.3-9 Imagine a straight pipe extending through the center of the earth and making an angle θ with the polar axis, as shown in Fig. P 5.3-9. When a mass is dropped through the pipe, neglecting friction and air resistance, the period of oscillation is 84 min. Set up the equation of motion when there is dry friction (Coulomb friction) between the mass and the pipe, and discuss the resulting paradox.

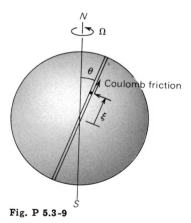

Fig. P 5.3-9

5.3-10 At Disneyland one can ride the Teacups, which are free to spin relative to a rotating platform. Figure P 5.3-10 shows one of the teacups whose spin axis A is at the distance $R = 12$ ft from the center of the platform, which is rotating at $\omega = 0.40$ rad/sec. A person sitting in the teacup is represented by a point mass m at a distance $r = 1.5$ ft from the spin axis. Determine the magnitude of the relative angular velocity ω_{rel} (spin) of the teacup to the rotating platform, such that, when m is closest to O, only the force of gravity acts on m.

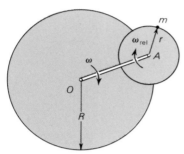

Fig. P 5.3-10

5.3-11   A space station in the form of a toroidal ring 30 ft in radius spins in order to create an artificial gravity of $\frac{1}{2}g$. Determine the ratio of the Coriolis force to that of the artificial gravity if an astronaut aboard moves with a velocity of 10 ft/sec.

5.3-12   Calculate the maximum Coriolis reaction acting on the catapult of an aircraft carrier if an airplane of 20,000 lb has a release velocity relative to the catapult of 145 ft/sec and the carrier turns with an angular velocity of $2\pi/8$ rad/min.

5.3-13   A man weighing 150 lb walks outward, without slipping, along a radius of a merry-go-round turntable which is 40 ft in diameter and which rotates at 10 rpm. If the man's velocity is 2 ft/sec relative to the turntable, what is the force transmitted by his shoes when he is 10 ft from the center?

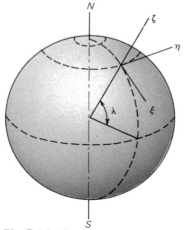

Fig. P 5.3-14

5.3-14   A projectile is fired with velocity v_0 from the earth's surface at latitude $\lambda°$N. The direction of v_0 is defined by the angles α, β, γ from the ξ, η, ζ axes at the earth's surface, as shown in Fig. P 5.3-14. Determine the ξ, η, ζ components of the acceleration of the projectile, neglecting the variation in g.

5.3-15   A hurricane wind of velocity 120 mph approaches Miami (latitude 25°N) from the south. How much and in what direction is the wind deflected because of the Coriolis force?

5.3-16   At a latitude $\lambda°$N a ball is projected with velocity v_0 on the surface of a smooth horizontal floor. Show that it starts to move clockwise on a circle of radius $p = v_0/(2\omega \sin \lambda)$, where ω is the angular velocity of the earth.

5.3-17   A bullet is fired toward the west from latitude 35°N with a muzzle velocity of 3,000 ft/sec and elevation of 30°. Neglecting air resistance, determine the deviation of the bullet because of the rotation of the earth.

5.3-18   From a position of $\lambda = 34°$N latitude it is desired to hit a target 8.0 miles toward the north using a gun with a muzzle velocity of 2,000 ft/sec. Determine how the gun should be aimed, neglecting air resistance.

5.3-19   A projectile is fired vertically upward. Determine the Coriolis deviation of the projectile as it returns to the earth, expressed in terms of the maximum height h and latitude λ. Compute its numerical value for a projectile at $\lambda = 35°$N reaching a height of 150 miles.

5.3-20   At latitude $\lambda°$S a projectile is fired at an elevation $\alpha°$ toward the east. Determine the latitude deviation of the projectile, and indicate whether it is north or south.

5.3-21   In what direction must a projectile be fired at latitude $\lambda°$S if it is to return to its starting point?

5.3-22   A wheel rotating about a fixed axis through its center C has a slot along which a mass m can slide (see Fig. P 5.3-22). The coefficient of friction between m and the slot is μ. At a given instant the angular velocity and acceleration of the wheel are ω and $\dot\omega$, and the slider has a relative velocity of $\mathbf{v}_{rel}$ toward the rim. Determine the relative acceleration $\mathbf{a}_{rel}$ of the mass m at this instant.

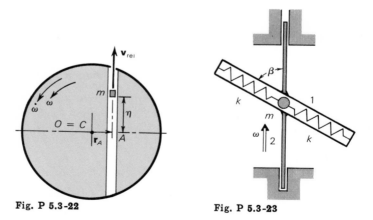

Fig. P 5.3-22   Fig. P 5.3-23

5.3-23   Consider the vibrating system shown in Fig. P 5.3-23, where a particle of mass m constrained by two springs, each of spring constant k, is to oscillate within a tube

1 that serves as a frictionless guide for the mass point. The tube is held by a shaft 2 forming a vertical axis about which the tube rotates with a constant angular velocity ω. With respect to this axis of rotation the tube axis is inclined by a constant angle β. In the case of no rotation the mass is at rest in line with the vertical shaft. If the mass is displaced in the rotating tube by a distance d from this equilibrium position and then released at time $t = 0$, (a) investigate the conditions under which the particle carries out periodic motion; (b) determine displacement, velocity, and acceleration as functions of time t; and (c) calculate the reactions of the tube to the inertia forces acting on the mass during the motion determined in (b).

5.4 THEOREMS OF MOMENTUM AND WORK IN RELATIVE MOTION

In Sec. 5.3 we found Eq. (5.3-3) as the expression for Newton's second law in a nonnewtonian frame of reference:

$$m\mathbf{a}_{rel} = \mathbf{F}_{rel} \tag{5.4-1}$$

where $\mathbf{F}_{rel}$ denotes all the forces acting on the particle of mass m, including the kinetic body forces. In view of the complete analogy of this equation to Newton's second law, all the previous theorems of momentum and work are also valid in the nonnewtonian reference frame. Thus we obtain, by the time integration of Eq. (5.4-1), the momentum relationship

$$\int_{t_1}^{t_2} \mathbf{F}_{rel}\, dt = m(\mathbf{v}_{rel_2} - \mathbf{v}_{rel_1}) \tag{5.4-2}$$

and, by the time integration of the force moment $\varrho \times \mathbf{F}_{rel} = \mathbf{M}_{rel} = \varrho \times m\mathbf{a}_{rel}$, the moment-of-momentum relationship

$$\int_{t_1}^{t_2} \mathbf{M}_{rel}\, dt = \varrho_2 \times m\mathbf{v}_{rel_2} - \varrho_1 \times m\mathbf{v}_{rel_1} \tag{5.4-3}$$

for a reference point fixed in the nonnewtonian reference frame.

Likewise when the force $\mathbf{F}_{rel}$ acts through a displacement $d\varrho$ in the moving coordinate system, the differential of the work done is

$$\mathbf{F}_{rel} \cdot d\varrho = [\mathbf{F} + \mathbf{F}_{cp} + (-2m\boldsymbol{\omega} \times \mathbf{v}_{rel})] \cdot d\varrho \tag{5.4-4}$$

Since $d\varrho$ is, by definition, in the same direction as $\mathbf{v}_{rel}$ and the vector $(\boldsymbol{\omega} \times \mathbf{v}_{rel})$ is perpendicular to $\mathbf{v}_{rel}$, the scalar product $(\boldsymbol{\omega} \times \mathbf{v}_{rel}) \cdot d\varrho = 0$. This expresses the fact that the Coriolis force does no work on the particle and Eq. (5.4-4) is reduced to

$$\mathbf{F}_{rel} \cdot d\varrho = (\mathbf{F} + \mathbf{F}_{cp}) \cdot d\varrho = dW_{rel} \tag{5.4-5}$$
$$dW_{rel} = dT_{rel} = \tfrac{1}{2}d(mv_{rel}^2)$$

The work done on the particle in moving from ϱ_1 to ϱ_2 is then—see Eq. (2.5-4)—

$$W_{rel_{1,2}} = \int_{\sigma_1}^{\sigma_2} (\mathbf{F}_{rel} \cdot \mathbf{1}_\sigma)\, d\sigma = \tfrac{1}{2}m(v_{rel_2}^2 - v_{rel_1}^2) \tag{5.4-6}$$

where σ is the coordinate[1] measured along the path of the particle in the moving ξ, η, ζ frame. Thus

$$W_{\text{rel}_{1,2}} = T_{\text{rel}_2} - T_{\text{rel}_1} \tag{5.4-7}$$

Although from a theoretical point of view these considerations look rather simple, the practical evaluation of the integrals in Eqs. (5.4-2), (5.4-3), and (5.4-6) poses great difficulties, except for a few special cases:

1 Nonnewtonian reference frame in pure translation with respect to an inertial frame. Then we have

$$\mathbf{F}_{\text{rel}} = \mathbf{F} - m\mathbf{a}_A \quad \text{and} \quad \mathbf{M}_{\text{rel}} = \varrho \times (\mathbf{F} - m\mathbf{a}_A)$$

Particularly simple is the case $\mathbf{a}_A = \text{const.}$

2 Nonnewtonian reference frame rotating with constant angular velocity ω with respect to an inertial frame. Besides, we require that $\mathbf{r}_A \equiv \mathbf{0}$, so that point 0 and A coincide at all times. Then we have

$$\mathbf{F}_{\text{rel}} = \mathbf{F} - 2m\omega \times \dot{\varrho} - m\omega \times (\omega \times \varrho)$$

Thus

$$\int_{t_1}^{t_2} \mathbf{F}_{\text{rel}}\, dt = \int_{t_1}^{t_2} \mathbf{F}\, dt - 2m\omega \times (\varrho_2 - \varrho_1) - m\omega \times \left(\omega \times \int_{t_1}^{t_2} \varrho\, dt\right) \tag{5.4-8}$$

This expression is already quite awkward, considering that its evaluation requires the knowledge of ϱ as a function of time. Besides, the force $\mathbf{F}$ must be stated in the rotating coordinates, which greatly complicates matters, because even a force $\mathbf{F}$ with constant direction with respect to an inertial frame changes direction with the angular velocity $-\omega$ with respect to the rotating reference frame. It is hardly worthwhile to write the corresponding expression for the time integral of the force moment.

For case 2, however, the work integral yields a rather simple expression:

$$\mathbf{F}_{\text{rel}} \cdot d\varrho = \mathbf{F} \cdot d\varrho - m[\omega \times (\omega \times \varrho)] \cdot d\varrho$$
$$= \mathbf{F} \cdot d\varrho + m(\omega \times \varrho) \cdot (\omega \times d\varrho)$$

or considering that $\omega = \text{const}$,

$$\mathbf{F}_{\text{rel}} \cdot d\varrho = \mathbf{F} \cdot d\varrho + m(\omega \times \varrho) \cdot d(\omega \times \varrho)$$

Thus

$$W_{\text{rel}_{1,2}} = \int_{\varrho_1}^{\varrho_2} \mathbf{F}_{\text{rel}} \cdot d\varrho = \int_{\varrho_1}^{\varrho_2} \mathbf{F} \cdot d\varrho + \tfrac{1}{2}m[(\omega \times \varrho_2)^2 - (\omega \times \varrho_1)^2] \blacktriangleleft \tag{5.4-9}$$

In contrast to Eq. (5.4-8) the work expression (5.4-9) can easily be evaluated when $\mathbf{F}$ is known as a function of ϱ, that is, stated in its ξ, η, ζ components.

[1] Corresponding to the path coordinate s in the inertial frame—see Eq. (2.5-4).

Then it is just as easy to calculate $\mathbf{v}_{rel}$ as a function of ϱ as to calculate $\mathbf{v}$ as a function of $\mathbf{r}$ when $\mathbf{F}$ is stated in inertial x, y, z coordinates (see Sec. 2.5). Although the concept of force potential can easily be established for these special cases of moving reference frames, we consider this topic beyond the scope of the present work.

ILLUSTRATIVE EXAMPLE 5.4-1
A spring-mass system rests on a smooth flatcar that accelerates with constant acceleration $\mathbf{a}_0$, as shown in Fig. 5.4-1. Determine the velocity of m relative to the car when a con-

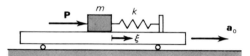

Fig. 5.4-1

stant force $\mathbf{P}$ is applied to m in the direction of $\mathbf{a}_0$. The mass of the car is assumed to be so large that its acceleration $\mathbf{a}_0$ is practically not influenced by P.
SOLUTION: The force on m is $F = P - k\xi$ (for $\xi = 0$, the spring is unstressed). The force F_{rel} producing the relative motion is then

$$F_{rel} = F + F_{cp} = P - k\xi - ma_0$$

Assuming $\dot{v}_{rel} = 0$ before P is applied, we also have $F_{rel} = 0$ before P is applied. Thus $\xi_0 = -ma_0/k$ denotes the position of m before the application of P, and the work theorem yields—see Eq. (5.4-6)—

$$\int_{\xi_0 = -ma_0/k}^{\xi} F_{rel}\, d\xi = (P - ma_0)\left(\xi + \frac{ma_0}{k}\right) - \frac{1}{2}k\xi^2 + \frac{1}{2}\frac{(ma_0)^2}{k} = \tfrac{1}{2}mv_{rel}^2$$

or
$$P\left(\xi + \frac{ma_0}{k}\right) - \frac{1}{2}k\left(\xi + \frac{ma_0}{k}\right)^2 = \tfrac{1}{2}mv_{rel}^2$$

Solving for v_{rel}, the velocity of m relative to the car is

$$v_{rel} = \sqrt{\frac{2P}{m}\left(\xi + \frac{ma_0}{k}\right) - \frac{k}{m}\left(\xi + \frac{ma_0}{k}\right)^2}$$

ILLUSTRATIVE EXAMPLE 5.4-2
On a train traveling with constant velocity $\mathbf{v}_A$, a ball of mass m is shot forward with velocity $\mathbf{v}_{rel_0}$ in the direction of motion of the train by a spring that is compressed through a distance σ and then released (see Fig. 5.4-2). Determine the work done by the train.
SOLUTION: The moving frame of reference attached to the train has no acceleration. Thus there are no kinetic body forces, and hence to an observer on the train the work done on m is

$$\int_0^\sigma k\xi\, d\xi = \tfrac{1}{2}k\sigma^2 = \tfrac{1}{2}mv_{rel_0}^2 \qquad (a)$$

which is the work done by the spring on the ball.

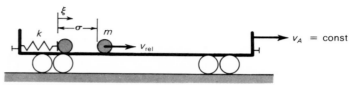

Fig. 5.4-2

To an observer on the ground, however, the change in the kinetic energy of the ball is

$$\tfrac{1}{2}m(v_A + v_{\mathrm{rel}_0})^2 - \tfrac{1}{2}mv_A{}^2 = \tfrac{1}{2}mv_{\mathrm{rel}_0}^2 + mv_A v_{\mathrm{rel}_0} \qquad (b)$$

Thus $mv_A v_{\mathrm{rel}_0}$ must be the work done by the train. This can also be shown as follows. The force acting on m is

$$m\mathbf{a} = m\frac{d\mathbf{v}}{dt} = m\frac{d}{dt}(\mathbf{v}_A + \mathbf{v}_{\mathrm{rel}}) = m\frac{d\mathbf{v}_{\mathrm{rel}}}{dt} \qquad (c)$$

where $\mathbf{a}$, that is, the acceleration of m with respect to the ground, is equal to the relative acceleration, because the velocity $\mathbf{v}_A$ of the train is specified as constant. This force acts through the fixed end of the spring, which moves through the distance $\mathbf{v}_A\,dt$. Hence the work done by the train is

$$\int_0^{t(v_{\mathrm{rel}_0})} m\frac{dv_{\mathrm{rel}}}{dt} v_A\,dt = \int_0^{v_{\mathrm{rel}_0}} mv_A\,dv_{\mathrm{rel}} = mv_A v_{\mathrm{rel}_0} \qquad (d)$$

ILLUSTRATIVE EXAMPLE 5.4-3

A particle of mass m rests in a radial slot in a horizontal disk rotating about its vertical axis with constant angular velocity ω (see Fig. 5.4-3). If released, what is its velocity relative to the disk when it leaves it? Neglect friction.

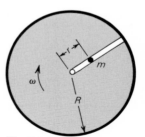

Fig. 5.4-3

SOLUTION: This problem is easily solved, using Eq. (5.4-9), considering that $\mathbf{F} = 0$, $(\boldsymbol{\omega} \times \boldsymbol{\varrho}_1)^2 = \omega^2 r^2$, and $(\boldsymbol{\omega} \times \boldsymbol{\varrho}_2)^2 = \omega^2 R^2$. Furthermore we have as an initial condition $v_{\mathrm{rel}_1} = 0$. Thus [see Eq. (5.4-7)]

$$\tfrac{1}{2}m\omega^2(R^2 - r^2) = \tfrac{1}{2}mv_{\mathrm{rel}2}^2$$

or

$$v_{\mathrm{rel}_2} = \omega\sqrt{R^2 - r^2}$$

PROBLEMS

5.4-1   A streetcar has two sliding doors coupled through gears so that, when closed, they cover the opening of width $2b$, and when open, they fit together in an enclosure, as shown in Fig. P 5.4-1.   If the streetcar accelerates with acceleration a_0 and the doors in the closed position are not locked, determine the velocities of the doors as they hit the end of the enclosure.   Assume the resisting force between each door and the floor to be $0.02w$, where w is the weight of each door.

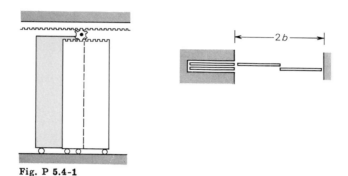

Fig. P 5.4-1

5.4-2   A freightcar decelerates with a = const.   Determine the velocity with which a box standing on the floor a distance l from the wall hits the wall (see Fig. P 5.4-2). Between the box and the floor there is Coulomb friction (μ_0, μ).   What is the limiting value of μ_0 for the box to stay at rest relative to the car?

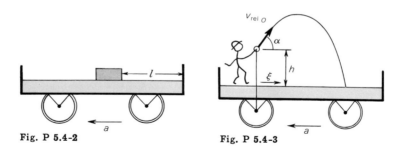

Fig. P 5.4-2   **Fig. P 5.4-3**

5.4-3   In a train decelerating with a = const, a ball is thrown with initial conditions v_{rel_0}, α, h, and $\xi = 0$, as shown in Fig. P 5.4-3.   Determine where it hits the floor.

5.4-4   A particle of mass m tied to a spring of spring constant k slides without friction in the groove of a disk rotating with angular speed ω (see Fig. P 5.4-4).   For $\omega = 0$ the mass is in equilibrium at the point ξ_0.   If released for a given constant

ω with the initial condition $v_{rel} = 0$ at $\xi = 0$, determine v_{rel} at ξ_1. What is the maximum displacement ξ_{max} that the mass can reach?

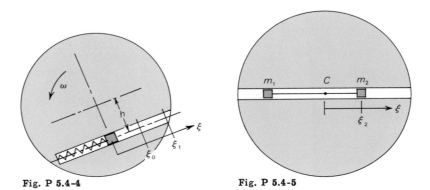

Fig. P 5.4-4   Fig. P 5.4-5

5.4-5   Two particles of mass m_1 and m_2 respectively, coupled by an inextensible string of length l, are sliding without friction in the groove of a rotating disk (see Fig. P 5.4-5). With initial conditions given as $\xi_{20} \neq l$ and $v_{rel} = 0$, determine v_{rel} at the instant when one of the particles passes through the center C of the disk.

5.4-6   Two particles of mass m_1 and m_2 respectively, coupled by an inextensible string slide in the hollow axis and the horizontal groove of a disk rotating with angular velocity ω (see Fig. P 5.4-6). For a given ω and the initial condition $v_{rel} = 0$ at ξ_0, find under what condition mass m_2 starts moving in the positive direction of ξ. Determine v_{rel} at $\xi = \xi_1$. Assume that there is no friction in the system.

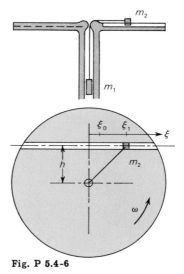

Fig. P 5.4-6

5.4-7   A particle of mass m restrained by a spring of spring constant k slides without friction in the groove of a cone rotating with angular velocity ω (see Fig. P 5.4-7). At $\omega = 0$, m is at rest at radius R_0. If for a given ω the particle is released with $v_{rel} = 0$ at R_0, determine (a) what maximum radius R_{max} it reaches, (b) what v_{rel} it has at $R < R_{max}$.

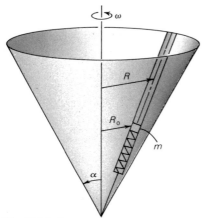

Fig. P 5.4-7

5.4-8   Consider the system in Prob. 5.4-7 with the same initial conditions but without the spring. Determine (a) in which direction the particle moves, (b) what maximum or minimum radius R_m it reaches, (c) what v_{rel} it has at some radius R within the possible range.

Fig. P 5.4-9

5.4-9   A string of length l with a particle of mass m at one end is wrapped around a drum of radius r that rotates with a constant ω (see Fig. P 5.4-9).   Determine the maximum relative velocity of the particle at the instant when the string is completely wound off the drum.   What is then the magnitude of the absolute velocity of the particle?   Which amount of energy must be supplied to the drum to keep its angular velocity constant?   Neglect gravity.

5.4-10   A string with a particle of mass m at one end is wrapped around a drum that is fixed on a rotating disk (see Fig. P 5.4-10).   Determine v_{rel} of the mass at point 2 after it is released with $v_{rel} = 0$ at point 1.   How large is the absolute velocity v_2? Neglect gravity.

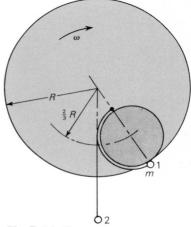

Fig. P 5.4-10

5.4-11   A particle of mass m at the end of a massless rod moves on a circular path about a point fixed on a horizontal disk that rotates with ω (see Fig. P 5.4-11).   What

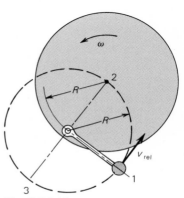

Fig. P 5.4-11

is the minimum relative velocity $v_{\text{rel}_{\min}}$ in position 1 that enables the mass to reach position 2? Determine v_{rel} in positions 2 and 3 for a given v_{rel} at 1.

5.4-12   The device shown schematically in Fig. P 5.4-12 is used as an absorber for torsional vibrations in reciprocating engines. Determine the magnitude of the velocity $\mathbf{v}_{\text{rel}}$ of the pendulous mass m for the location $\theta = 0$ after it is released at the small angle θ_0. ($\omega = $ const.) Neglect gravity.

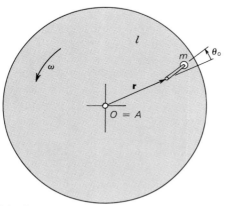

Fig. P 5.4-12

GENERAL MOTION OF RIGID BODIES

6.1 BASIC KINEMATIC RELATIONS

To describe the motion of a rigid body L with respect to a reference body K, we use the results obtained in the study of relative motion.[1] Our treatment is based on the theorem[2] that the most general displacement of a rigid body can be produced by superimposing, on the translation of the body, its rotation about an axis through a body point A that, because of the translation, has already reached its final location. This point is called the reference point A, and it serves as the origin of the ξ, η, ζ coordinates fixed in the body L (see Fig. 6.1-1). Then every point P, fixed in the rigid body L,

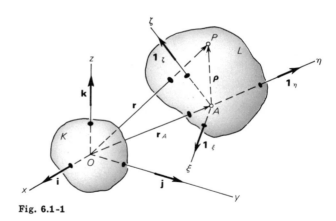

Fig. 6.1-1

is located relative to the origin of the ξ, η, ζ system by

$$\varrho = \xi \mathbf{1}_\xi + \eta \mathbf{1}_\eta + \zeta \mathbf{1}_\zeta$$

such that $\xi = \text{const}$, $\eta = \text{const}$, and $\zeta = \text{const}$.

According to Fig. 6.1-1 the position of every point P in the body L is

---

[1] The reader is advised to review Secs. 5.1 and 5.2.

[2] Since we did not prove it, we accepted it as a more or less obvious axiom. This theorem is due to the French mathematician M. Chasles (born 1793 in Epernon, France; died 1880 in Paris). Euler had already formulated the theorem concerning the rotation about a fixed point, which was then generalized by Chasles. For an exhaustive treatment see J. S. Beggs, "Advanced Mechanism," The Macmillan Company, New York, 1966.

described in the x, y, z coordinates tied to the reference frame K by

$$\mathbf{r} = x\mathbf{i} + y\mathbf{j} + z\mathbf{k}$$

or $\qquad \mathbf{r} = \mathbf{r}_A + \mathbf{\varrho} = x_A\mathbf{i} + y_A\mathbf{j} + z_A\mathbf{k} + \xi\mathbf{1}_\xi + \eta\mathbf{1}_\eta + \zeta\mathbf{1}_\zeta$ $\qquad$ (6.1-1)

Differentiating Eq. (6.1-1), we obtain, for the velocity $\mathbf{v}$ of any body point P with respect to the reference frame K,

$$\dot{\mathbf{r}} = \mathbf{v} = \dot{\mathbf{r}}_A + \dot{\mathbf{\varrho}}$$

or—see Eq. (5.2-10) for $|\mathbf{\varrho}| = \text{const}$—

$$\mathbf{v} = \mathbf{v}_A + \mathbf{\omega} \times \mathbf{\varrho} \qquad (6.1\text{-}2)$$
where $\qquad \mathbf{v}_A = \dot{x}_A\mathbf{i} + \dot{y}_A\mathbf{j} + \dot{z}_A\mathbf{k}$ $\qquad\qquad$ (6.1-3)

is the velocity of the base point A and $\mathbf{\omega}$ the angular velocity of L with respect to the reference body K, which can be expressed in either the x, y, z or the ξ, η, ζ coordinates:

$$\mathbf{\omega} = \omega_x\mathbf{i} + \omega_y\mathbf{j} + \omega_z\mathbf{k} \qquad (6.1\text{-}4)$$
or $\qquad \mathbf{\omega} = \omega_\xi\mathbf{1}_\xi + \omega_\eta\mathbf{1}_\eta + \omega_\zeta\mathbf{1}_\zeta$ $\qquad\qquad$ (6.1-5)

Differentiating Eq. (6.1-2) once more, we obtain the acceleration $\mathbf{a}$ of any point in the body L with respect to the reference frame K:

$$\mathbf{a} = \dot{\mathbf{v}} = \dot{\mathbf{v}}_A + \dot{\mathbf{\omega}} \times \mathbf{\varrho} + \mathbf{\omega} \times \dot{\mathbf{\varrho}}$$

or since $\dot{\mathbf{\varrho}} = \mathbf{\omega} \times \mathbf{\varrho}$—see Eq. (5.2-10) for $|\mathbf{\varrho}| = \text{const}$—

$$\mathbf{a} = \mathbf{a}_A + \dot{\mathbf{\omega}} \times \mathbf{\varrho} + \mathbf{\omega} \times (\mathbf{\omega} \times \mathbf{\varrho}) \qquad \blacktriangleleft \quad (6.1\text{-}6)$$

Expanding the triple vector product, we may also write

$$\mathbf{a} = \mathbf{a}_A + \dot{\mathbf{\omega}} \times \mathbf{\varrho} + (\mathbf{\omega} \cdot \mathbf{\varrho})\mathbf{\omega} - \omega^2\mathbf{\varrho} \qquad (6.1\text{-}7)$$
with $\qquad \dot{\mathbf{\omega}} = \dot{\omega}_\xi\mathbf{1}_\xi + \dot{\omega}_\eta\mathbf{1}_\eta + \dot{\omega}_\zeta\mathbf{1}_\zeta$ $\qquad\qquad$ (6.1-8)

When one point, say Q, of the body L has zero velocity with respect to the reference frame K, then the vector $\mathbf{\omega}$ drawn through this fixed point defines the instantaneous axis of rotation in the sense that the velocity of any body point P relative to K is computed simply by

$$\mathbf{v}_P = \mathbf{\omega} \times \mathbf{\varrho}_{QP}$$

Often it is possible to locate this axis by inspection (see Illustrative Example 6.1-1).

ILLUSTRATIVE EXAMPLE 6.1-1

The vertical shaft 1 and arm 2 in Fig. 6.1-2 rotate with angular velocity ω_z. The wheel on the arm rolls on its track without slipping. Determine the angular velocity ω_u of the wheel relative to the arm.

SOLUTION: Consider the wheel to be the moving body L, and the track part of the reference body K. Then, because there is no slipping, the point Q of contact with the track is a point on the instantaneous axis. A second point on this axis is found by imagining a line along the axis of the arm to be part of the body L. On this line the point A also has zero velocity with respect to the reference body K. Hence the straight line AQ is the instantaneous axis of rotation in the sense defined above.

The angular velocity of the body L, that is, the wheel, with respect to the track is represented by the vector ω directed along the line AQ (see Fig. 6.1-2). With the wheel

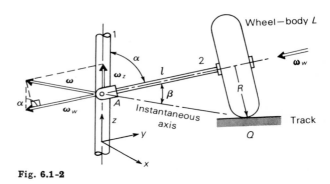

Fig. 6.1-2

rotating about the arm with angular velocity ω_w with respect to a reference frame containing the z and instantaneous axis, as well as the arm, and with the arm rotating with respect to the x, y, z frame with angular velocity ω_z, the resultant angular velocity ω of the wheel (body L) must be the sum of ω_w and ω_z, as shown in Fig. 6.1-2. Dropping a perpendicular line from the end of the ω vector on ω_w, we find

$$\omega_w = \omega_z \cos \alpha + (\omega_z \sin \alpha) \cot \beta$$

$$= \omega_z \left(\cos \alpha + \frac{l}{R} \sin \alpha \right)$$

In engineering practice ω_w is usually called the eigenspin of the wheel, usually denoted by $\dot{\phi}$.

The instantaneous axis AQ rotating about the z axis generates a conical surface that is called the space cone (see Fig. 6.1-3). A line passing through point A and any fixed

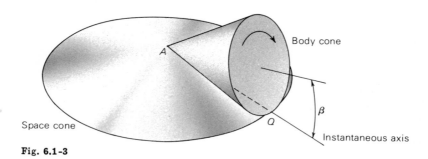

Fig. 6.1-3

point on the rim of the wheel generates a second cone that is the body cone. The body cone rolls on the space cone with the instantaneous axis AQ as the line of contact. The space cone is fixed in the reference body K, and the body cone is tied to the body L.

ILLUSTRATIVE EXAMPLE 6.1-2

At the bottom of a rolling pullout from a dive, the centripetal acceleration of the center of mass of an airplane is $4g$, and its forward speed is 500 mph. Both values are stationary for the instant under consideration. The roll is executed under uniform acceleration of $\ddot{\phi} = 0.10$ rad/sec² clockwise looking forward in the direction of flight, and at the instant under consideration the wings are horizontal with a roll rate of $\dot{\phi} = 0.80$ rad/sec, also clockwise. Determine the velocity and acceleration of a point on the wing tip ($\xi = 0$. $\eta = 15$ ft, $\zeta = 0$), where ξ is forward along the longitudinal axis and η is along the left wing.

SOLUTION: To calculate the velocity and acceleration of any point on the airplane, we need to determine the angular velocity and angular acceleration of the airplane. From the equation for the centripetal acceleration we can find the radius of curvature of the path of the airplane at the lowest point:

$$\frac{v^2}{R} = 4g \qquad R = \frac{v^2}{4g} = \frac{(500 \times {}^{88}\!/_{60})^2}{4 \times 32.2} = 4,190 \text{ ft}$$

In the following we treat the problem in two ways:

1   Using the airplane as a moving reference frame, such that the ξ, η, ζ axes are fixed in the airplane and oriented as stated above.

2   Using a moving frame of reference, such that the origin of the ξ, η, ζ coordinates is fixed to the airplane and the ξ axis is identical to that in (1), but the ζ axis remains in the vertical plane and thus the η axis is always horizontal.

Thus in case 1 we use a reference frame whose angular velocity ω is identical to that of the airplane, and in case 2 the angular velocity ω of the reference frame is different from the angular velocity Ω of the airplane.

1. Because of the roll of the airplane we have

$$\omega_\xi = \dot{\phi} = 0.80 \text{ rad/sec}$$

and referring to Fig. 6.1-4 and noting that the magnitude of the airplane's angular velocity

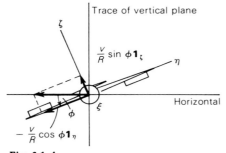

Fig. 6.1-4

due to its curved flight path is v/R, we have

$$\omega_\eta = -\frac{v}{R}\cos\phi\,\mathbf{1}_\eta \quad\text{and}\quad \omega_\zeta = \frac{v}{R}\sin\phi\,\mathbf{1}_\zeta$$

Thus we obtain for the angular velocity of the airplane, as well as of the moving frame of reference, with respect to the ground,

$$\boldsymbol{\omega} = \dot\phi\mathbf{1}_\xi - \frac{v}{R}\cos\phi\,\mathbf{1}_\eta + \frac{v}{R}\sin\phi\,\mathbf{1}_\zeta \tag{a}$$
$$\boldsymbol{\omega} = 0.80\,\mathbf{1}_\xi - 0.175\cos\phi\,\mathbf{1}_\eta + 0.175\sin\phi\,\mathbf{1}_\zeta$$

That is, for $\phi = 0$ (horizontal wings),

$$\boldsymbol{\omega} = 0.80\,\mathbf{1}_\xi - 0.175\,\mathbf{1}_\eta \quad \text{rad/sec} \tag{b}$$

Hence we find from Eq. (a) for the angular acceleration—see Eq. (6.1-8)—

$$\dot{\boldsymbol{\omega}} = \ddot\phi\mathbf{1}_\xi - \left(\frac{\dot vR - \dot Rv}{R^2}\cos\phi - \frac{v}{R}\dot\phi\sin\phi\right)\mathbf{1}_\eta + \left(\frac{\dot vR - \dot Rv}{R^2}\sin\phi + \frac{v}{R}\dot\phi\cos\phi\right)\mathbf{1}_\zeta$$

or with $\ddot\phi = 0.10$ rad/sec², $\dot v = 0$, $\dot R = 0$, and $\phi = 0$,

$$\dot{\boldsymbol{\omega}} = 0.10\,\mathbf{1}_\xi + 0.175\times0.80\,\mathbf{1}_\zeta = 0.10\,\mathbf{1}_\xi + 0.14\,\mathbf{1}_\zeta \quad\text{rad/sec}^2 \tag{c}$$

The velocity of the point on the wing tip can now be found from Eq. (6.1-2) as

$$\begin{aligned}\mathbf{v} &= \mathbf{v}_A + \boldsymbol{\omega}\times\boldsymbol{\varrho}\\ &= (500\times{}^{88}\!/_{60})\mathbf{1}_\xi + (0.80\,\mathbf{1}_\xi - 0.175\,\mathbf{1}_\eta)\times(15\,\mathbf{1}_\eta)\\ &= 733\,\mathbf{1}_\xi + 12\,\mathbf{1}_\zeta \quad\text{ft/sec}\end{aligned} \tag{d}$$

and the acceleration from Eq. (6.1-6) as

$$\begin{aligned}\mathbf{a} &= \mathbf{a}_A + \dot{\boldsymbol{\omega}}\times\boldsymbol{\varrho} + \boldsymbol{\omega}\times(\boldsymbol{\omega}\times\boldsymbol{\varrho})\\ &= 4g\mathbf{1}_\zeta + (0.10\,\mathbf{1}_\xi + 0.14\,\mathbf{1}_\zeta)\times(15\,\mathbf{1}_\eta) + (0.80\,\mathbf{1}_\xi - 0.175\,\mathbf{1}_\eta)\times(12\,\mathbf{1}_\zeta)\\ &= -4.20\,\mathbf{1}_\xi - 9.6\,\mathbf{1}_\eta + 130.3\,\mathbf{1}_\zeta\end{aligned} \tag{e}$$

2. This time we must distinguish between the angular velocity $\boldsymbol{\omega}$ of the moving frame of reference and the angular velocity $\boldsymbol{\Omega}$ of the airplane, because the moving frame of reference does not roll with the airplane. Here they are linked to each other by the relationship

$$\boldsymbol{\Omega} = \boldsymbol{\omega} + \dot\phi\mathbf{1}_\xi \tag{f}$$

From our discussion of case 1 we easily see that the components of the angular velocity of the airplane are the same in this case:

$$\begin{aligned}\Omega_\xi &= \dot\phi = 0.80 \text{ rad/sec}\\ \Omega_\eta &= -\frac{v}{R} = -0.175 \text{ rad/sec}\\ \Omega_\zeta &= 0\end{aligned} \tag{g}$$

and those of the moving reference frame are

$$\omega_\xi = \omega_\zeta = 0 \quad\text{and}\quad \omega_\eta = -\frac{v}{R} = -0.175 \text{ rad/sec} \tag{h}$$

which now differ from those of the airplane.

The angular acceleration of the airplane is now found, referring to Eq. (5.2-13), as

$$\dot{\Omega} = \overset{\frown}{\dot{\Omega}} + \omega \times \Omega$$
$$= \overset{\frown}{\dot{\Omega}} + \omega \times (\omega + \phi \mathbf{1}_\xi) \qquad \text{See Eq. } (f)$$
$$= \overset{\frown}{\dot{\Omega}} + \omega \times \phi \mathbf{1}_\xi$$

or with the data above

$$\dot{\Omega} = \ddot{\phi} \mathbf{1}_\xi - \frac{\dot{v}R - \dot{R}v}{R^2} \mathbf{1}_\eta + \left(-\frac{v}{R} \mathbf{1}_\eta \times \phi \mathbf{1}_\xi \right)$$

With $\dot{v} = 0$, $\dot{R} = 0$ we have, then, for the angular acceleration of the airplane

$$\dot{\Omega} = 0.10\ \mathbf{1}_\xi + 0.175 \times 0.80\ \mathbf{1}_\zeta$$
$$= 0.10\ \mathbf{1}_\xi + 0.14\ \mathbf{1}_\zeta \qquad \text{rad/sec}^2 \qquad (i)$$

which is identical to that given in Eq. (c), because the ξ, η, ζ coordinate systems coincide in both cases for the instant under consideration ($\phi = 0$). On the other hand, the angular acceleration $\dot{\omega}$ of the moving reference frame is zero for $\dot{v} = 0$ and $\dot{R} = 0$, as Eqs. (h) easily show.

If we now continue to compute the velocity and acceleration of the airplane's wing tip in the frame of reference of case 2, we have to use Eqs. (5.2-14) and (5.2-17):

$$\mathbf{v} = \mathbf{v}_A + \omega \times \varrho + \mathbf{v}_{\text{rel}} \qquad (j)$$
and
$$\mathbf{a} = \mathbf{a}_A + \dot{\omega} \times \varrho + \omega \times (\omega \times \varrho) + \mathbf{a}_{\text{rel}} + 2\omega \times \mathbf{v}_{\text{rel}} \qquad (k)$$

Because of the roll we have for the wing tip

$$\mathbf{v}_{\text{rel}} = \phi \mathbf{1}_\xi \times \varrho = 12\ \mathbf{1}_\zeta \qquad \text{ft/sec}$$
and
$$\mathbf{a}_{\text{rel}} = \ddot{\phi} \mathbf{1}_\xi \times \varrho - \dot{\phi}^2 \varrho$$
$$= 1.5\ \mathbf{1}_\zeta - 9.6\ \mathbf{1}_\eta \qquad \text{ft/sec}^2$$

It is left to the reader to evaluate these expressions (j) and (k) and to verify that they yield the same results as Eqs. (d) and (e), respectively.

PROBLEMS

6.1-1   A circular cone has a height $OC = 10$ in. and an angle $AOB = 90°$ (see Fig. P 6.1-1). It rolls on a horizontal plane without slipping, so that point C moves in a circle once every 2 sec. Determine the velocity of point B and the acceleration of points A and C.

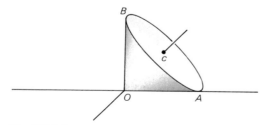

Fig. P 6.1-1

6.1-2   In Prob. 6.1-1 determine the angular velocity of the diameter AB and the eigen-spin of the cone, that is, the angular velocity of the cone with respect to the reference frame $OABC$.

6.1-3   A cone of semiangle α rolls without slipping on a horizontal xy plane so that its axis has the angular velocity $\dot{\psi}$ with respect to the x, y, z frame, as shown in Fig. P 6.1-3.   Determine the eigenspin $\dot{\phi}$ of the cone, that is, the angular velocity

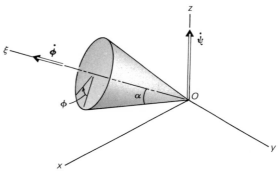

Fig. P 6.1-3

of the cone relative to the ξz plane rotating with angular velocity $\dot{\psi}$ (velocity of precession).

6.1-4   A cone 1 of half angle α and height h rolls on an identical cone 2 fixed in the vertical position.   The plane formed by the two cone axes rotates with angular velocity Ω, as shown in Fig. P 6.1-4.   Determine the angular velocity ω of the rolling cone and furthermore the angular velocity of a radial line r in the base of the rolling cone relative to the rotating plane formed by the axes of the two cones (that is, the eigenspin of the cone $\dot{\phi} = \omega - \Omega$).

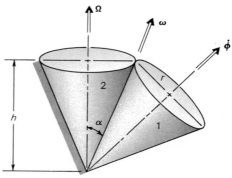

Fig. P 6.1-4

6.1-5   A 60° cone rotates without slipping on a stationary cone of 120° so that its axis
of symmetry OC moves in a horizontal plane through O (see Fig. P 6.1-5). If
the 60° cone makes 1 revolution around the z axis in 1 min, determine the eigenspin and the angular velocity of the cone.

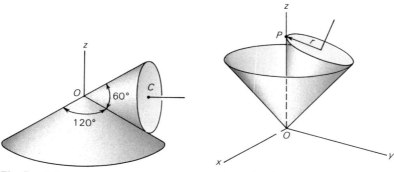

Fig. P 6.1-5   **Fig. P 6.1-6**

6.1-6   A 45° cone rolls inside a 90° cone without slipping, as shown in Fig. P 6.1-6. If
the spin axis of the 45° cone makes 1 revolution about the z axis in 2 sec, determine its eigenspin, as well as the angular velocity of the cone.

6.1-7   The axis of a rocket fired in the vertical z direction deviates through small angles
θ_ξ and θ_η, where ξ and η are the pitch and yaw axes fixed in the rocket (see Fig.
P 6.1-7).   It is desired to express the acceleration g due to gravity in the negative
z direction in terms of the rocket-fixed axes ξ, η, ζ as follows: $g = \alpha\mathbf{1}_\xi + \beta\mathbf{1}_\eta + \gamma\mathbf{1}_\zeta$.

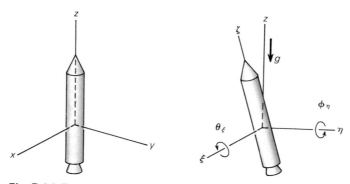

Fig. P 6.1-7

6.1-8   The axis of symmetry (ζ axis) of a rotor makes an angle of 30° with the space-
fixed z axis. The spin of the rotor relative to the ζz plane is 100 rpm, and
the ζz plane rotates about the z axis at 10 rpm. Determine the half angles
of the space and body cones of the rotor.

6.1-9   A symmetrical satellite is spinning and precessing, as shown in Fig. P 6.1-9 (both eigenspin $|\dot{\phi}|$ and precessional speed $\dot{\psi}$ are constants). An accelerometer is mounted at a point $(0,b,h)$ in the body-fixed axes ξ, η, ζ. Determine what this accelerometer measures in terms of b, h, $\dot{\phi}$, $\dot{\psi}$, θ.

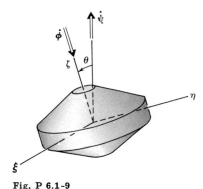

Fig. P 6.1-9

6.1-10   A gyro wheel of radius r spins about the axis ζ with angular velocity ω_ζ relative to the gimbal frame of reference, while the gimbal rotates about the space-fixed z axis with angular velocity ω_z (see Fig. P 6.1-10). Determine the velocity and acceleration of points A and B on the opposite ends of the diameter at the instant when it is vertical.

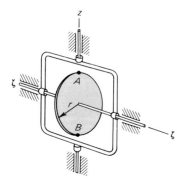

Fig. P 6.1-10

6.1-11   If in Prob. 6.1-10 the wheel rotates slowly at $\omega_\zeta = 10$ rps while $\omega_z = 6$ rps, determine the magnitude and direction of the angular velocity and angular acceleration of the wheel.

6.1-12   The node line $\varkappa$ perpendicular to the ζz plane rotates relative to the fixed x, y, z axes with angular speed $\dot{\psi}$ (precessional speed), while the wheel rotates at a speed $\dot{\phi}$ (eigenspin) relative to the $\varkappa$, ζ, z frame (see Fig. P 6.1-12).   Give the x, y, z coordinates of the point P in the above space in terms of the eulerian angles ϕ, ψ, θ.

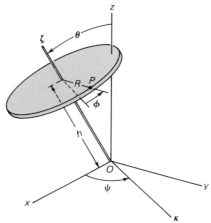

Fig. P **6.1-12**

6.1-13   In Prob. 6.1-12 determine the velocity and acceleration of P.

6.1-14   The wheels of an airplane on takeoff leave the ground at 110 mph.   With the wheels spinning at this speed, the landing gear is retracted by rotation about A at an angular velocity of 3 rad/sec.   Determine the acceleration of the point P in the position shown in Fig. P 6.1-14, using the axes indicated.

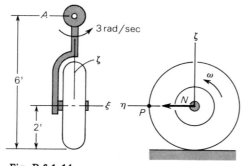

Fig. P **6.1-14**

6.1-15   At the lowest point of a vertical dive, the airplane shown in Fig. P 6.1-15 is moving with speed v in a circular path of radius R.   Write, in terms of unit vectors $\mathbf{1}_\xi$, $\mathbf{1}_\eta$, $\mathbf{1}_\zeta$, the components of the acceleration of a point on the propeller a distance c from the hub if it is spinning clockwise with angular speed θ as seen by the pilot.

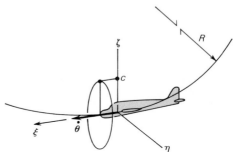

Fig. P 6.1-15

6.2 MOMENTS AND PRODUCTS OF INERTIA

MOMENTS OF INERTIA

After our brief treatment of the most important kinematic relationships we consider, as a preliminary step before turning to the dynamics of a rigid body, certain concepts necessary for the description of the mass distribution of an extended body.   In Chap. 4 we saw that the mass m and the center of mass of a body are not sufficient to define its mass properties.   There the reader was first familiarized with the concept of moment of inertia, which, in body-fixed coordinates taken about the ζ axis, was defined as—see Eq. (4.3-4b)—

$$I_\zeta = \int_m (\xi^2 + \eta^2) \, dm \qquad \blacktriangleleft \quad (6.2\text{-}1)$$

Consequently, the moments of inertia about the ξ and η axes are

$$I_\xi = \int_m (\eta^2 + \zeta^2) \, dm \qquad (6.2\text{-}2)$$

and
$$I_\eta = \int_m (\zeta^2 + \xi^2) \, dm \qquad (6.2\text{-}3)$$

respectively.

PRODUCTS OF INERTIA

Besides, we now encounter certain mass integrals, known as the products of inertia:

$$J_{\xi\eta} = J_{\eta\xi} = \int_m \xi\eta \, dm \qquad \blacktriangleleft \quad (6.2\text{-}4)$$

$$J_{\eta\zeta} = J_{\zeta\eta} = \int_m \eta\zeta \, dm \qquad (6.2\text{-}5)$$

$$J_{\zeta\xi} = J_{\xi\zeta} = \int_m \zeta\xi \, dm \qquad (6.2\text{-}6)$$

Although the moments of inertia are necessarily positive quantities, the products of inertia may be positive, negative, or zero, depending on the direction of the body-fixed coordinate system. We consider, for example, Fig. 6.2-1, where Fig. 6.2-1a shows a coordinate system for which $J_{\xi\eta}$ is

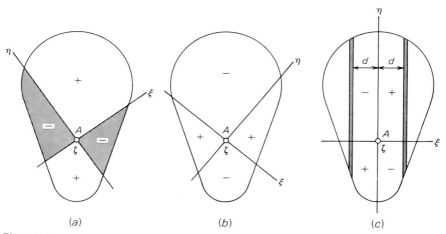

(a)   (b)   (c)

Fig. 6.2-1

positive; Fig. 6.2-1b, one for which $J_{\xi\eta}$ is negative; and Fig. 6.2-1c, one for which $J_{\xi\eta}$ is zero. Here the $\eta\zeta$ plane is a plane of symmetry, and so we have

$$J_{\xi\eta} = J_{\zeta\xi} = 0$$

because all infinitesimal mass elements dm in planes $\xi = \text{const} = d$ have their "opposite numbers" in plane $\xi = -d$. If there are two planes of symmetry, for example, the $\xi\eta$ and $\eta\zeta$ planes, then all products of inertia vanish:

$$J_{\xi\eta} = J_{\eta\zeta} = J_{\zeta\xi} = 0$$

At the end of Sec. 6.3 it is shown that for any arbitrary body point as coordinate origin there is one rectangular coordinate system such that the products of inertia vanish. These axes are called the *principal axes*, and the corresponding moments of inertia the *principal moments of inertia*. In order to distinguish the principal moments of inertia, they are denoted by the letter I, that is, I_ξ, I_η, and I_ζ, and the moments of inertia determined for axes that are not principal are denoted by the letter J, that is, J_ξ, J_η, J_ζ, which is also used for the products of inertia $J_{\xi\eta}$, $J_{\eta\zeta}$, and $J_{\zeta\xi}$. The reader is asked to consider why the moment of inertia I_ζ, as defined in Chap. 4, is principal.

We also show that of the three principal moments of inertia, in general, one is the largest and one is the smallest moment of inertia that can be found for any axis through the origin A of the coordinate system. If the origin of the principal axes coincides with the center of mass, we call the associated moments of inertia the *central principal moments of inertia*.

POLAR MOMENT OF INERTIA

While the moments and products of inertia above were referred to body-fixed coordinate axes, we define the polar moment of inertia of a body with respect to the body-fixed reference point A (pole A) by the equation

$$I_A = \int_m \rho^2 \, dm = \int_m (\xi^2 + \eta^2 + \zeta^2) \, dm$$
$$= \tfrac{1}{2} \int_m (\eta^2 + \zeta^2) \, dm + \tfrac{1}{2} \int_m (\zeta^2 + \xi^2) \, dm + \tfrac{1}{2} \int_m (\xi^2 + \eta^2) \, dm$$

or $I_A = \tfrac{1}{2}(J_\xi + J_\eta + J_\zeta) = \tfrac{1}{2}(I_\xi + I_\eta + I_\zeta)$ (6.2-7)

Equation (6.2-7) shows that the sum of the three moments of inertia is invariant with respect to the choice of the ξ, η, ζ system. This relationship is often useful in computing the moment of inertia about an axis when there is symmetry about the pole A. Then, for any ξ, η, ζ system with origin in the pole A, we have $I_\xi = I_\eta = I_\zeta$, and Eq. (6.2-7) yields

$$I_\xi = I_\eta = I_\zeta = \tfrac{2}{3} I_A$$

For example, when the moment of inertia of a homogeneous solid sphere of radius R about its diameter is to be determined, the polar moment of inertia can easily be found by taking concentric spheres of thickness $d\rho$ as mass elements dm, so that $dm = \gamma 4\pi\rho^2 \, d\rho$ (γ = density of the body):

$$I_A = \int_m \rho^2 \, dm = \gamma \int_0^R 4\pi\rho^4 \, d\rho = \gamma \frac{4\pi R^5}{5} = \tfrac{3}{5} mR^2$$

with $m = \gamma \tfrac{4}{3} R^3 \pi$

Hence, as the moment of inertia about a diameter (any diameter is a principal axis), we find

$$I_\xi = \tfrac{2}{3} I_A = \tfrac{2}{5} mR^2$$

PARALLEL-AXES TRANSFORMATION

We assume that the moments and products of inertia are known for a ξ, η, ζ system whose origin is the center of mass of the body; that is,

$$\int_m \xi \, dm = \int_m \eta \, dm = \int_m \zeta \, dm = 0$$

Now we wish to know the moments and products of inertia about ξ', η', ζ' axes parallel to the ξ, η, ζ system, however, with an origin A not coinciding with the center of mass C, which, in the body-fixed ξ', η', ζ' system, is defined by ξ'_C, η'_C, and ζ'_C (see Fig. 6.2-2). Then, by definition—see, for example,

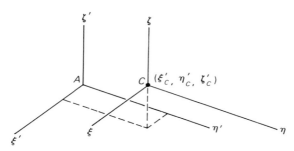

Fig. 6.2-2

Eq. (6.2-1)—with $\xi' = \xi'_C + \xi$, $\eta' = \eta'_C + \eta$, and $\zeta' = \zeta'_C + \zeta$, we have

$$J_{\zeta'} = \int_m (\xi'^2 + \eta'^2)\, dm = \int_m [(\xi'_C + \xi)^2 + (\eta'_C + \eta)^2]\, dm$$
$$= (\xi'^2_C + \eta'^2_C)m + J_{\zeta} \qquad \blacktriangleleft \quad (6.2\text{-}8)$$

since $\quad J_{\zeta} = \int_m (\xi^2 + \eta^2)\, dm \quad$ and $\quad \int_m \xi\, dm = \int_m \eta\, dm = 0$

Equally we find

$$J_{\xi'} = (\eta'^2_C + \zeta'^2_C)m + J_{\xi} \qquad (6.2\text{-}9)$$

and

$$J_{\eta'} = (\zeta'^2_C + \xi'^2_C)m + J_{\eta} \qquad (6.2\text{-}10)$$

It is easily recognized from Eqs. (6.2-8) to (6.2-10) that of all moments of inertia referred to parallel axes those referred to axes through the center of mass are the smallest.

For the products of inertia the parallel-axes theorem[1] yields, in the same manner as above,

$$J_{\xi'\eta'} = J_{\eta'\xi'} = J_{\xi\eta} + \xi'_C\eta'_C m \qquad \blacktriangleleft \quad (6.2\text{-}11)$$
$$J_{\eta'\zeta'} = J_{\zeta'\eta'} = J_{\eta\zeta} + \eta'_C\zeta'_C m \qquad (6.2\text{-}12)$$
$$J_{\zeta'\xi'} = J_{\xi'\zeta'} = J_{\zeta\xi} + \zeta'_C\xi'_C m \qquad (6.2\text{-}13)$$

Finally, if the polar moment about the center of mass is denoted by I_C and we want to know the polar moment with respect to point A, then we easily find

$$I_A = I_C + r_C^2 m \qquad \blacktriangleleft \quad (6.2\text{-}14)$$

with

$$r_C^2 = \xi'^2_C + \eta'^2_C + \zeta'^2_C$$

From Eq. (6.2-14) it is evident that the polar moment of inertia about the center of mass is smaller than that about any other point.

---

[1] In the European literature it is usually known as Steiner's theorem (born 1796 in Solothurn, Switzerland; died 1863 in Bern).

ILLUSTRATIVE EXAMPLE 6.2-1

Determine the moments and products of inertia of the solid circular cylinder of mass m, radius R, and length L about the ξ', η', ζ' axes placed as shown in Fig. 6.2-3.

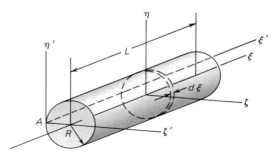

Fig. 6.2-3

SOLUTION: We consider the thin disk of mass $(m/L) \, d\xi$ with symmetry and therefore principal axes ξ, η, ζ shown in Fig. 6.2-3.   Its moment of inertia about the axes η and ζ is (see the Appendix)

$$dI_\eta = dI_\zeta = \frac{m}{L} \, d\xi \, \frac{R^2}{4}$$

Since η and ζ pass through the center of mass of the infinitesimal disk, the parallel-axes theorem can be used to find its moment of inertia about the ζ' and η' axes as follows—see Eqs. (6.2-8) and (6.2-10)—

$$dJ_{\zeta'} = dI_\zeta + \frac{m}{L} \, d\xi' \xi'^2$$

$$dJ_{\eta'} = dI_\eta + \frac{m}{L} \, d\xi'(\xi'^2 + R^2)$$

Integrating from $\xi' = 0$ to $\xi' = L$, $J_{\zeta'}$ and $J_{\eta'}$ are

$$J_{\zeta'} = \int_0^L \frac{m}{L} \frac{R^2}{4} \, d\xi' + \int_0^L \frac{m}{L} \, \xi'^2 \, d\xi'$$

$$= m \left(\frac{R^2}{4} + \frac{L^2}{3} \right)$$

$$J_{\eta'} = m \left(\frac{R^2}{4} + \frac{L^2}{3} + R^2 \right) = m \left(\frac{5}{4} R^2 + \frac{L^2}{3} \right)$$

The moment of inertia about the symmetry axis ξ is simply

$$I_\xi = \int_0^L \frac{m}{L} \frac{R^2}{2} \, d\xi = \frac{mR^2}{2}$$

and again by using the parallel-axes theorem—see Eq. (6.2-9)—

$$J_{\xi'} = m \left(\frac{R^2}{2} + R^2 \right) = \tfrac{3}{2} m R^2$$

Since the $\zeta'\xi'$ plane is a plane of symmetry, the products of inertia $J_{\eta'\zeta'}$ and $J_{\xi'\eta'}$ are zero. In view of the fact that the ξ axis is an axis of symmetry the infinitesimal products of inertia $dJ_{\xi\eta}$, $dJ_{\eta\zeta}$, and $dJ_{\zeta\xi}$ are all zero, and we have—see Eq. (6.2-13)—

$$dJ_{\zeta'\xi'} = R\xi' \frac{m}{L} d\xi'$$

and thus

$$J_{\zeta'\xi'} = R\frac{m}{L} \int_0^L \xi' \, d\xi' = mR\frac{L}{2}$$

ANGULAR TRANSFORMATION

We now study the case where the origin O of body-fixed x, y, z axes and the origin A of body-fixed ξ, η, ζ axes coincide, although the directions of the ξ, η, ζ axes differ from those of the x, y, z axes, as shown in Fig. 6.2-4. Here

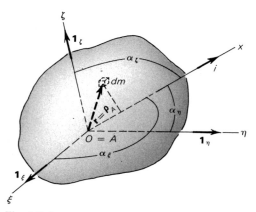

Fig. 6.2-4

only the x axis has been shown, together with the ξ, η, ζ frame, since the results around the y and z axes are easily found by substitution of y and z, respectively, for x.

The components of the unit vector $\mathbf{i}$ are specified by the direction cosines $\cos \alpha_\xi = l_{\xi x}$, $\cos \alpha_\eta = l_{\eta x}$, and $\cos \alpha_\zeta = l_{\zeta x}$ of the x axis relative to the ξ, η, ζ axes, so that

$$\mathbf{i} = l_{\xi x}\mathbf{1}_\xi + l_{\eta x}\mathbf{1}_\eta + l_{\zeta x}\mathbf{1}_\zeta \qquad (6.2\text{-}15)$$

The position of the mass element dm is defined by the vector

$$\boldsymbol{\varrho} \equiv \mathbf{r} = \xi\mathbf{1}_\xi + \eta\mathbf{1}_\eta + \zeta\mathbf{1}_\zeta$$

Its perpendicular distance from the x axis is $(y^2 + z^2)^{1/2} = |\boldsymbol{\varrho} \times \mathbf{i}|$, and hence the square of the perpendicular distance between dm and the x axis is

$$y^2 + z^2 = (\varrho \times i) \cdot (\varrho \times i) = \begin{vmatrix} 1_\xi & 1_\eta & 1_\zeta \\ \xi & \eta & \zeta \\ l_{\xi x} & l_{\eta x} & l_{\zeta x} \end{vmatrix} \cdot \begin{vmatrix} 1_\xi & 1_\eta & 1_\zeta \\ \xi & \eta & \zeta \\ l_{\xi x} & l_{\eta x} & l_{\zeta x} \end{vmatrix}$$

$$= (l_{\zeta x}\eta - l_{\eta x}\zeta)^2 + (l_{\xi x}\zeta - l_{\zeta x}\xi)^2 + (l_{\eta x}\xi - l_{\xi x}\eta)^2$$

$$= (\xi^2 + \eta^2)l_{\zeta x}{}^2 + (\xi^2 + \zeta^2)l_{\eta x}{}^2 + (\eta^2 + \zeta^2)l_{\xi x}{}^2$$
$$- 2\xi\eta l_{\xi x}l_{\eta x} - 2\xi\zeta l_{\xi x}l_{\zeta x} - 2\eta\zeta l_{\eta x}l_{\zeta x}$$

The moment of inertia about the x axis being the integral of the mass elements multiplied by the square of their normal distance from the x axis, we obtain, from this equation, the result

$$J_x = l_{\zeta x}{}^2 J_\zeta + l_{\eta x}{}^2 J_\eta + l_{\xi x}{}^2 J_\xi - 2l_{\xi x}l_{\eta x}J_{\xi\eta} - 2l_{\xi x}l_{\zeta x}J_{\xi\zeta} - 2l_{\eta x}l_{\zeta x}J_{\eta\zeta} \quad (6.2\text{-}16)$$

Thus with the moments and products of inertia known with respect to the ξ, η, ζ axes, the moment of inertia J_x about an axis x defined by the direction cosines $l_{\xi x}, l_{\eta x}$, and $l_{\zeta x}$ is available. In like manner the moments of inertia about the y and z axes can be computed by replacing the subscript x by y and z, respectively.

The product of inertia J_{yz} is defined by the equation

$$J_{yz} = \int_m yz \, dm = \int_m (\varrho \cdot j)(\varrho \cdot k) \, dm \quad (6.2\text{-}17)$$

Hence to determine the product yz in the ξ, η, ζ coordinates, we require the components of the unit vectors j and k in these coordinates:

$$j = l_{\xi y}1_\xi + l_{\eta y}1_\eta + l_{\zeta y}1_\zeta \quad (6.2\text{-}18)$$
$$k = l_{\xi z}1_\xi + l_{\eta z}1_\eta + l_{\zeta z}1_\zeta \quad (6.2\text{-}19)$$

The product yz then becomes

$$yz = (\varrho \cdot j)(\varrho \cdot k) = (\xi l_{\xi y} + \eta l_{\eta y} + \zeta l_{\zeta y})(\xi l_{\xi z} + \eta l_{\eta z} + \zeta l_{\zeta z})$$
$$= \xi^2 l_{\xi y}l_{\xi z} + \eta^2 l_{\eta y}l_{\eta z} + \zeta^2 l_{\zeta y}l_{\zeta z} + \xi\eta(l_{\xi y}l_{\eta z} + l_{\xi z}l_{\eta y})$$
$$+ \xi\zeta(l_{\xi y}l_{\zeta z} + l_{\xi z}l_{\zeta y}) + \eta\zeta(l_{\eta y}l_{\zeta z} + l_{\eta z}l_{\zeta y}) \quad (6.2\text{-}20)$$

From the relationship—see Eqs. (6.2-18) and (6.2-19)—

$$j \cdot k = l_{\xi y}l_{\xi z} + l_{\eta y}l_{\eta z} + l_{\zeta y}l_{\zeta z} = 0$$

we have

$$\xi^2 l_{\xi y}l_{\xi z} = -\xi^2(l_{\eta y}l_{\eta z} + l_{\zeta y}l_{\zeta z})$$

and likewise

$$\eta^2 l_{\eta y}l_{\eta z} = -\eta^2(l_{\xi y}l_{\xi z} + l_{\zeta y}l_{\zeta z})$$
$$\zeta^2 l_{\zeta y}l_{\zeta z} = -\zeta^2(l_{\xi y}l_{\xi z} + l_{\eta y}l_{\eta z})$$

Thus the first three terms of Eq. (6.2-20) can be replaced by

$$-(\xi^2 + \eta^2)l_{\zeta y}l_{\zeta z} - (\xi^2 + \zeta^2)l_{\eta y}l_{\eta z} - (\eta^2 + \zeta^2)l_{\xi y}l_{\xi z}$$

The product of inertia J_{yz} can then be expressed in terms of the moments and products of inertia in the ξ, η, ζ frame:

$$J_{yz} = -l_{\zeta y}l_{\zeta z}J_\zeta - l_{\eta y}l_{\eta z}J_\eta - l_{\xi y}l_{\xi z}J_\xi + (l_{\xi y}l_{\eta z} + l_{\xi z}l_{\eta y})J_{\xi\eta}$$
$$+ (l_{\xi y}l_{\zeta z} + l_{\xi z}l_{\zeta y})J_{\xi\zeta} + (l_{\eta y}l_{\zeta z} + l_{\eta z}l_{\zeta y})J_{\eta\zeta} \quad (6.2\text{-}21)$$

In summary, the moments and products of inertia about the x, y, z axes, whose directions relative to the ξ, η, ζ axes are defined by their respective cosines, can be expressed in terms of the moments and products of inertia about the ξ, η, ζ axes by the equations

$$J_a = l_{\xi a}{}^2 J_\xi + l_{\eta a}{}^2 J_\eta + l_{\zeta a}{}^2 J_\zeta - 2l_{\xi a}l_{\eta a}J_{\xi\eta} - 2l_{\xi a}l_{\zeta a}J_{\xi\zeta}$$
$$- 2l_{\eta a}l_{\zeta a}J_{\eta\zeta} \quad \blacktriangleleft \quad (6.2\text{-}22)$$

$$-J_{ab} = l_{\xi a}l_{\xi b}J_\xi + l_{\eta a}l_{\eta b}J_\eta + l_{\zeta a}l_{\zeta b}J_\zeta - (l_{\xi a}l_{\eta b} + l_{\xi b}l_{\eta a})J_{\xi\eta}$$
$$- (l_{\xi a}l_{\zeta b} + l_{\xi b}l_{\zeta a})J_{\xi\zeta} - (l_{\eta a}l_{\zeta b} + l_{\eta b}l_{\zeta a})J_{\eta\zeta} \quad \blacktriangleleft \quad (6.2\text{-}23)$$

The subscripts a and b are either x and y respectively or y and z respectively or z and x respectively.

In the next section it is shown that the fundamental dynamic relationships are expressed in rather simple form when they are written in terms of the principal moments of inertia. Thus it is worthwhile to show how the principal moments of inertia, as well as the direction of the principal axes, are determined. However, in order to spare the beginner certain mathematical difficulties, we refrain from deriving the results below in purely geometric fashion. On the other hand, the interested reader will find a rather simple "dynamic" derivation of the cubic equation (6.2-25) for the determination of the principal moments of inertia at the end of Sec. 6.3.

1   The three principal moments of inertia $I_{\xi'}$, $I_{\eta'}$, $I_{\zeta'}$, where the orthogonal axes ξ', η', ζ' define the principal axes, are obtained from the determinant

$$\begin{vmatrix} J_\xi - I & -J_{\xi\eta} & -J_{\xi\zeta} \\ -J_{\eta\xi} & J_\eta - I & -J_{\eta\zeta} \\ -J_{\zeta\xi} & -J_{\zeta\eta} & J_\zeta - I \end{vmatrix} = 0 \qquad (6.2\text{-}24)$$

which, on expansion, leads to the cubic equation

$$I^3 - (J_\xi + J_\eta + J_\zeta)I^2 + (J_\xi J_\eta + J_\eta J_\zeta + J_\zeta J_\xi - J_{\xi\eta}{}^2$$
$$- J_{\eta\zeta}{}^2 - J_{\zeta\xi}{}^2)I - (J_\xi J_\eta J_\zeta - 2J_{\xi\eta}J_{\eta\zeta}J_{\zeta\xi}$$
$$- J_\xi J_{\eta\zeta}{}^2 - J_\eta J_{\zeta\xi}{}^2 - J_\zeta J_{\xi\eta}{}^2) = 0 \quad (6.2\text{-}25)$$

Equation (6.2-25) yields, in general, three different values $I_{\xi'}$, $I_{\eta'}$, and $I_{\zeta'}$.

2   The direction of the three principal axes ξ', η', ζ', defined by the nine direction cosines, is found from the following set of homogeneous equations:

$$(J_\xi - I_a)l_{\xi a} - J_{\xi\eta}l_{\eta a} - J_{\xi\zeta}l_{\zeta a} = 0$$
$$-J_{\eta\xi}l_{\xi a} + (J_\eta - I_a)l_{\eta a} - J_{\eta\zeta}l_{\zeta a} = 0 \qquad (6.2\text{-}26)$$
$$-J_{\zeta\xi}l_{\xi a} - J_{\zeta\eta}l_{\eta a} + (J_\zeta - I_a)l_{\zeta a} = 0$$

For example, in order to find the direction of the principal axis ξ', we substitute ξ' for the subscript a in Eqs. (6.2-26) and for I_a the value $I_{\xi'}$ found above. Of course, the homogeneous Eqs. (6.2-26) yield only the ratios of the direction cosines, for example, $l_{\xi\xi'}/l_{\eta\xi'}$ and $l_{\zeta\xi'}/l_{\eta\xi'}$. The absolute values are then found, considering that

$$l_{\xi\xi'}^2 + l_{\eta\xi'}^2 + l_{\zeta\xi'}^2 = 1$$

which is a well-known relationship for the direction cosines and follows, for example, immediately from Eq. (6.2-18), because

$$\mathbf{1}_{\xi'} = l_{\xi\xi'}\mathbf{1}_\xi + l_{\eta\xi'}\mathbf{1}_\eta + l_{\zeta\xi'}\mathbf{1}_\zeta$$

and thus $\qquad \mathbf{1}_{\xi'} \cdot \mathbf{1}_{\xi'} = l_{\xi\xi'}^2 + l_{\eta\xi'}^2 + l_{\zeta\xi'}^2 = 1$

The reader may note that the determinant (6.2-24) is the determinant of the homogeneous Eqs. (6.2-26), which yield a solution for the direction cosines only if the determinant vanishes.

3 Of the three principal moments one is the largest and one is the smallest moment of inertia that can be obtained for axes through the origin of the ξ, η, ζ axes. The proof of this property, if carried out, serves simultaneously to prove the existence of the principal axes, which at the beginning of this section were defined to yield zero products of inertia.

4 Furthermore, we have the useful relationships

$$I_\xi + I_\eta > I_\zeta \qquad I_\eta + I_\zeta > I_\xi \qquad I_\zeta + I_\xi > I_\eta$$

In which special idealized case do we have $I_\xi + I_\eta = I_\zeta$?

ILLUSTRATIVE EXAMPLE 6.2-2

The rotor of a gyro wheel has the following moments of inertia about the gimbal-fixed ξ, η, ζ axes:

$$I_{w\xi} = I_{w\eta} = A \qquad I_{w\zeta} = C$$

Moreover, the moments of inertia of the gimbal, supporting the rotor, are (see Fig. 6.2-5)

$$I_{g\xi} \qquad I_{g\eta} \qquad I_{g\zeta}$$

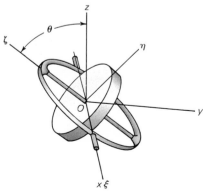

Fig. 6.2-5

Determine the moments and products of inertia of the gimbal-wheel assembly about the space-fixed x, y, z axes for any angle θ.

SOLUTION: We first sum the moments of inertia about the ξ, η, ζ axes:

$$I_\xi = A + I_{o\xi}$$
$$I_\eta = A + I_{o\eta}$$
$$I_\zeta = C + I_{o\zeta}$$

Since the ξ, η, ζ axes are principal axes, considering that the $\xi\eta$ as well as $\eta\zeta$ and $\xi\zeta$ planes are planes of symmetry, the moment of inertia about any axis a is found from Eq. (6.2-22) to be

$$J_a = l_{\xi a}{}^2 I_\xi + l_{\eta a}{}^2 I_\eta + l_{\zeta a}{}^2 I_\zeta$$

Substituting x, y, and z for a in succession and considering that $l_{\xi x} = 1$, $l_{\eta x} = l_{\zeta x} = l_{\xi y} = l_{\xi z} = 0$, $l_{\eta y} = l_{\zeta z} = \cos \theta$, and $l_{\eta z} = -l_{\zeta y} = \sin \theta$, we find, for the moments of inertia,

$$J_x = I_\xi = A + I_{o\xi}$$
$$J_y = I_\eta \cos^2 \theta + I_\zeta \sin^2 \theta = (A + I_{o\eta}) \cos^2 \theta + (C + I_{o\zeta}) \sin^2 \theta$$
$$J_z = I_\eta \sin^2 \theta + I_\zeta \cos^2 \theta = (A + I_{o\eta}) \sin^2 \theta + (C + I_{o\zeta}) \cos^2 \theta$$

and for the products of inertia—see Eq. (6.2-23)—

$$\begin{aligned}
J_{xy} &= 0 \\
J_{yz} &= -\cos \theta \sin \theta \, I_\zeta + \sin \theta \cos \theta \, I_\eta \\
&= \sin \theta \cos \theta \, (I_\eta - I_\zeta) \\
&= (A - C + I_{o\eta} - I_{o\zeta}) \sin \theta \cos \theta \\
J_{zx} &= 0
\end{aligned}$$

PROBLEMS

6.2-1   Determine the moments of inertia J_η, J_ζ and the product of inertia $J_{\eta\zeta}$ of a toroid with homogeneous mass distribution (see Fig. P 6.2-1).   Assume that $d \ll D$.

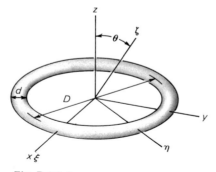

Fig. P 6.2-1

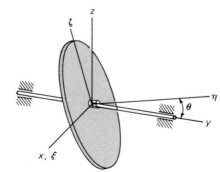

Fig. P 6.2-2

6.2-2   A thin uniform disk of radius R is mounted on a shaft with its normal at an angle θ with the shaft.   Determine J_z, J_{zx}, and J_{yz} for the position shown in Fig. P 6.2-2.

6.2-3   A thin uniform disk of radius R is at an angle θ with the xy plane, as shown in Fig. P 6.2-3.   Determine J_z and J_{yz}.

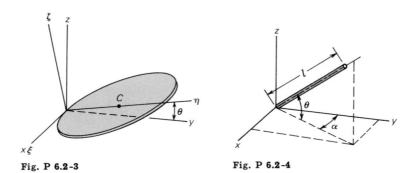

Fig. P 6.2-3   Fig. P 6.2-4

6.2-4   Determine the quantities J_z, J_{yz}, J_{zx} for the thin homogeneous rod of mass m shown in Fig. P 6.2-4.

6.2-5   Determine the ratio between the diameter and the length of a homogeneous cylinder, such that any axis through its center of mass is a principal axis.

6.2-6   Determine the principal moments of inertia for a homogeneous body of mass m (see Fig. P 6.2-6).

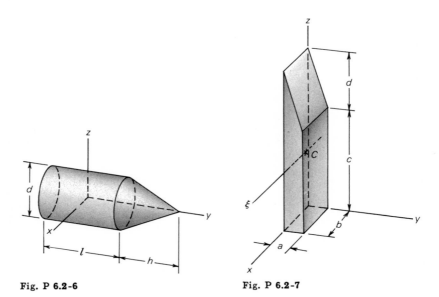

Fig. P 6.2-6   Fig. P 6.2-7

6.2-7   Determine the central moment of inertia I_ξ of the body shown in Fig. P 6.2-7. $a = 1$ in., $b = 2$ in., $c = 3$ in., $d = 1$ in., $\rho = 10^{-4}$ lb sec²/in.⁴

6.2-8   Determine the moments of inertia of a homogeneous rectangular block (see Fig. P 6.2-8) about three space diagonals and about two plane diagonals lying in the xy plane. $a = 1$ in., $b = 2$ in., $h = 3$ in., $\rho = 10^{-4}$ lb sec²/in.⁴

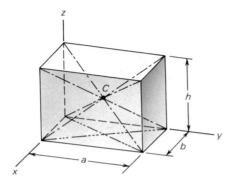

Fig. P 6.2-8

6.2-9   Figure P 6.2-9 shows a homogeneous rectangular block of mass m_2 hanging at an angle θ under a parachute of mass m_1 that forms a hollow half sphere.   Neglecting the mass of the suspension strings, determine the moment of inertia of the entire system about the vertical z axis.

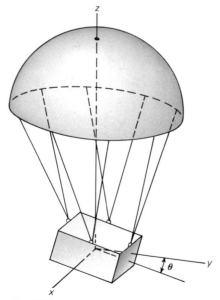

Fig. P 6.2-9

6.2-10 Determine the moment of inertia J_ξ of the homogeneous body of mass m shown in Fig. P 6.2-10. The cylinder is hollow, and the half sphere is solid. $d = 2$ in., $D = 4$ in., $l = 10$ in., $m = 10^{-2}$ lb sec²/in.

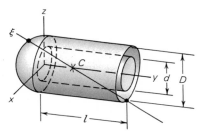

Fig. P 6.2-10

6.2-11 Determine the moment of inertia J_z and the products of inertia J_{xy}, J_{xz} of the solid homogeneous body of rotational symmetry of mass m consisting of a cone and a half sphere shown in Fig. P 6.2-11. $h = 2$ in., $R = 1$ in., $\rho = 10^{-4}$ lb sec²/in.⁴

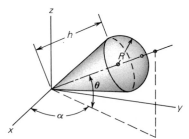

Fig. P 6.2-11

6.2-12 To a homogeneous cylinder of mass m a particle of mass m_1 is attached, as shown in Fig. P 6.2-12. Determine the orientation of the principal axes through point A.

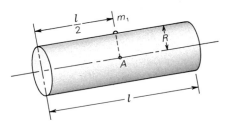

Fig. P 6.2-12

6.2-13   What is the moment of inertia J_η of the hollow cone of mass m about a generating line shown in Fig. P 6.2-13? $d_i = 2$ in., $d = 4$ in., $D = 6$ in., $h = 6$ in., $\rho = 10^{-4}$ lb sec²/in.⁴

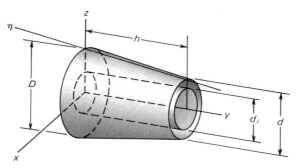

Fig. P 6.2-13

6.2-14   Determine the moment of inertia J_ζ of the homogeneous buoy shown in Fig. P 6.2-14.   The mass of the rod connecting the float and the spherical head may be neglected. $a = 1$ in., $h = 2$ in., $l = 1$ in., $D = 2$ in., $m_1 = 10^{-2}$ lb sec²/in., $m_2 = m_1/2$.

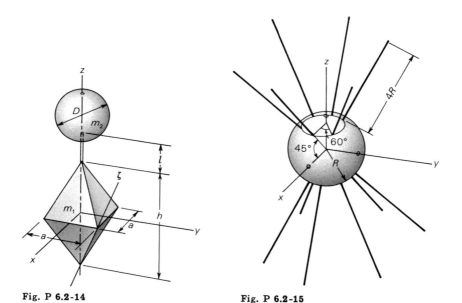

Fig. P 6.2-14   **Fig. P 6.2-15**

6.2-15   Determine the central principal moments of inertia and the direction of the principal axes of a homogeneous spherical satellite (mass m_1) carrying antennas each of mass m_2 and length $4R$ (see Fig. P 6.2-15).

6.2-16   Figure P 6.2-16 shows a thin-walled closed oil tank of mass m with axes ξ, ς. Determine J_η, J_ς, and $J_{\eta\varsigma}$. $h/D = 2$.

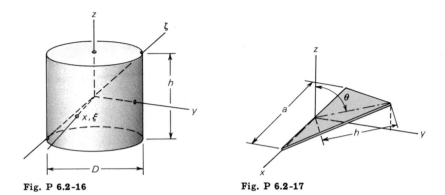

Fig. P 6.2-16   Fig. P 6.2-17

6.2-17   Determine the moment of inertia J_z of the homogeneous thin plate of mass m shown in Fig. P 6.2-17.

6.2-18   Determine the moment of inertia J_ς of the homogeneous thin-walled cone of mass m shown in Fig. P 6.2-18.

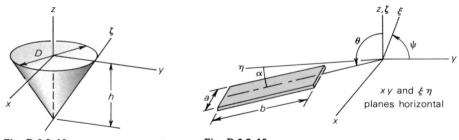

Fig. P 6.2-18   Fig. P 6.2-19

6.2-19   Figure P 6.2-19 shows the position relative to an x, y, z coordinate system of a helicopter rotor blade (a thin homogeneous rectangular plate of constant thickness and mass m).   Determine J_x, J_y, J_z, J_{xy}. $a = 6$ in., $b = 12$ in., $c = 2$ in., $m = 10^{-2}$ lb sec^2/in., $\alpha = 30°$, $\psi = 30°$, $\theta = 60°$.

6.3   BASIC DYNAMIC RELATIONSHIPS FOR A RIGID BODY
IN GENERAL MOTION

MOMENTUM

The derivation of Eq. (4.4-1) concerning the momentum of a rigid body in plane motion shows that it is also valid for three-dimensional motion (see

Sec. 4.4 and also Sec. 3.2).   There we obtained the momentum as the product of the mass and the velocity of its center of mass with respect to an inertial reference frame:

$$\mathbf{G} = \int_m \mathbf{v} \, dm = m\mathbf{v}_C \tag{6.3-1}$$

and its time rate of change was

$$\mathbf{F} = \frac{d\mathbf{G}}{dt} = \frac{d}{dt}(m\mathbf{v}_C) \tag{6.3-2}$$

where $\mathbf{F}$ is the resultant of all external forces acting on the body.   Integration of the force equation with respect to time then yields the theorem that impulse equals change in momentum:

$$\hat{\mathbf{F}} = \int_{t_1}^{t_2} \mathbf{F} \, dt = m[\mathbf{v}_C(t_2) - \mathbf{v}_C(t_1)] \tag{6.3-3}$$

MOMENT OF MOMENTUM

When we dealt with the theorem of moment of momentum of a closed system of particles in Sec. 3.3, we found the following fundamental relationship—see Eq. (3.3-8)—

$$\mathbf{M}_O = \dot{\mathbf{H}}_O \tag{6.3-4}$$

where $\mathbf{M}_O$ is the resultant moment of all external forces and couples acting on the system of particles and $\mathbf{H}_O$ its total moment of momentum, both referred to the point O fixed in an inertial reference frame.   Since a rigid body is simply a very special case of a system of particles, as we pointed out in Sec. 4.1, Eq. (3.3-8) also holds for a rigid body.   Hence, the relationship—see Eq. (3.3-14)—

$$\mathbf{M}_C = \dot{\mathbf{h}}_C \tag{6.3-5a}$$

is also valid in the general motion of a rigid body.   Here $\mathbf{M}_C$ is the resultant moment of all external forces referred to the center of mass C, and $\mathbf{h}_C$ is the moment of momentum of the rigid body defined in a reference frame translating[1] with the center of mass C.   Now we let $\mathbf{h}_C$ be described in coordinates that rotate with respect to an inertial frame with angular velocity $\boldsymbol{\omega}$, and then we may rewrite Eq. (6.3-5a), in view of Eq. (5.1-11),

$$\mathbf{M}_C = \overset{\frown}{\dot{\mathbf{h}}}_C + \boldsymbol{\omega} \times \mathbf{h}_C \tag{6.3-5b}$$

or in ξ, η, ζ coordinates

$$\begin{aligned} M_\xi &= \dot{h}_\xi - h_\eta \omega_\zeta + h_\zeta \omega_\eta \\ M_\eta &= \dot{h}_\eta - h_\zeta \omega_\xi + h_\xi \omega_\zeta \\ M_\zeta &= \dot{h}_\zeta - h_\xi \omega_\eta + h_\eta \omega_\xi \end{aligned} \tag{6.3-6}$$

---

[1] That is, a reference frame not rotating with respect to an inertial frame of reference.   Of course, because of the acceleration of C, the reference frame may be nonnewtonian.

Equations (6.3-4) and (6.3-5) immediately yield the following mathematical expression for the theorem of moment of momentum of a rigid body in general motion:

$$\int_{t_1}^{t_2} \mathbf{M}_O \, dt = \mathbf{H}_O(t_2) - \mathbf{H}_O(t_1) \tag{6.3-7}$$

and

$$\int_{t_1}^{t_2} \mathbf{M}_C \, dt = \mathbf{h}_C(t_2) - \mathbf{h}_C(t_1) \tag{6.3-8}$$

respectively.

We now determine $\mathbf{h}_C$ for a rigid body, using the concept of its moments and products of inertia. The moment of momentum of a rigid body about the center of mass C in a reference frame translating with point C is (see Fig. 6.3-1)

$$\mathbf{h}_C = \int_m \varrho_C \times (\boldsymbol{\omega} \times \varrho_C) \, dm = \boldsymbol{\omega} \int_m \varrho_C^2 \, dm - \int_m (\boldsymbol{\omega} \cdot \varrho_C)\varrho_C \, dm \tag{6.3-9}$$

where $\boldsymbol{\omega}$ is the angular velocity of the moving body with respect to an inertial reference body, and consequently $\boldsymbol{\omega} \times \varrho_C$ is the velocity of any mass element

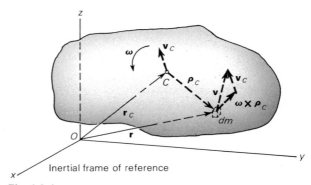

Inertial frame of reference

Fig. 6.3-1

dm with respect to a reference frame translating with C in an inertial reference frame. The moment of momentum $\mathbf{h}_C$ is suitably expressed in terms of the body coordinates ξ, η, ζ having their origin in C. With the vectors

$$\boldsymbol{\omega} = \omega_\xi \mathbf{1}_\xi + \omega_\eta \mathbf{1}_\eta + \omega_\zeta \mathbf{1}_\zeta \tag{6.3-10}$$

$$\varrho_C = \xi \mathbf{1}_\xi + \eta \mathbf{1}_\eta + \zeta \mathbf{1}_\zeta \tag{6.3-11}$$

the two integrals on the right side of Eq. (6.3-9) become

$$\int_m \rho_C^2 \, dm = \int_m (\xi^2 + \eta^2 + \zeta^2) \, dm \tag{6.3-12}$$

$$\int_m (\boldsymbol{\omega} \cdot \varrho_C)\varrho_C \, dm = \int_m (\omega_\xi \xi + \omega_\eta \eta + \omega_\zeta \zeta)(\xi \mathbf{1}_\xi + \eta \mathbf{1}_\eta + \zeta \mathbf{1}_\zeta) \, dm \tag{6.3-13}$$

and the equation for $\mathbf{h}_C$ takes the form

$$\mathbf{h}_C = \int_m \{[\omega_\xi(\eta^2 + \zeta^2) - \omega_\eta\xi\eta - \omega_\zeta\xi\zeta]\mathbf{1}_\xi + [-\omega_\xi\eta\xi + \omega_\eta(\zeta^2 + \xi^2)$$
$$- \omega_\zeta\eta\zeta]\mathbf{1}_\eta + [-\omega_\xi\zeta\xi - \omega_\eta\zeta\eta + \omega_\zeta(\xi^2 + \eta^2)]\mathbf{1}_\zeta\} \, dm \quad (6.3\text{-}14)$$

Referring to the definitions of the moments and products of inertia in Sec. 6.2, Eq. (6.3-14) can then be expressed in terms of these quantities as

$$\mathbf{h}_C = (J_\xi\omega_\xi - J_{\xi\eta}\omega_\eta - J_{\xi\zeta}\omega_\zeta)\mathbf{1}_\xi + (-J_{\eta\xi}\omega_\xi + J_\eta\omega_\eta - J_{\eta\zeta}\omega_\zeta)\mathbf{1}_\eta$$
$$+ (-J_{\zeta\xi}\omega_\xi - J_{\zeta\eta}\omega_\eta + J_\zeta\omega_\zeta)\mathbf{1}_\zeta \quad (6.3\text{-}15)$$

or concisely and more elegantly in matrix notation,

$$\begin{bmatrix} h_\xi \\ h_\eta \\ h_\zeta \end{bmatrix} = \begin{bmatrix} J_\xi & -J_{\xi\eta} & -J_{\xi\zeta} \\ -J_{\eta\xi} & J_\eta & -J_{\eta\zeta} \\ -J_{\zeta\xi} & -J_{\zeta\eta} & J_\zeta \end{bmatrix} \begin{bmatrix} \omega_\xi \\ \omega_\eta \\ \omega_\zeta \end{bmatrix} \quad (6.3\text{-}16)$$

where the square matrix on the right side is known as the inertia matrix. If the body-fixed axes ξ, η, ζ happen to be central principal axes, then the products of inertia vanish, and we have

$$\mathbf{h}_C = \omega_\xi I_\xi\mathbf{1}_\xi + \omega_\eta I_\eta\mathbf{1}_\eta + \omega_\zeta I_\zeta\mathbf{1}_\zeta \quad (6.3\text{-}17)[1]$$

With Eq. (6.3-17) we obtain from Eqs. (6.3-6) the important relationships

$$\begin{aligned} M_\xi &= I_\xi\dot{\omega}_\xi - (I_\eta - I_\zeta)\omega_\eta\omega_\zeta \\ M_\eta &= I_\eta\dot{\omega}_\eta - (I_\zeta - I_\xi)\omega_\zeta\omega_\xi \\ M_\zeta &= I_\zeta\dot{\omega}_\zeta - (I_\xi - I_\eta)\omega_\xi\omega_\eta \end{aligned} \quad \blacktriangleleft \quad (6.3\text{-}18)$$

These are the so-called *Euler's equations of motion*.

The moment of momentum about a fixed point O is easily found, once $\mathbf{h}_C = \mathbf{H}_C$ is known (see Fig. 6.3-1):

$$\mathbf{H}_O = \mathbf{h}_C + \mathbf{r}_C \times m\mathbf{v}_C \quad (6.3\text{-}19)$$

If O is fixed in inertial space, as well as in L, then (see Fig. 6.3-2)

$$\mathbf{H}_O = \int_m \boldsymbol{\varrho} \times (\boldsymbol{\omega} \times \boldsymbol{\varrho}) \, dm$$

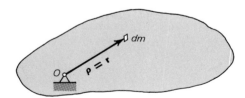

Fig. 6.3-2

[1] This equation demonstrates the fundamental difference (from a dynamic point of view) between plane and three-dimensional motion of a rigid body. The directions of the instantaneous axis of rotation $\boldsymbol{\omega}$ and of the moment-of-momentum vector $\mathbf{h}_C$ no longer coincide, as they did in the case of plane motion discussed in Chap. 4.

If ξ, η, ζ are now body-fixed coordinates with the fixed point O as origin, then Eq. (6.3-14) immediately follows with $\mathbf{H}_O$ as its left side. Furthermore, with ξ, η, ζ as principal axes through O we have correspondingly— see Eq. (6.3-16)—

$$\mathbf{H}_O = \omega_\xi I_\xi \mathbf{1}_\xi + \omega_\eta I_\eta \mathbf{1}_\eta + \omega_\zeta I_\zeta \mathbf{1}_\zeta \qquad (6.3\text{-}20)$$

Then also Euler's equations (6.3-18) are identically valid for the reference point O fixed both in an inertial reference frame and in the body, since $\mathbf{H}_O$, like $\mathbf{h}_C$, is expressed in the body coordinates ξ, η, ζ. By the way, the opposites of $\mathbf{M}_C$ and $\mathbf{M}_O$ are called the gyroscopic moments about C and O, respectively.

ILLUSTRATIVE EXAMPLE 6.3-1
The inertial properties of the airplane shown in Fig. 6.3-3 are given by the matrix of the moments and products of inertia below. What control-surface torques are necessary in order to execute a steady roll along a straight line in the direction of flight?

$$\begin{bmatrix} J_\xi & 0 & -J_{\xi\zeta} \\ 0 & J_\eta & 0 \\ -J_{\zeta\xi} & 0 & J_\zeta \end{bmatrix}$$

SOLUTION: Since the ξ, η, ζ axes through the center of mass C are not principal axes, Eq. (6.3-15) must be used for the calculation of the moment of momentum $\mathbf{h}_C$. With only $\omega_\xi \neq 0$ (only rolling), we have

$$\mathbf{h}_C = \omega_\xi (J_\xi \mathbf{1}_\xi - J_{\zeta\xi} \mathbf{1}_\zeta)$$

Then we find, by means of Eq. (6.3-5b), considering that for a steady roll $\dot{\boldsymbol{\omega}}_C = \mathbf{0}$, and thus also $\overset{\frown}{\dot{\mathbf{h}}}_C = \mathbf{0}$,

$$\mathbf{M}_C = \boldsymbol{\omega} \times \mathbf{h}_C = \omega_\xi \mathbf{1}_\xi \times \omega_\xi (J_\xi \mathbf{1}_\xi - J_{\zeta\xi} \mathbf{1}_\zeta)$$

or
$$\mathbf{M}_C = \omega_\xi^2 J_{\zeta\xi} \mathbf{1}_\eta$$

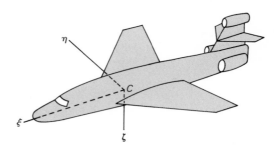

Fig. 6.3-3

Assuming $J_{\zeta\xi}$ to be positive, it is seen that the maneuver requires a downward force on the tail in order to produce the above pitching torque by means of the elevators.[1] Besides, a torque about the ξ axis is necessary to overcome the rolling drag in order to have $\boldsymbol{\omega} = \omega_\xi \mathbf{1}_\xi = $ const.

[1] Explain this by means of the concept of centrifugal force.

KINETIC ENERGY; WORK AND ENERGY THEOREMS

All theorems that were derived in Sec. 2.5 are also valid for a rigid body. The only necessary amplification concerns the expression for the kinetic energy and the work done by the external forces.   We consider a rigid body moving in an inertial x, y, z frame of reference.   According to Eq. (2.5-6) the kinetic energy of the mass particle dm is then defined by (see Fig. 6.3-2)

$$dT = \tfrac{1}{2}v^2\, dm = \tfrac{1}{2}\mathbf{v}\cdot\mathbf{v}\, dm$$

or with—see Eq. (6.1-2)—

$$\mathbf{v} = \mathbf{v}_C + \boldsymbol{\omega}\times\boldsymbol{\varrho}_C$$

$$dT = \tfrac{1}{2}\mathbf{v}_C\cdot\mathbf{v}_C\, dm + \mathbf{v}_C\cdot(\boldsymbol{\omega}\times\boldsymbol{\varrho}_C)\, dm + \tfrac{1}{2}(\boldsymbol{\omega}\times\boldsymbol{\varrho}_C)\cdot(\boldsymbol{\omega}\times\boldsymbol{\varrho}_C)\, dm \quad (6.3\text{-}21)$$

Integrating over the entire mass m of the body, the second term drops out, since $\int_m \boldsymbol{\varrho}_C\, dm = \mathbf{0}$, and we obtain

$$T = \tfrac{1}{2}m\mathbf{v}_C\cdot\mathbf{v}_C + \tfrac{1}{2}\int_m (\boldsymbol{\omega}\times\boldsymbol{\varrho}_C)\cdot(\boldsymbol{\omega}\times\boldsymbol{\varrho}_C)\, dm \quad (6.3\text{-}22)$$

Thus the kinetic energy of a rigid body consists essentially of two parts— see Eqs. (4.5-2) and (4.5-3)—$T = T_{\text{trans}} + T_{\text{rot}}$:

(1)
$$T_{\text{trans}} = \tfrac{1}{2}m\mathbf{v}_C\cdot\mathbf{v}_C \quad (6.3\text{-}23)$$

expressing the kinetic energy of translation, as if all body points had the same velocity as the center of mass or as if the entire mass m were concentrated in the center of mass.   Furthermore we recognize that in view of $\mathbf{G} = m\mathbf{v}_C$ we may also write, instead of Eq. (6.3-23),

(2)
$$T_{\text{trans}} = \tfrac{1}{2}\mathbf{v}_C\cdot\mathbf{G} \qquad \text{See Eq. (4.5-5)} \quad (6.3\text{-}24)$$
$$T_{\text{rot}} = \tfrac{1}{2}\int_m (\boldsymbol{\omega}\times\boldsymbol{\varrho}_C)\cdot(\boldsymbol{\omega}\times\boldsymbol{\varrho}_C)\, dm \quad (6.3\text{-}25)$$

expressing the kinetic energy due to the rotation of a rigid body about an axis assumed to pass parallel to $\boldsymbol{\omega}$ through the center of mass. T_{rot} is the kinetic energy computed in a reference frame translating with the center of mass.   It can also be expressed as—see Eq. (4.5-5)—

$$T_{\text{rot}} = \tfrac{1}{2}\boldsymbol{\omega}\cdot\mathbf{h}_C \quad (6.3\text{-}26)$$

since from the properties of the spate product $\mathbf{a}\cdot(\mathbf{b}\times\mathbf{c}) = \mathbf{c}\cdot(\mathbf{a}\times\mathbf{b})$

$$\boldsymbol{\omega}\cdot\mathbf{h}_C = \int_m \boldsymbol{\omega}\cdot[\boldsymbol{\varrho}_C\times(\boldsymbol{\omega}\times\boldsymbol{\varrho}_C)]\, dm = \int_m (\boldsymbol{\omega}\times\boldsymbol{\varrho}_C)\cdot(\boldsymbol{\omega}\times\boldsymbol{\varrho}_C)\, dm = 2T_{\text{rot}}$$

Equation (6.3-26) is easily evaluated for central principal axes of the rotating body—see Eq. (6.3-16)—

$$T_{\text{rot}} = \tfrac{1}{2}(\omega_\xi^2 I_\xi + \omega_\eta^2 I_\eta + \omega_\zeta^2 I_\zeta) \quad (6.3\text{-}27)$$

If ξ, η, ζ are not principal axes through C, then Eq. (6.3-26) yields with reference to Eq. (6.3-14)

$$T_{\text{rot}} = \tfrac{1}{2}\omega_\xi^2 J_\xi + \tfrac{1}{2}\omega_\eta^2 J_\eta + \tfrac{1}{2}\omega_\zeta^2 J_\zeta - \omega_\xi\omega_\eta J_{\xi\eta} - \omega_\eta\omega_\zeta J_{\eta\zeta} - \omega_\zeta\omega_\xi J_{\zeta\xi}$$

$$(6.3\text{-}28)$$

From here on it is easy to establish the work theorem for a rigid body. We denote the resultant of all external forces by $\mathbf{F}$ and that of the moments of all external forces and couples about the center of mass by $\mathbf{M}_C$. Then

$$\int_{t_1}^{t_2} \mathbf{F} \cdot \mathbf{v}_C \, dt + \int_{t_1}^{t_2} \mathbf{M}_C \cdot \boldsymbol{\omega} \, dt = W_{1,2} \qquad (6.3\text{-}29)$$

represents the work done by all external forces and couples in the time interval $\langle t_1, t_2 \rangle$. We saw in Sec. 3.4—see Eq. (3.4-3)—that

$$W_{1,2} = T_2 - T_1 \qquad (6.3\text{-}30)$$

Substituting

$$\mathbf{F} \, dt = d\mathbf{G} = m \, d\mathbf{v}_C$$

from Eq. (6.3-2) in the first term of Eq. (6.3-29), we obtain

$$\int_{t_1}^{t_2} \mathbf{F} \cdot \mathbf{v}_C \, dt = m \int_{v_{C1}}^{v_{C2}} \mathbf{v}_C \cdot d\mathbf{v}_C = \tfrac{1}{2}m(v_{C2}^2 - v_{C1}^2) = T_{2,\text{trans}} - T_{1,\text{trans}}$$

$$(6.3\text{-}31)$$

Hence we conclude from Eqs. (6.3-29) to (6.3-31) that

$$\int_{t_1}^{t_2} \mathbf{M}_C \cdot \boldsymbol{\omega} \, dt = T_{2,\text{rot}} - T_{1,\text{rot}} \qquad (6.3\text{-}32)$$

We have shown that the work done by the resultant of all external forces applied to the center of mass brings about a change in the translatory kinetic energy—see Eq. (6.3-31)—and that the work done by the resultant moment of all external forces and couples about the center of mass leads to a change in the rotatory kinetic energy of a rigid body—see Eq. (6.3-32). In case all external forces are conservative forces, their potential is denoted by U; then the theorem of the conservation of energy yields

$$T + U = E = \text{const} \qquad (6.3\text{-}33)$$
or
$$T_1 + U_1 = T_2 + U_2 \qquad (6.3\text{-}34)$$

DETERMINATION OF THE PRINCIPAL MOMENTS OF INERTIA
AND THE PRINCIPAL AXES

Given the moments and products of inertia about the arbitrary axes ξ, η, ζ, it is often necessary to determine the principal moments of inertia and the direction of the principal axes.[1] We start with arbitrary ξ, η, ζ axes, about which the moment of momentum is stated by the matrix equation (6.3-16) as

$$\begin{bmatrix} h_\xi \\ h_\eta \\ h_\zeta \end{bmatrix} = \begin{bmatrix} J_\xi & -J_{\xi\eta} & -J_{\xi\zeta} \\ -J_{\eta\xi} & J_\eta & -J_{\eta\zeta} \\ -J_{\zeta\xi} & -J_{\zeta\eta} & J_\zeta \end{bmatrix} \begin{bmatrix} \omega_\xi \\ \omega_\eta \\ \omega_\zeta \end{bmatrix} \qquad (6.3\text{-}16)$$

[1] See the end of Sec. 6.2.

Here ω_ξ, ω_η, ω_ζ are the components of the resultant angular-velocity vector $\boldsymbol{\omega}$. Now if $\boldsymbol{\omega}$ is such that its direction coincides with one of the principal axes ξ', η', or ζ', then, also, $\mathbf{h}$ and $\boldsymbol{\omega}$ coincide, and we may write

$$\mathbf{h} = I\boldsymbol{\omega} = I\omega_\xi \mathbf{1}_\xi + I\omega_\eta \mathbf{1}_\eta + I\omega_\zeta \mathbf{1}_\zeta \tag{6.3-35}$$

where I denotes any of the three principal moments of inertia $I_{\xi'}$, $I_{\eta'}$, or $I_{\zeta'}$. Thus, substituting Eq. (6.3-35) in Eq. (6.3-16), we obtain

$$\begin{bmatrix} I\omega_\xi \\ I\omega_\eta \\ I\omega_\zeta \end{bmatrix} = \begin{bmatrix} J_\xi & -J_{\xi\eta} & -J_{\xi\zeta} \\ -J_{\eta\xi} & J_\eta & -J_{\eta\zeta} \\ -J_{\zeta\xi} & -J_{\zeta\eta} & J_\zeta \end{bmatrix} \begin{bmatrix} \omega_\xi \\ \omega_\eta \\ \omega_\zeta \end{bmatrix} \tag{6.3-36}$$

or

$$\begin{bmatrix} J_\xi - I & -J_{\xi\eta} & -J_{\xi\zeta} \\ -J_{\eta\xi} & J_\eta - I & -J_{\eta\zeta} \\ -J_{\zeta\xi} & -J_{\zeta\eta} & J_\zeta - I \end{bmatrix} \begin{bmatrix} \omega_\xi \\ \omega_\eta \\ \omega_\zeta \end{bmatrix} = 0 \tag{6.3-37}$$

For this equation to be satisfied, the determinant

$$\begin{vmatrix} J_\xi - I & -J_{\xi\eta} & -J_{\xi\zeta} \\ -J_{\eta\xi} & J_\eta - I & -J_{\eta\zeta} \\ -J_{\zeta\xi} & -J_{\zeta\eta} & J_\zeta - I \end{vmatrix} = 0 \tag{6.3-38}$$

must be zero, which leads to three values of I, namely, $I_{\xi'}$, $I_{\eta'}$, and $I_{\zeta'}$, which are the principal moments of inertia[1]—see Eq. (6.2-24).

Substitution of, say, $I_{\xi'}$ into Eq. (6.3-37) leads to ratios of the angular-velocity components ω_ξ, ω_η, and ω_ζ defining the directions of the ξ, η, ζ axes with respect to the principal axis ξ'. Likewise we find the directions with respect to the principal axes η' and ζ', respectively—see also Eqs. (6.2-26).

ILLUSTRATIVE EXAMPLE 6.3-2
A symmetric satellite (see Fig. 6.3-4) with central principal moments of inertia $I_\xi = I_\eta = A$ and $I_\zeta = C$ spins freely in space with angular velocity $\boldsymbol{\omega}$. Assuming a moment-free condition, determine the relationship between the orientation of its axis of symmetry with respect to the moment-of-momentum vector $\mathbf{h}_C$ and the kinetic energy.

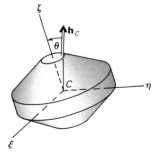

Fig. 6.3-4

---

[1] Equation (6.3-38) shows that the principal moments of inertia turn out to be the characteristic numbers of the inertia matrix.

SOLUTION: With central body-fixed axes ξ, η, ζ the equations for the moment of momentum (6.3-17) and the kinetic energy (6.3-27) yield ($|h_C| = h$)

$$h^2 = A^2(\omega_\xi^2 + \omega_\eta^2) + C^2\omega_\zeta^2$$
$$2T = A(\omega_\xi^2 + \omega_\eta^2) + C\omega_\zeta^2$$

Multiplying the second equation by A and subtracting,

$$h^2 - 2TA = C(C - A)\omega_\zeta^2$$

Letting the angle between the axis ζ and the space-fixed vector $\mathbf{h}_C$ (no moment acting on the satellite) be θ, the component of $\mathbf{h}_C$ along the ζ axis is

$$C\omega_\zeta = h \cos \theta$$

Thus ω_ζ can be eliminated between the last two equations to obtain the relationship

$$h^2 - 2TA = \frac{h^2}{C}(C - A)\cos^2 \theta$$

or

$$T = \frac{h^2}{2C}\left[1 + \left(\frac{C}{A} - 1\right)\sin^2 \theta\right]$$

Figure 6.3-5 shows a plot of T versus θ for various values of C/A, which can take on values from 0 (infinitely thin rod) to 2 (infinitely thin disk). We assume that the

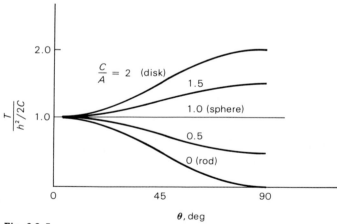

Fig. 6.3-5

satellite has been set in motion so that the vector $\mathbf{h}_C$ and axis ζ ($\theta = 0$) coincide. In the case $C/A > 1$, Fig. 6.3-5 shows that T is then a minimum, that is, that work would have to be done on the satellite to supply the necessary additional kinetic energy to tilt axis ζ away from the vector $\mathbf{h}_C$. Since it was assumed that the satellite is spinning freely, no increase in the kinetic energy is possible, so that the satellite remains at $\theta = 0$, which means that the symmetry axis ζ is a stable axis of rotation for satellites with $C/A > 1$ (disklike bodies). Similar reasoning then leads to the statement that slender bodies with $C/A < 1$ cannot perform stable rotations about the ξ axis ($T_{\min}$ is then found for $\theta = 90°$—see Fig. 6.3-5).

ILLUSTRATIVE EXAMPLE 6.3-3

The wheel shown in Fig. 6.3-6 is considered a thin disk of mass m and radius r. It rolls without slipping in an inclined position on a horizontal table, in such way that the normal

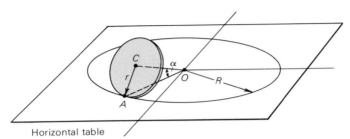

Horizontal table

Fig. 6.3-6

on the center C of the disk passes through the center O of the circular track. Determine its kinetic energy in terms of the angular velocity Ω. An observer located at point O would have to turn with Ω about his vertical axis in order to keep the disk in view.

SOLUTION: We consider the disk the bottom of a circular cone whose apex is at point O. Then the total angular velocity ω of the disk is directed along the instantaneous axis AO, since both points A and O are at rest. Thus (see Fig. 6.3-7) we find $\omega = \Omega/\tan \alpha$.

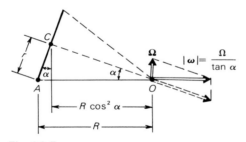

Fig. 6.3-7

Splitting ω into its components along OC and AC, we obtain $\Omega \cos^2 \alpha/\sin \alpha$ and $\Omega \cos \alpha$ respectively. Therefore we have

$$T_{\text{rot}} = \frac{1}{2} \frac{mr^2}{2} \Omega^2 \frac{\cos^4 \alpha}{\sin^2 \alpha} + \frac{1}{2} \frac{mr^2}{4} \Omega^2 \cos^2 \alpha \qquad (a)$$

Since the velocity of the center of the wheel C is

$$v_C = r \cos \alpha \frac{\Omega}{\tan \alpha} = \Omega r \frac{\cos^2 \alpha}{\sin \alpha}$$

we obtain

$$T_{\text{trans}} = \tfrac{1}{2}mv_C{}^2 = \tfrac{1}{2}mr^2\Omega^2 \frac{\cos^4 \alpha}{\sin^2 \alpha} \tag{b}$$

With $\sin \alpha = r/R$ we find from Eqs. (a) and (b)

$$T = T_{\text{rot}} + T_{\text{trans}} = \tfrac{1}{2}m\Omega^2(\tfrac{3}{2}R^2 \cos^4 \alpha + \tfrac{1}{4}r^2 \cos^2 \alpha)$$

PROBLEMS

6.3-1   A slender homogeneous rod of length l is hinged at its upper end to a vertical shaft that rotates at a constant speed ω (see Fig. P 6.3-1).   Determine the steady angle θ between the shaft and the vertical.

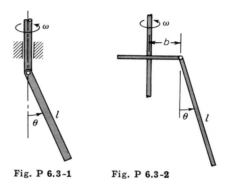

Fig. P 6.3-1   Fig. P 6.3-2

6.3-2   A uniform slender bar hinged to a hub of radius b rotates with a constant angular speed ω about a vertical shaft (see Fig. P 6.3-2).   Determine the angle θ and the magnitude and line of action of the centrifugal force as a function of b.

6.3-3   A helicopter blade of weight w (assume uniform) and length l rotates at a constant speed ω about a vertical shaft and at a constant angle θ (see Fig. P 6.3-3). Determine the magnitude and line of action of the centrifugal force acting on the blade (the lift on the blade is balancing the weight at angle θ).

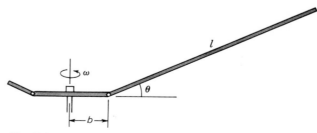

Fig. P 6.3-3

6.3-4   A homogeneous rod, bent into a right angle with legs of length a and b, is pinned to a vertical shaft that rotates with a constant angular velocity ω (see Fig. P 6.3-4). Show that the steady angular position taken by the rod is related to ω by the equation

$$\omega^2 = 3g \frac{b^2 \cos \theta - a^2 \sin \theta}{(b^2 - a^2) \sin 2\theta}$$

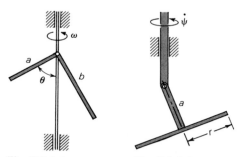

Fig. P 6.3-4   Fig. P 6.3-5

6.3-5   A thin disk of radius r and mass m has a stem of length a that is pinned to a vertical shaft, as shown in Fig. P 6.3-5. Show that, if $r < 2a$, it is unstable if $\dot\psi > 4ga/(4a^2 - r^2)$. Show also that it is stable at all $\dot\psi$ if $r > 2a$.

6.3-6   A uniform bar of length l is supported by a cord of length b attached to its center. When rotated, the bar can take either of the two configurations shown in Fig. P 6.3-6. Assuming zero friction at the post, determine the angle θ for each case. If slightly disturbed the bar flies out, provided ω is sufficient. Determine the angles θ and ϕ and the minimum value of ω^2.

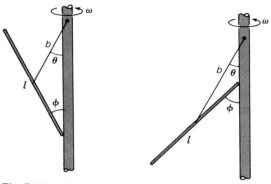

Fig. P 6.3-6

6.3-7   A gyro wheel of moment of inertia C about the ζ axis and A about the ξ axis spins
with speed n rps in a gimbal that can turn about the ξ axis, as shown in Fig.
P 6.3-7.   The gimbal axis ξ is connected to a pulley of radius r with a weight w
that can be attached to it.   The moment of inertia of the gimbal and the pulley
about the ξ axis is B.   Determine the bearing reactions at D and E when the
weight w has fallen through a distance h from the horizontal position of the
gimbal.

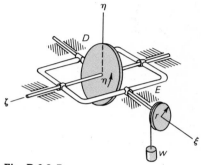

Fig. P 6.3-7

6.3-8   Establish the relationships for the angular momentum and the kinetic energy
of a symmetric body such that $I_\xi = I_\eta = A$ and $I_\zeta = C$.

6.3-9   The body referred to in Prob. 6.3-8 is suspended in such a way that the sum of all
force moments about its center of mass vanishes.   Show that $|\omega|$ is then constant.

6.3-10   The spin axis of the homogeneous top shown in Fig. P 6.3-10 rotates about the
vertical axis with an angular velocity $\dot{\psi}$ at a constant angle θ.   Establish the
expressions of $\mathbf{H}_O$, $\dot{\mathbf{H}}_O$, and the kinetic energy T.   Does T vary with time t?
If not, why not?

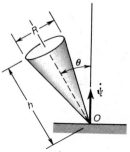

Fig. P 6.3-10

6.4 MISCELLANEOUS FIRST PROBLEMS IN MECHANICS FOR A RIGID BODY IN GENERAL MOTION

It will be remembered (see Sec. 2.2) that first problems in mechanics exist when the kinematics of a body's motion is completely known and the associated forces and moments responsible for it are sought. Although this kind of problem is quite simple, it is of great practical importance, especially in the field of machine dynamics. The mathematical simplicity of first problems is evident, since it is necessary only to substitute the given kinematic information and the inertial properties of a body into the right sides of Eqs. (6.3-2) and (6.3-18) in order to determine the unknown forces and force moments, respectively. Since these equations together represent six scalar equations, they permit, naturally, the determination only of six unknowns (see the three-dimensional case of statics of a rigid body).

In simple situations, for example, those encountered in the dynamics of a rigid body rotating about a fixed axis, no reference to the eulerian equations (6.3-18) is usually necessary, because in such cases the fundamental relationships between the force moment and the time rate of change of the body's moment of momentum are easily derived *ab ovo*. We now deal with a number of miscellaneous first problems in mechanics.

DYNAMICS OF A RIGID BODY ROTATING ABOUT A FIXED AXIS

As the simplest case of rigid-body dynamics, except pure translation, which was covered in Chap. 2, we first treat the rotation of a rigid body about an axis fixed in an inertial frame of reference (see Fig. 6.4-1). We let the

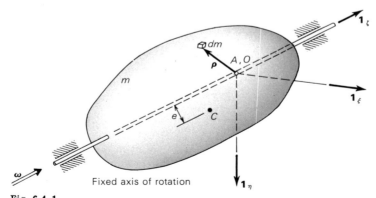

Fig. 6.4-1

origin A of the body-fixed ξ, η, ζ coordinates coincide with an arbitrary point O on the axis of rotation so that the ζ axis coincides with the axis of rotation and $\mathbf{v}_A = \mathbf{v}_O \equiv \mathbf{0}$. Considering that the angular velocity of the body and, thus, of the ξ, η, ζ coordinates is $\boldsymbol{\omega} = \omega_\zeta \mathbf{1}_\zeta$, Eq. (6.3-16), which is also valid for a simultaneously body- and space-fixed reference point, yields the following components of $\mathbf{H}_O$:

$$
\begin{aligned}
H_\xi &= -\omega_\zeta J_{\xi\zeta} \\
H_\eta &= -\omega_\zeta J_{\eta\zeta} \\
H_\zeta &= \omega_\zeta J_\zeta
\end{aligned}
\tag{6.4-1}
$$

Now, although $\mathbf{H}_O$ is a vectorial quantity defined with respect to an inertial frame, it is stated in the rotating ξ, η, ζ coordinates, and thus its time rate of change in an inertial frame is—see Eq. (5.1-11)—

$$
\dot{\mathbf{H}}_O = \overset{\frown}{\dot{\mathbf{H}}}_O + \boldsymbol{\omega} \times \mathbf{H}_O
\tag{6.4-2}
$$

Substituting Eqs. (6.4-1), we obtain according to Eq. (6.3-4) in ξ, η, ζ coordinates

$$
\begin{aligned}
M_\xi &= -\dot{\omega}_\zeta J_{\xi\zeta} + \omega_\zeta{}^2 J_{\eta\zeta} \\
M_\eta &= -\dot{\omega}_\zeta J_{\eta\zeta} - \omega_\zeta{}^2 J_{\xi\zeta} \\
M_\zeta &= \dot{\omega}_\zeta J_\zeta
\end{aligned}
\tag{6.4-3}
$$

The moment $\mathbf{M}_O$ is the moment of all external forces, including, of course, the reactions of the bearings.

We note from Eqs. (6.4-3) that even for the case in which $\boldsymbol{\omega}$ is constant, a force moment (rotating with the body) is exerted by the bearings on the rotating shaft unless the axis of rotation (ζ axis) is a principal axis ($J_{\eta\zeta} = J_{\xi\zeta} = 0$). When $J_{\eta\zeta}$ and $J_{\xi\zeta}$ are not zero, the rotating body is said to be dynamically unbalanced, a most unwelcome situation that must be remedied as much as possible on a balancing machine to ensure quiet running conditions.[1] Naturally, for this purpose it is also necessary to have the center of mass on the axis of rotation, because otherwise the bearing forces have to counteract the centrifugal force $me\omega^2$ (see Fig. 6.4-1). The process of removing the eccentricity e of the center of mass is called static balancing. The reader is invited to ponder the reason for choosing the terms *dynamic* and *static balancing*.

A direct application of Euler's equations (6.3-18) is possible when the principal axes ξ, η, ζ through O are known,[2] together with the principal

[1] Referring to footnote 1 on page 202, we point out that plane motion, that is, motion parallel to the $\xi\eta$ plane, is not possible without the constraining moments M_ξ and M_η unless the products of inertia $J_{\eta\zeta}$ and $J_{\xi\zeta}$ vanish.

[2] This is, for example, the case in problems like that treated in Illustrative Example 6.4-1.

moments of inertia I_ξ, I_η, and I_ζ (see Fig. 6.4-2).   All we have to do, then, is to resolve the angular velocity vector $\boldsymbol{\omega}$, which is permanently directly

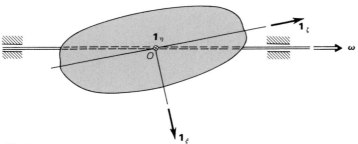

Fig. 6.4-2   Principal axes.

along the fixed axis of rotation, in terms of components along the body-fixed principal axes.   For didactic reasons, however, we do not use this formal procedure, but rather we use this case for illustrating the relationship between the force moment and the moment of momentum.   For the latter we have—see Eq. (6.3-20)—

$$\mathbf{H}_O = I_\xi \omega_\xi \mathbf{1}_\xi + I_\eta \omega_\eta \mathbf{1}_\eta + I_\zeta \omega_\zeta \mathbf{1}_\zeta \qquad (6.4\text{-}4)$$

It is evident that $\mathbf{H}_O$ must have a different direction[1] from $\boldsymbol{\omega}$, since $\mathbf{H}_O$ was obtained by multiplying the three components of $\boldsymbol{\omega}$ with, in general, different principal moments of inertia.   As the principal axes rotate with the body, the moment-of-momentum vector $\mathbf{H}_O$ also rotates about the axis of rotation with the instantaneous angular velocity $\boldsymbol{\omega}$ (see Fig. 6.4-3), and its magnitude

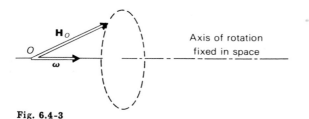

Fig. 6.4-3

is changed simultaneously with a change in the angular speed.   Therefore, the direction of $\mathbf{H}_O$ and also, in general, its magnitude change with respect

[1] Except when ω coincides with a principal axis.

to the inertial reference frame as the body rotates. Because of this time rate of change of $\mathbf{H}_O$ the moment of the external forces about the shaft is— see Eqs. (6.4-2) and (5.1-11)—

$$\mathbf{M}_O = \dot{\mathbf{H}}_O = \overset{\frown}{\dot{\mathbf{H}}}_O + \boldsymbol{\omega} \times \mathbf{H}_O \qquad (6.4\text{-}5)$$

Since the direction of $\boldsymbol{\omega}$ does not change, the first term $\overset{\frown}{\dot{\mathbf{H}}}_O$ on the right side of this equation describes the moment that is solely responsible here for the "stretching" of $\mathbf{H}_O$ (change of magnitude), and the second term $\boldsymbol{\omega} \times \mathbf{H}_O$ represents the moment causing the "swinging" (change of direction) of $\mathbf{H}_O$ (see Fig. 6.4-4).

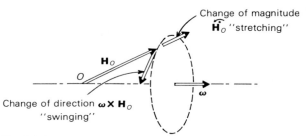

Fig. 6.4-4

ILLUSTRATIVE EXAMPLE 6.4-1
We consider a thin disk of mass m mounted on a massless rigid shaft (see Fig. 6.4-5). The plane of the disk is not quite normal to the shaft, so that the principal ξ axis does not coincide with the axis of rotation. We calculate the bearing reactions due to this assembly fault when the shaft rotates with constant angular velocity $\boldsymbol{\omega}$, as shown in Fig. 6.4-5.

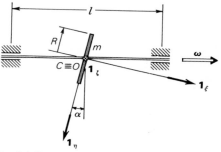

Fig. 6.4-5

SOLUTION: At any instant the angular velocity ω may be split into two components:

$$\omega = (\omega \cos \alpha)\mathbf{1}_\xi + (-\omega \sin \alpha)\mathbf{1}_\eta \qquad (a)$$

With $I_\xi = mR^2/2$ and $I_\eta = mR^2/4$ (see the Appendix) and $\dot{\omega} = \mathbf{0}$ we have from Eqs. (6.3-18)

$$M_\xi = M_\eta = 0 \qquad (b)$$

and

$$M_\zeta = mR^2\omega^2 \frac{\sin \alpha \cos \alpha}{4} \qquad (c)$$

When α is very small, so that $\sin \alpha \approx \alpha$ and $\cos \alpha \approx 1$, then Eq. (c) may simply be written

$$M_\zeta = \frac{mR^2\omega^2\alpha}{4} \qquad (d)$$

Equations (c) and (d), respectively, represent the moment exerted by the bearing reactions on the shaft. Hence these reactions act at this instant, as shown in Fig. 6.4-6.

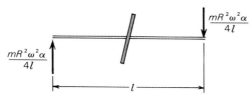

Fig. 6.4-6

They rotate with the shaft. Does it make any difference, as far as these reactions are concerned, whether the disk is mounted in the middle of the shaft or nearer to one of the bearings? Does the direction of ω influence the directions of the reactions?

It is interesting also for the engineer to discuss this problem from the point of view that the shaft is no longer considered rigid. In Fig. 6.4-7 the

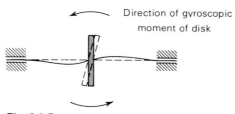

Direction of gyroscopic
moment of disk

Fig. 6.4-7

thick lines show the case of the flexible shaft, where the disk is "straightened up" because of the action of the gyroscopic moment[1] of the disk. Hence,

[1] See page 353.

if we have only one disk on a shaft, as in the early Laval steam turbines, then a very flexible shaft is beneficial. On the other hand, when we consider a modern turbine shaft (see Fig. 6.4-8), the gyroscopic moment of the rotor

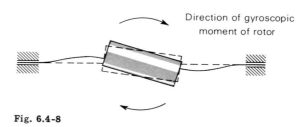

Fig. 6.4-8

tends to enlarge the "obliqueness" of the rotor. Hence such turbine rotors need to be very stiff. The reader is invited to reason out the different directions of the gyroscopic moments in Figs. 6.4-7 and 6.4-8 without using the derived formulas (use the concept of centrifugal forces).

DYNAMICS OF A RIGID BODY ROTATING ABOUT A MOVING AXIS
We encounter this case most often when a rotating body is mounted on a moving vehicle, for example, a turbine rotor on a boat. We let the rotor rotate about its spin axis with the angular velocity ω_a with respect to the vehicle, while the vehicle turns with the angular velocity ω_b in an inertial reference frame. Then the moment of momentum of the rotor $\mathbf{h}_C$ is to be computed considering that it rotates with respect to the inertial frame with the angular velocity $\omega_a + \omega_b$. In view of Eqs. (6.3-5) and (6.3-6) the question of what ω is to be used in the evaluation of these equations arises. We consider only two alternatives:

1 $\mathbf{h}_C$ is described in ξ, η, ζ coordinates fixed in the rotor with their origin at C. Then, obviously, we have to use $\omega = \omega_a + \omega_b$ in Eqs. (6.3-5).

2 $\mathbf{h}_C$ is described in ξ, η, ζ coordinates fixed in the moving vehicle. Then we have to use $\omega = \omega_b$ in Eqs. (6.3-5).

In case 1 Euler's equations (6.3-18) are immediately applicable, simply substituting $\omega_\xi = \omega_{a\xi} + \omega_{b\xi}$, and so forth. On the other hand, the application of case 2 causes, in general, great difficulties, because—except for the special case discussed below—the moments of inertia of the rotor with respect to the chosen ξ, η, ζ coordinate axes vary with time because of the angular velocity ω_a of the rotor with respect to these axes. Besides, they are, in general, no longer principal axes. However, for the usual case in which the rotor has rotational symmetry such that the center of mass C is on the spin axis, we may use alternative 2 with advantage. We tie the ξ, η, ζ coordinates to the vehicle in such way that their origin coincides with C and the ξ axis with the spin axis. Then I_ξ, I_η, I_ζ are central principal moments of inertia and $I_\eta = I_\zeta$, and furthermore I_ξ, I_η, I_ζ are constants, not depending on the angular position of the rotor with respect to the vehicle. Considering that $\omega_{a\eta} = \omega_{a\zeta} = 0$, we then have

$$
\begin{aligned}
h_\xi &= (\omega_{a\xi} + \omega_{b\xi})I_\xi \\
h_\eta &= \omega_{b\eta}I_\eta \\
h_\zeta &= \omega_{b\zeta}I_\zeta = \omega_{b\zeta}I_\eta
\end{aligned}
\tag{6.4-6}
$$

Hence Eq. (6.3-5b) becomes, with $\boldsymbol{\omega} \equiv \boldsymbol{\omega}_b$,

$$
\mathbf{M}_C = \dot{\mathbf{h}}_C + \boldsymbol{\omega}_b \times \mathbf{h}_C
$$

or in coordinates

$$
\begin{aligned}
M_\xi &= (\dot{\omega}_{a\xi} + \dot{\omega}_{b\xi})I_\xi \\
M_\eta &= \dot{\omega}_{b\eta}I_\eta - \omega_{b\zeta}\omega_{b\xi}I_\eta + (\omega_{a\xi} + \omega_{b\xi})\omega_{b\zeta}I_\xi \\
M_\zeta &= \dot{\omega}_{b\zeta}I_\eta - (\omega_{a\xi} + \omega_{b\xi})\omega_{b\eta}I_\xi + \omega_{b\eta}\omega_{b\xi}I_\eta
\end{aligned}
\tag{6.4-7}
$$

ILLUSTRATIVE EXAMPLE 6.4-2

The shaft of a marine turbine rotates about its spin axis with constant angular speed Ω with respect to the ship, while the ship travels with constant speed v through a circular curve of radius R. We determine the forces exerted by the bearings on the shaft on account of the ship's turn.

SOLUTION: We fix the coordinates ξ, η, ζ in the rotor, as shown in Fig. 6.4-9 (case 1). Hence we have $\omega_{a\xi} = \Omega$, $\omega_{a\eta} = \omega_{a\zeta} = 0$, and with the magnitude of ω_b as v/R, we easily

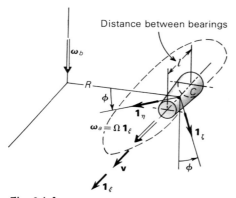

Fig. 6.4-9

find $\omega_{b\xi} = 0$, $\omega_{b\eta} = (v/R) \sin \phi$, $\omega_{b\zeta} = (v/R) \cos \phi$. Thus with $\dot\phi = \Omega = $ const we substitute in Euler's equations (6.3-18)

$$\omega_\xi = \Omega \qquad \omega_\eta = \frac{v}{R} \sin \phi \qquad \omega_\zeta = \frac{v}{R} \cos \phi$$

and

$$\dot\omega_\xi = 0 \qquad \dot\omega_\eta = \frac{v}{R} \Omega \cos \phi \qquad \dot\omega_\zeta = -\frac{v}{R} \Omega \sin \phi$$

and obtain, considering that because of the rotational symmetry of the shaft $I_\eta = I_\zeta$,

$$M_\xi = 0$$

$$M_\eta = I_\eta \frac{v}{R} \Omega \cos \phi - (I_\zeta - I_\xi) \frac{v}{R} \Omega \cos \phi = I_\xi \frac{v}{R} \Omega \cos \phi$$

$$M_\zeta = -\left[I_\zeta \frac{v}{R} \Omega \sin \phi + (I_\xi - I_\eta) \frac{v}{R} \Omega \sin \phi \right] = -I_\xi \frac{v}{R} \Omega \sin \phi$$

Thus we find the result that the force moment exerted by the bearings on the shaft is of constant magnitude

$$M_C = I_\xi \frac{v}{R} \Omega$$

and of constant direction, since its vector always points normal to the ξ axis in the horizontal plane, as shown in Fig. 6.4-10.

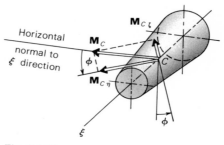

Fig. 6.4-10

The moment $\mathbf{M}_C$ is exerted on the shaft by the two bearing forces, which form a couple, each force being of magnitude

$$I_\xi \frac{v}{lR} \Omega \qquad l = \text{distance between bearings}$$

The front (rear) bearing force is constantly directed upward (downward). Thus the shaft pin exerts a downward (upward) pressure on the bearing, and the ship always dips at the bow. In order to find the total bearing forces due to the ship's turn, the forces necessary for the acceleration of the shaft's center of mass also have to be taken into account—see Eq. (6.3-2).   The acceleration of the center of mass is

$$\mathbf{a}_C = \frac{v^2}{R}\,(\cos\phi\,\mathbf{1}_\eta + \sin\phi\,\mathbf{1}_\zeta)$$

and thus, assuming the center of mass in the middle between the bearings, each bearing reaction amounts to $mv^2/2R$ acting in the horizontal direction opposite and parallel to the radius R of the turn.

ALTERNATIVE SOLUTION: In view of the rotational symmetry of the turbine rotor $(I_\eta = I_\zeta)$ we now fix the ξ, η, ζ axes in the boat, again in such a way that the ξ axis coincides with the spin axis (case 2). Then Eqs. (6.4-7) apply. If we place the η axis horizontal in the direction of the center of the ship's circular path, we easily see from Fig. 6.4-9 that

$$\omega_{b\xi} = 0 \qquad \omega_{b\eta} = 0 \qquad \omega_{b\zeta} = \frac{v}{R} = \text{const}$$

Thus with $\omega_{a\xi} = \Omega = \text{const}$, $\omega_{a\eta} = \omega_{a\zeta} = 0$, Eqs. (6.4-7) yield

$$M_\xi = 0 \qquad M_\eta = I_\xi\Omega\frac{v}{R} \qquad M_\zeta = 0$$

which, considering the horizontal orientation of the η axis, is the same result as found above (see also Fig. 6.4-10).

ILLUSTRATIVE EXAMPLE 6.4-3

Figure 6.4-11 shows a crusher (gyroscopic mill) in which the pressure of the wheels due to their weight is enhanced by the gyroscopic forces.   Assuming pure rolling of the middle-wheel plane, determine the gyroscopic force for each wheel.

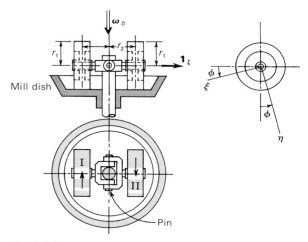

Mill dish

Pin

Fig. 6.4-11

SOLUTION: The ξ, η, ζ axes are fixed in the wheel, as shown in Fig. 6.4-11, and thus we apply Euler's equations (6.3-18).   The moving horizontal axis (wheel axle) rotates with constant angular velocity ($\dot{\omega}_b = 0$) with respect to an inertial reference frame:

$$\boldsymbol{\omega}_b = \omega_b(\sin\phi\ \mathbf{1}_\xi + \cos\phi\ \mathbf{1}_\eta) \qquad \text{where } \omega_b = |\boldsymbol{\omega}_b|$$

Assuming no slipping, we find that

$$\boldsymbol{\omega}_a = \dot\phi\mathbf{1}_\zeta = \omega_b\frac{r_2}{r_1}\mathbf{1}_\zeta$$

Thus we have to substitute in Euler's equations (6.3-18), considering that $\boldsymbol{\omega} = \boldsymbol{\omega}_a + \boldsymbol{\omega}_b$,

$$\omega_\xi = \omega_b\sin\phi \qquad \omega_\eta = \omega_b\cos\phi \qquad \omega_\zeta = \omega_b\frac{r_2}{r_1}$$

$$\dot\omega_\xi = \omega_b{}^2\frac{r_2}{r_1}\cos\phi \qquad \dot\omega_\eta = -\omega_b{}^2\frac{r_2}{r_1}\sin\phi \qquad \dot\omega_\zeta = 0$$

The moment $\mathbf{M}_C$, which can now be evaluated by means of the eulerian equations (6.3-18), is the force couple exerted by the central pin on the wheel axle and by the mill dish on the wheel ($I_\xi = I_\eta$):

$$M_\xi = I_\xi\omega_b{}^2\frac{r_2}{r_1}\cos\phi - (I_\eta - I_\zeta)\omega_b{}^2\frac{r_2}{r_1}\cos\phi = I_\zeta\omega_b{}^2\frac{r_2}{r_1}\cos\phi$$

$$M_\eta = -I_\eta\omega_b{}^2\frac{r_2}{r_1}\sin\phi - (I_\xi - I_\zeta)\omega_b{}^2\frac{r_2}{r_1}\sin\phi = -I_\zeta\omega_b{}^2\frac{r_2}{r_1}\sin\phi$$

$$M_\zeta = 0$$

Hence the moment $\mathbf{M}_C$ is always directed horizontally in the $\xi\eta$ plane, as shown in Fig. 6.4-12, and thus the force couple mentioned above acts on the wheel, as shown in Fig. 6.4-13.

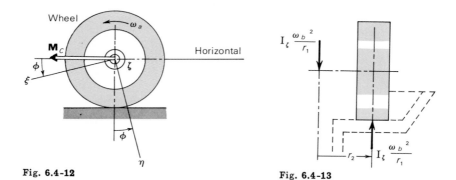

Fig. 6.4-12   Fig. 6.4-13

Thus the wheel of mass m presses on the mill dish with its weight mg plus the gyroscopic force $I_\zeta\omega_b{}^2/r_1$, which in practical designs often amounts to more than the weight.

In the design of the bearings for the vertical central shaft one has to consider that the gyroscopic forces of the two wheels exert a lifting force on it equal to $2I_\zeta\omega_b{}^2/r_1$. The reader is invited to apply the alternative procedure (case 2) to this problem also. Furthermore he should ponder the consequences when, instead of the hinged connection of the horizontal wheel shafts to the vertical central shaft, the horizontal shaft is designed as shown in Fig. 6.4-14. Why do we then no longer have the gyroscopic effect discussed above?

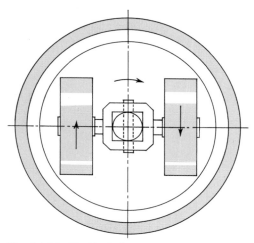

Fig. 6.4-14   Faulty design of crusher.

PROBLEMS

6.4-1   A rectangular thin plate of total weight w is spun about its geometric axis, as shown in Fig. P 6.4-1. Determine the total tensile force at any position x from the axis of rotation.

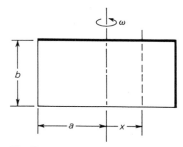

Fig. P 6.4-1

6.4-2   A thin homogeneous circular plate of mass m is rotated about its diameter with angular speed ω (see Fig. P 6.4-2). Determine the tensile force at distance x from the axis of rotation.

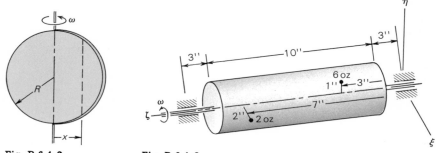

Fig. P 6.4-2   Fig. P 6.4-3

6.4-3   The rotor shown in Fig. P 6.4-3 has unbalances that are to be corrected by removing weights at the end planes 2 in. from the rotor axis. Determine the amount and the position of the weights to be removed. The 2-oz unbalance is located parallel to the ξ axis, and the 6-oz unbalance parallel to the η axis, as shown.

6.4-4   A symmetric rotor has unbalances w_1 and w_2, as shown in Fig. P 6.4-4. Determine the products of inertia $I_{\xi\zeta}$ and $I_{\eta\zeta}$ and the bearing reactions at A and B when the rotation speed is ω.

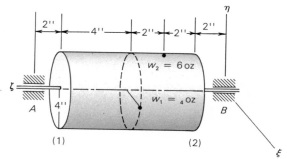

Fig. P 6.4-4

6.4-5   If the rotor in Prob. 6.4-4 is to be balanced by removing mass at planes 1 and 2, determine the amount and the position of the mass to be removed at the circumference in each plane.

6.4-6   A rotor has unbalance weights w_1, w_2, and w_3, as shown in Fig. P 6.4-6.   Determine the unbalance moments M_ξ and M_η, as well as the bearing reactions at A and B.

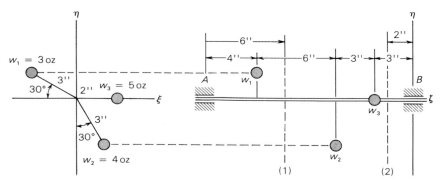

Fig. P 6.4-6

6.4-7   If the rotor in Prob. 6.4-6 is to be balanced by adding masses in planes 1 and 2, determine the amount and the position of the weight to be added in each plane 2 in. from the rotor axis.

6.4-8   A right circular homogeneous cylinder of weight w, length $2l$, and radius R rotates with constant angular velocity ω about an axis that makes an angle α with the axis of the cylinder.   Determine the forces on the bearings that are a distance h from the center of the cylinder.

6.4-9   A circular cylinder of weight w, length h, and diameter $2R$ is spun about a horizontal axis through its center and passing through the circumference of the end planes (see Fig. P 6.4-9).   Determine the bearing reactions at A and B with distance l between them when rotated at a speed ω, with $\dot{\omega}$ = const.

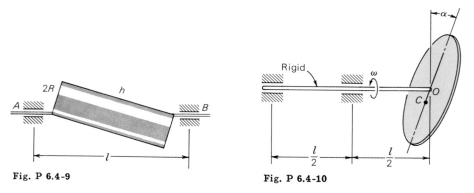

Fig. P 6.4-9   **Fig. P 6.4-10**

6.4-10   A thin homogeneous disk of radius R and mass m is mounted at an angle $90° - \alpha$ with the shaft.   Its center of mass is located by the eccentricity $OC = e$, as shown in Fig. P 6.4-10.   When rotated at a constant speed ω, determine the dynamical reaction of the bearings.

6.4-11   For a constant torque M acting along the z axis, find the forces on the bearings that have equal distance from the center, as shown in Fig. P 6.4-11, when the rotor has reached the angular velocity ω.

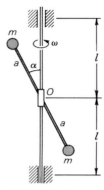

Fig. P 6.4-11

6.4-12   A 10-lb homogeneous slender bar 12 ft long is welded at its center to a heavy axle at an angle of 30°, as shown in Fig. P 6.4-12.   When rotated at a speed of 1,000 rpm, determine the forces on the bearings.   What is the bending moment at the weld?

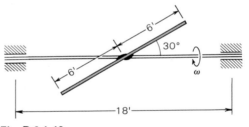

Fig. P 6.4-12

6.4-13   Determine the moment of momentum of a homogeneous thin-walled pipe of rectangular cross section and weight 32.2 lb with sides 3 by 5 by 12 in., rotating with an angular velocity of 10 rad/sec about the main diagonal passing through its center.

6.4-14   A thin rectangular plate of weight w, as shown in Fig. P 6.4-14, rotates about a horizontal axis through its diagonal with constant angular speed ω.   Determine the reaction of the bearings A and B with distance l between them.

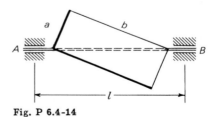

Fig. P 6.4-14

6.4-15   A thin wheel (mass m) is mounted on an axle pivoted at Q that rotates about a vertical line through Q, as shown in Fig. P 6.4-15.   Determine its moment of momentum about C and its kinetic energy, assuming no slipping of the wheel on the ground.

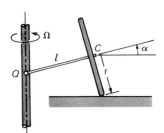

Fig. P 6.4-15

6.4-16   The rotor of an electric motor has its axis of spin perpendicular to the longitudinal axis of a ship, as shown in Fig. P 6.4-16.   If the ship rolls with a maximum angle of 15° and a period of 25 sec (harmonic motion), determine the maximum reaction of the bearings.   The rotor moment of inertia is 20 lb ft sec², the distance between the bearings is 36 in., and the speed of the rotor is 1,800 rpm.

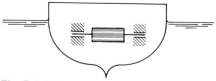

Fig. P 6.4-16

6.4-17   In an old automobile, the two front wheels are attached directly to a one-piece axle, so that the plane of the wheels rotates with the axle.   If the front left wheel drops into a hole in the road, determine the gyroscopic moment of the wheel acting on the front end of the car, and state whether it tends to make the front of the car turn to the left or right.   How is this avoided in the modern, individually suspended wheel?

6.4-18   The rotating parts of an automobile engine have a moment of inertia of 160 lb ft sec².   At 60 mph it rotates at 2,000 rpm counterclockwise, as viewed from the rear.   If a left turn of radius 800 ft is made at 60 mph, determine how much the gyroscopic couple affects the pressure on the front and rear wheels, which are 128 in. apart.

6.4-19   In a certain automobile, the engine is mounted crosswise, so that its rotation axis is normal to the direction of motion.   In which direction should the engine rotate in order to stabilize the car on turns?

6.4-20   A single-engine airplane has a three-bladed propeller weighing 122 lb with a radius of gyration of 1.45 ft.   Determine the gyroscopic moment exerted by the propeller on the airplane when making a horizontal turn to the left of ½-mile radius at a speed of 160 mph with the propeller rotating clockwise at 1,000 rpm, as viewed from the rear.   How is this moment counteracted?

6.4-21 The turboprop engine and the three-bladed propeller of a single-engine airplane
        have the weights w, radii of gyration k, and rotational speeds as given in Fig.
        P 6.4-21. (Note that the propeller rotates clockwise and the engine counter-

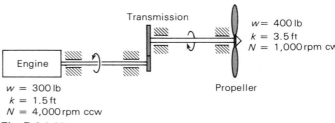

Transmission

$w = 400 \text{ lb}$
$k = 3.5 \text{ ft}$
$N = 1,000 \text{ rpm cw}$

Engine

Propeller

$w = 300 \text{ lb}$
$k = 1.5 \text{ ft}$
$N = 4,000 \text{ rpm ccw}$

Fig. P 6.4-21

clockwise, as viewed from the rear.) If the airplane makes a horizontal turn
to the left at a rate of 4°/sec, determine the gyroscopic moment exerted on the
airplane, indicating which way it tends to turn the nose. Ignore the moment of
inertia of the transmission gears.

6.4-22 The three-bladed propeller on a single-engine airplane has a moment of inertia
        of 90 lb ft sec² about its spin axis. With the propeller rotating at 1,800 rpm
        clockwise as seen by the pilot, the plane makes a left turn in a horizontal circle
        of radius R at a speed of 100 mph, maintaining an angle of bank of 45°. Deter-
        mine the moments that the pilot must exert through the use of the ailerons,
        elevators, and rudder to balance the gyroscopic moment of the propeller. Is
        the pitching moment of the elevators nose up or nose down?

6.4-23 A single-engine airplane has a 250-lb three-bladed propeller with radius of
        gyration of 2.0 ft. With the propeller rotating at 1,500 rpm, the airplane under-
        goes a maneuver, horizontally turning through an angle of 90° in 16 sec. Deter-
        mine the gyroscopic moment imposed on the propeller-shaft bearings.

6.4-24 A solid circular cylinder of mass m, length l, and radius r rotates with angular
        velocity ω_a relative to a platform that rotates about its vertical axis with angular
        velocity ω_b, as shown in Fig. P 6.4-24. Determine the gyroscopic forces exerted by
        the cylinder on its bearings, whose distance is L.

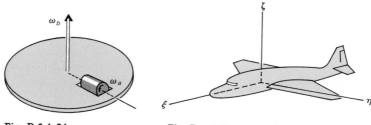

ω_b

ω_a

ζ

ξ

η

Fig. P 6.4-24   **Fig. P 6.4-25**

6.4-25 The principal moments of inertia of a certain airplane are $I_\xi = 0.5I$, $I_\eta = 0.6I$,
        and $I_\zeta = I$. If the airplane turns with constant angular velocity $\omega = \omega(0.50 \, \mathbf{1}_\xi + 0.866 \, \mathbf{1}_\eta)$, determine the aerodynamic torque about each axis. See Fig.
        P 6.4-25.

6.4-26   The body-fixed axes ξ, η, ζ of the airplane shown in Fig. P 6.4-25 are principal axes with $I_\xi = 5,000$ lb ft sec², $I_\eta = 4,000$ lb ft sec², and $I_\zeta = 8,000$ lb ft sec². While undergoing flight test, the airplane is put into a maneuver consisting of a steady roll of 0.2 rps about the ξ axis while diving in a vertical circle with constant speed $v_\xi = 500$ mph and normal acceleration of $5g$. Determine the torque that the control surfaces must exert about the ξ, η, ζ axes as a function of the roll angle θ of the left wing measured from the normal to the vertical plane.

6.4-27   If the wheel in Prob. 6.1-10 weighs w lb and the distance between the horizontal bearings is h, determine the bearing reactions at A and B due to ω_ζ and ω_z. The moment of inertia of the wheel about its spin axis is I_ζ.

6.4-28   The axle of an ore crusher wheel of mass m (solid cylinder) rotates with angular velocity $\dot\psi$ about the vertical axis, as shown in Fig. P 6.4-28. Determine the force between the wheel and the track. Consider the wheel in pure rolling motion in its center plane.

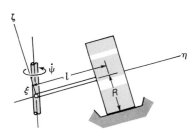

Fig. P 6.4-28

6.5 MISCELLANEOUS PROBLEMS IN GYRO DYNAMICS

In the treatment of these problems we confine ourselves to a detailed investigation of the steady-state motion of a rigid body of rotational symmetry[1] and only occasionally discuss its small nutations[2] (mostly fast oscillations) superimposed on the steady (mostly slow) precession due to the initial conditions. The theory presented here is of great practical importance for the understanding of all gyroscopic instruments—such as the gyrocompass, rate gyro, integrating gyro, gyro horizon, stable platform, in short all mechanical elements involved in conventional and inertial navigation—and of the behavior of spinning missiles, gyroscopic ship stabilization, gyrostabilized monorail vehicles, and other similar devices and phenomena. Again, all our considerations are based on the fundamental equations (6.3-4) and (6.3-5).

SLOW AND FAST PRECESSION OF THE HEAVY TOP

The top shown in Fig. 6.5-1 is a body of rotational symmetry about the spin axis ζ, which is rotating about a fixed point O on this axis. Its center

[1] It is not necessary that the body be geometrically symmetrical, but its mass distribution must be such that $I_\xi = I_\eta$ and that the center of mass is on the ζ axis.

[2] Nutation, from the Latin *nutatio*, nodding.

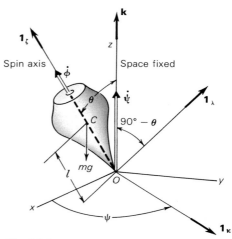

Fig. 6.5-1

of mass has a distance l from point O, which serves as common origin for the orthogonal ζ, κ, λ axes as well as the space-fixed x, y, z axes. In steady precession the body-fixed spin axis ζ describes a circular cone of half angle θ about the z axis, and the node axis κ† (line of intersection between the planes normal to $\dot{\phi}$ and $\dot{\psi}$, respectively; κ is not a body-fixed axis) sweeps the xy plane with the constant angular velocity of precession $\dot{\psi}$. The constant eigenspin $\dot{\phi}$ of the top, that is, the top's angular speed with respect to the ζ, κ, λ frame of reference, is usually high compared with $\dot{\psi}$. The weight of the top points in negative z direction and produces the force moment

$$\mathbf{M}_O = mgl \sin \theta \, \mathbf{1}_\kappa \tag{6.5-1}$$

about the node axis κ.

We first consider the case that $\dot{\phi}$ is so large compared with $\dot{\psi}$ that the moment of momentum can simply be written (with sufficient accuracy for practical purposes)—see Eq. (6.3-4)—

$$\mathbf{H}_O = I_{\text{spin}} \dot{\phi} \mathbf{1}_\zeta \qquad I_\zeta \equiv I_{\text{spin}}$$

Considering that $\mathbf{H}_O$ is expressed in ζ, κ, λ coordinates (here the κ and λ components are zero, because we neglected $\dot{\psi}$ compared with $\dot{\phi}$), which rotate with $\boldsymbol{\omega} = \dot{\psi}\mathbf{k}$ with respect to an inertial frame of reference, we have for the time rate of change of $\mathbf{H}_O$

$$\dot{\mathbf{H}}_O = \overset{\frown}{\mathbf{H}}_O + \dot{\psi}\mathbf{k} \times \mathbf{H}_O$$

† The Greek letter κ is used, because in the classical German literature on gyroscopes this line is called *Knotenlinie*.

Because $\dot\phi$ is constant, we have $\widehat{\mathbf{H}}_O = \mathbf{0}$, and thus we obtain

$$\dot{\mathbf{H}}_O = \boldsymbol{\omega} \times \mathbf{H}_O = \dot\psi\mathbf{k} \times I_{\text{spin}}\dot\phi\mathbf{1}_\zeta = I_{\text{spin}}\dot\psi\dot\phi \sin\theta\, \mathbf{1}_\kappa \qquad (6.5\text{-}2)$$

since $\mathbf{k} \times \mathbf{1}_\zeta = \sin\theta\,\mathbf{1}_\kappa$ (see Fig. 6.5-1). Therefore Eq. (6.3-4) yields with Eqs. (6.5-1) and (6.5-2)

$$mgl \sin\theta = I_{\text{spin}}\dot\psi\dot\phi \sin\theta$$

and the angular speed of precession is

$$\dot\psi = \frac{mgl}{I_{\text{spin}}\dot\phi} \qquad\blacktriangleleft\qquad (6.5\text{-}3)$$

which verifies our initial statement that $\dot\psi$ is constant when $\dot\phi$ is constant and our assumption that $\dot\psi$ is very small when $\dot\phi$ is very large, as is usually the case in gyroscopic instruments. Note also that Eq. (6.5-3) is independent of θ and that $\dot\psi$ is proportional to the product of the top's weight and the distance l of the center of gravity from the pivot.

If $\dot\psi$ is not neglected in the calculation of $\mathbf{H}_O$, we obtain by inspection of Fig. 6.5-1

$$\mathbf{H}_O = (\dot\phi + \dot\psi \cos\theta)I_{\text{spin}}\mathbf{1}_\zeta + \dot\psi \sin\theta\, I_{\text{normal}}\mathbf{1}_\lambda$$

where I_{normal} is the moment of inertia of the body about any axis normal to the spin axis through point O. With $\widehat{\dot{\mathbf{H}}}_O = \mathbf{0}$ we find, considering that in regular precession $\mathbf{H}_O$ the ζ, κ, λ coordinate axes rotate with the constant angular velocity $\dot\psi\mathbf{k}$,

$$\begin{aligned}
\dot{\mathbf{H}}_O &= \dot\psi\mathbf{k} \times [(\dot\phi + \dot\psi \cos\theta)I_{\text{spin}}\mathbf{1}_\zeta + \dot\psi \sin\theta\, I_{\text{normal}}\mathbf{1}_\lambda] \\
&= I_{\text{spin}}(\dot\psi\dot\phi + \dot\psi^2 \cos\theta) \sin\theta\, \mathbf{1}_\kappa - \dot\psi^2 \cos\theta \sin\theta\, I_{\text{normal}}\mathbf{1}_\kappa
\end{aligned}$$

Since $\mathbf{M}_O = mgl \sin\theta\, \mathbf{1}_\kappa$, Eq. (6.3-4) yields

$$mgl = \dot\psi^2 \cos\theta\, (I_{\text{spin}} - I_{\text{normal}}) + \dot\psi\dot\phi I_{\text{spin}}$$

This quadratic equation in $\dot\psi$ is usually rewritten by eliminating $\dot\phi$ in favor of $\omega_{\text{spin}} = \dot\phi + \dot\psi \cos\theta$, which is the projection of the total angular velocity $\boldsymbol{\omega} = \dot{\boldsymbol{\phi}} + \dot{\boldsymbol{\psi}}$ on the spin axis:[1]

$$I_{\text{normal}}\dot\psi^2 \cos\theta - I_{\text{spin}}\dot\psi\omega_{\text{spin}} + mgl = 0$$

[1] Consider that the top's steady precessional motion is brought about as follows. The top is first given the eigenspin $\dot\phi$, its spin axis ζ held fixed at an arbitrary angle θ with the vertical z axis. Then it is given the proper impulse such that θ remains constant and the ζz plane rotates about the z axis with one of the precessional angular velocities $\dot\psi$ determined by Eqs. (6.5-4) and (6.5-5). The total angular velocity of the top is then $\boldsymbol\omega = \dot{\boldsymbol\phi} + \dot{\boldsymbol\psi}$. If the initial impulse is not exactly right, the steady state cannot occur, and nutations (high-frequency oscillations) are superimposed on the steady precession (Fig. 6.5-3 for the case of slow precession).

This equation has two solutions:

$$\dot\psi_1 = \frac{I_{\text{spin}}\omega_{\text{spin}}}{2I_{\text{normal}}\cos\theta}\left(1 - \sqrt{1 - \frac{4I_{\text{normal}}\cos\theta\, mgl}{I_{\text{spin}}^2\omega_{\text{spin}}^2}}\right) \blacktriangleleft \quad (6.5\text{-}4)$$

$$\dot\psi_2 = \frac{I_{\text{spin}}\omega_{\text{spin}}}{2I_{\text{normal}}\cos\theta}\left(1 + \sqrt{1 - \frac{4I_{\text{normal}}\cos\theta\, mgl}{I_{\text{spin}}^2\omega_{\text{spin}}^2}}\right) \blacktriangleleft \quad (6.5\text{-}5)$$

Equation (6.5-4) yields the small value $\dot\psi_1$, a slow motion of the spin axis, known as the slow precession. It vanishes when the external moment vanishes ($l \to 0$). For large ω_{spin} we find (considering that $\sqrt{1-x} \approx 1 - x/2$ for $|x| \ll 1$) that

$$\dot\psi_1 \approx \frac{mgl}{I_{\text{spin}}\omega_{\text{spin}}} \qquad \text{with } \omega_{\text{spin}} \approx \dot\phi \qquad (6.5\text{-}6)$$

where ω_{spin} is about equal to $\dot\phi$, since $\dot\psi_1$ is very small. Hence, as we have already seen—see Eq. (6.5-3)—the slow precession decreases with increasing eigenspin $\dot\phi$.

Equation (6.5-5) yields the large value $\dot\psi_2$, fast motion of the spin axis, known as the fast precession,[1] which, in contrast to the slow precession $\dot\psi_1$, increases for large eigenspin $\dot\phi$ about in proportion to $\dot\phi$. It is, however, hardly possible to give a top with large $\dot\phi$ exactly the right impulse in order to bring about a steady fast precession. When this is tried in practical tests, the result is almost invariably the so-called pseudoregular precession, consisting of a "mixture" of slow precession with superimposed nutations (see Fig. 6.5-3), the nutations having an angular velocity about equal to that of the fast precession $\dot\psi_2$ (see the footnote on page 380 and the footnote on this page).

When the external moment vanishes, that is, when in our case points O and C coincide, Eq. (6.5-5) yields

$$\dot\psi_2 = \frac{I_{\text{spin}}\omega_{\text{spin}}}{I_{\text{normal}}\cos\theta} \qquad (6.5\text{-}7)$$

for the fast precession of a symmetrical body in torque-free motion. Furthermore note that for $l = 0$ (no external moment) the slow precession $\dot\psi_1$, as given by Eq. (6.5-4), is zero. We return briefly to the study of this torque-free motion in the next paragraph.

Both the slow and the fast precession are possible only if the radicand in Eqs. (6.5-4) and (6.5-5) is positive. This is the case, or in other words, a

[1] In the classic literature on gyroscopes (see, for example, the works by M. Schuler, one of the great pioneers in the development of the theory and design of gyroscopic instruments at the beginning of this century) the slow and fast precessions are called regular precession and regular nutation, respectively. This makes sense, because the nutations shown in Fig. 6.5-3 (see also the end of the footnote on page 380) almost take place with the angular velocity of the fast precession $\dot\psi_2$—see Eqs. (6.5-5) and (6.5-7).

stable motion is possible, only if

$$\omega_{\text{spin}}^2 > 4 \frac{I_{\text{normal}}}{I_{\text{spin}}} \frac{mgl}{I_{\text{spin}}} \cos\theta \qquad \blacktriangleleft \quad (6.5\text{-}8)$$

Hence we see that for a "standing-up" top ($\cos\theta > 0$) both the slow precession and the fast precession become unstable when the spin ω_{spin} drops under the value demanded by inequality (6.5-8).

For a gyro pendulum ($\cos\theta < 0$), however, inequality (6.5-8) is always satisfied; that is, no unstable motions are possible, whatever the magnitude of the spin ω_{spin}. Considering the special case $\theta = 0$, that is, the sleeping top with no regular precession, since $\mathbf{M}_o = \mathbf{0}$, the stability relationship (6.5-8) becomes

$$\omega_{\text{spin}}^2 > 4 \frac{I_{\text{normal}}}{I_{\text{spin}}} \frac{mgl}{I_{\text{spin}}} \qquad (6.5\text{-}9)$$

This expression is often used to determine the spin of missiles and projectiles necessary for their stable motion. Referring to Fig. 6.5-2, the drag $\mathbf{D}$

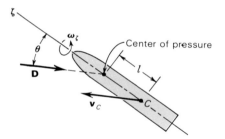

Fig. 6.5-2   Spin stabilization of a projectile.

coincides with the spin axis as long as the velocity $\mathbf{v}_C$ of the projectile points in the direction of the spin axis. As soon as $\mathbf{v}_C$ deviates from this direction, the drag $\mathbf{D}$ does also, and its line of action passes at an angle θ through the center of pressure (determined by the aerodynamic properties) ahead of the center of mass. Thus $\mathbf{D}$ "produces" a moment $Dl \sin\theta$ about the center of mass C, exactly as the weight produces a moment $mgl \sin\theta$ about the fixed point O of the heavy top. Hence we replace mgl by Dl in the relationship (6.5-9), and we obtain, as criterion for the stabilizing spin of the projectile,

$$\omega_{\text{spin}}^2 > 4 \frac{I_{\text{normal}}}{I_{\text{spin}}} \frac{Dl}{I_{\text{spin}}} \qquad (6.5\text{-}10)$$

As pointed out above, the steady precession almost never occurs in its pure form. Usually we have a superposition (see Fig. 6.5-3) of slow precession

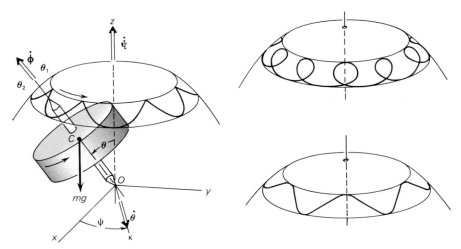

Fig. 6.5-3   Possible forms of nutation.

and nutations, which for high eigenspin $\dot{\phi}$ occur with an angular velocity about equal to that of the fast precession.   Then the angle θ is no longer constant, but oscillates between two limiting angles θ_1 and θ_2.   The exact analytical treatment of this general case requires the use of mathematical tools beyond the scope of the present work.

ILLUSTRATIVE EXAMPLE 6.5-1
If, from the apex of a top, a string is wound clockwise, as shown in Fig. 6.5-4, determine the direction of the steady precession.

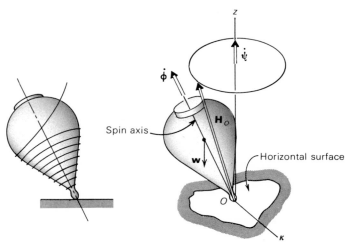

Fig. 6.5-4

SOLUTION: Looking toward the origin along the node axis (axis κ in Fig. 6.5-4), the moment of the weight is a vector toward the positive end of the node axis, and the relationship $\mathbf{M}_O = \dot{\mathbf{H}}_O$ requires the vector $\mathbf{H}_O$ to precess accordingly with $\dot{\psi}$ directed in the positive z direction, as shown in Fig. 6.5-4. Since the eigenspin $\dot{\phi}$ is generally much larger than the regular precession $\dot{\psi}$, the moment-of-momentum vector $\mathbf{H}_O$ lies very close to the spin axis. If the string is wound counterclockwise from the apex, so that $\dot{\phi}$ is negative, the reader should verify that $\dot{\psi}$ is also negative.

TORQUE-FREE MOTION OF A SYMMETRICAL RIGID BODY
In the preceding paragraph we found that, lacking an external moment about the center of mass C of a symmetrical rigid body, the only possible rotational motion consists of a constant fast precession, from now on, for the sake of brevity, called precession:[1]

$$\dot{\psi}_2 = \frac{I_{\text{spin}}\omega_{\text{spin}}}{I_{\text{normal}} \cos \theta} \qquad \blacktriangleleft \quad (6.5\text{-}7)$$

superimposed on the constant eigenspin $\dot{\phi}$. We saw, furthermore, that the direction of the angular velocity vector $\dot{\psi}$ defines an axis fixed in inertial space and that the spin axis, and therefore also the eigenspin vector $\dot{\phi}$, precesses at constant angle θ about this space-fixed axis with constant angular velocity $\dot{\psi}$ (see Fig. 6.5-5). Now, since an external moment $\mathbf{M}_C$

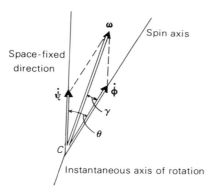

Fig. 6.5-5

is absent, we have—see Eqs. (6.3-5)—$\mathbf{h}_C = $ const, which therefore must coincide with the space-fixed precession angle $\dot{\psi}$. The total angular velocity ω of the rotating body is again

$$\omega = \dot{\phi} + \dot{\psi} \qquad (6.5\text{-}11)$$

The relationship between θ and γ (see Fig. 6.5-5) is easily established.

[1] In the classic literature on gyroscopes it is called nutation (see the footnote on page 381).

Considering that $\omega_{\text{spin}} \equiv \omega \cos \gamma$, Eq. (6.5-7) yields

$$\omega \cos \gamma = \dot\psi \, \frac{I_{\text{normal}}}{I_{\text{spin}}} \cos \theta$$

and Fig. (6.5-5) shows that

$$\omega \sin \gamma = \dot\psi \sin \theta$$

Division of these two equations then yields

$$\tan \gamma = \tan \theta \, \frac{I_{\text{spin}}}{I_{\text{normal}}} \qquad \blacktriangleleft \quad (6.5\text{-}12)$$

Since $\boldsymbol{\omega}$ lies in one plane with $\dot{\boldsymbol\psi}$ and $\dot{\boldsymbol\phi}$, the vector $\boldsymbol{\omega}$, which coincides by its very definition with the instantaneous axis of rotation, also rotates at constant angle $\theta - \gamma$ (see Fig. 6.5-5) about the space-fixed axis with the constant angular velocity $\dot\psi$, thereby describing a conical surface fixed in space, usually called the space cone. Hence, one may picture the motion of a symmetrical rigid body as pure rolling of a body cone (half angle γ) on a space cone (half angle $\theta - \gamma$) with angular velocity $\boldsymbol{\omega}$ (see Fig. 6.5-6).

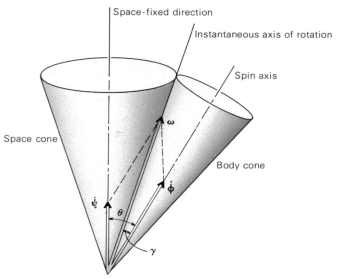

Fig. 6.5-6

Finally we rewrite Eq. (6.5-7) by substituting $\omega_{\text{spin}} = \dot\phi + \dot\psi \cos \theta$:

$$\dot\psi = \frac{\dot\phi}{\cos \theta} \, \frac{I_{\text{spin}}}{I_{\text{normal}} - I_{\text{spin}}} \qquad \blacktriangleleft \quad (6.5\text{-}13)$$

Remember that in the case of torque-free motion I_{normal} is the moment of inertia of the symmetrical body about any axis normal to the spin axis through the center of mass C. Now Eq. (6.5-13) serves to discuss two different cases:

(a)
$$0 < \frac{I_{\text{spin}}}{I_{\text{normal}}} < 1 \qquad \text{slender body}$$

Then $I_{\text{normal}} - I_{\text{spin}} > 0$, and thus also $\cos\theta$ is positive, that is, we have $0° < \theta < 90°$. Therefore the motion of a slender symmetrical body is as shown in Fig. 6.5-6, the body cone rolling "outside" around the space cone. Thus an observer riding on the spin axis around the space-fixed axis with the precessional velocity $\dot{\psi}$ sees the body spinning about its spin axis in the same direction as he rotates about the space-fixed axis. This type of motion is called direct precession.

(b)
$$1 < \frac{I_{\text{spin}}}{I_{\text{normal}}} < 2 \qquad \text{oblate body}[1]$$

Then $I_{\text{normal}} - I_{\text{spin}} < 0$, and thus also $\cos\theta$ is negative, that is, we have $90° < \theta < 180°$. Therefore, the motion of an oblate symmetrical body is as shown in Fig. 6.5-7, the body cone rolling around the space cone, enclosing

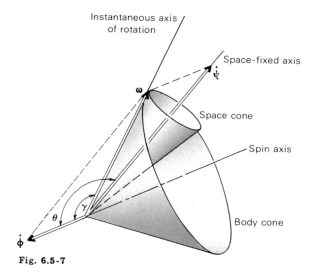

Fig. 6.5-7

[1] Answer yourself the question why I_{spin} cannot be larger than $2I_{\text{normal}}$.

the latter.   Thus an observer riding on the spin axis around the space-fixed axis with the angular velocity $\dot{\psi}$ sees the body spinning about its spin axis in the opposite direction as he rotates about the space-fixed axis.   This type of motion is called retrograde precession.

ILLUSTRATIVE EXAMPLE 6.5-2
A missile with $I_{\text{spin}}/I_{\text{normal}} = \frac{1}{20}$ spins at a speed $\omega_{\text{spin}} = 10\pi$ rad/sec and precesses at an angle $\theta = 5°$ with a fixed direction in an inertial reference frame.   Determine the precessional velocity $\dot{\psi}$ and the angle γ between the resultant angular-velocity vector $\boldsymbol{\omega}$ and the longitudinal axis (spin axis).
SOLUTION: Figure 6.5-8 shows the various angular-velocity and moment-of-momentum

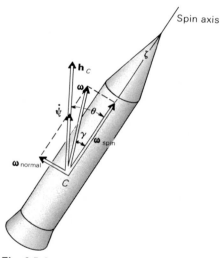

Fig. 6.5-8

vectors.   The precessional speed is given by Eq. (6.5-7):

$$\dot{\psi} = \frac{I_{\text{spin}}\omega_{\text{spin}}}{I_{\text{normal}}\cos\theta} = \frac{10\pi}{20 \times 0.999} = 1.572 \text{ rad/sec}$$

that is, about $\frac{1}{20}$ of the spin rate.   Since $I_{\text{normal}} > I_{\text{spin}}$, we clearly have direct precession.

The angle γ between the spin axis and the vector $\boldsymbol{\omega}$ is obtained from—see Eq. (6.5-12)—

$$\tan\gamma = \frac{I_{\text{spin}}}{I_{\text{normal}}}\tan\theta = \frac{1}{20} \times 0.0875$$

$$\gamma = 0.00438 \text{ rad}$$

Thus the body cone is only $\frac{1}{20}$ as wide as the space cone, as shown in Fig. 6.5-9.

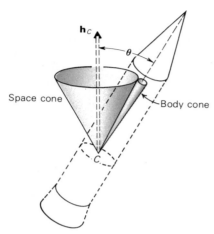

Fig. 6.5-9

ILLUSTRATIVE EXAMPLE 6.5-3
An oblate symmetric satellite is characterized by the relationship $I_{\text{spin}}/I_{\text{normal}} = 1.40$. It is spin-stabilized in space, so that it has angular momentum $h_C{}^\circ = I_{\text{spin}}\omega_{\text{spin}}$ about its axis of symmetry (see Fig. 6.5-10). Hence, the spin ω_{spin} equals the eigenspin $\dot\phi$. At

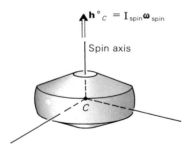

Fig. 6.5-10

time t it encounters a meteor that imparts a moment impulse $\int_t^{t+\Delta t} M_C\,dt = \hat M_C$ about a central axis normal to the spin axis (Δt very short). Describe its subsequent angular motion and draw the space and body cones.

SOLUTION: The moment impulse results in a change of moment of momentum:

$$\hat M_C = \Delta h_C = I_{\text{normal}}\omega_{\text{normal}}$$

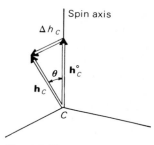

Fig. 6.5-11

where $\Delta \mathbf{h}_C$ is normal to the spin axis, as shown in Fig. 6.5-11. The new moment-of-momentum vector $\mathbf{h}_C$ then remains fixed in magnitude and direction after the impact, since the satellite is torque-free. The problem is that of torque-free motion for which the initial conditions are $\omega_{\text{normal}} = \hat{M}_C / I_{\text{normal}}$ and ω_{spin} as given, with $\mathbf{h}_C = \text{const}$.

For the torque-free motion, the angles between the new $\mathbf{h}_C$, the spin axis, and $\boldsymbol{\omega}$ remain constant, and the plane containing these vectors rotates about the new $\mathbf{h}_C$ with constant angular velocity. The angle between this $\mathbf{h}_C$ vector and the spin axis is found by referring to Fig. 6.5-11:

$$\tan \theta = \frac{\Delta h_C}{h_C{}^\circ} = \frac{\hat{M}}{I_{\text{spin}}\omega_{\text{spin}}}$$

The angle γ between the spin axis and the $\boldsymbol{\omega}$ vector is found from Eq. (6.5-12):

$$\tan \gamma = \frac{I_{\text{spin}}}{I_{\text{normal}}} \tan \theta = 1.40 \frac{\hat{M}}{I_{\text{spin}}\omega_{\text{spin}}}$$

The space and body cones can then be drawn as shown in Fig. 6.5-12.

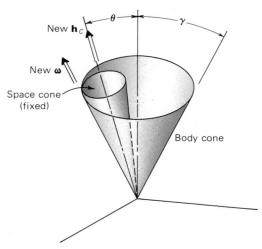

Fig. 6.5-12

In conclusion let us treat a few gyroscopic instruments. Here the concept of the gyroscopic moment, as defined in Sec. 6.3, following the derivation of Euler's equations (6.3-18), and as used also in Sec. 6.4 (see Figs. 6.4-7 and 6.4-8 and also Illustrative Example 6.4-3), is very useful. Because gyro wheels spin with very high constant angular velocity compared with the angular velocity of the vehicle to which the instrument is tied, the moment of momentum $\mathbf{h}_C$ with respect to an inertial frame of the gyro may safely be taken to be that of the wheel alone, computed with respect to the frame (inner gimbal), which carries the bearings of the wheel. As this gimbal rotates with angular velocity $\boldsymbol{\omega}$ in an inertial reference frame, the bearings exert the force couple of moment on the wheel—see Eqs. (6.3-5)—

$$\mathbf{M}_C = \boldsymbol{\omega} \times \mathbf{h}_C \qquad (6.5\text{-}14)$$

because $\overset{\frown}{\mathbf{h}}_C = \mathbf{0}$, owing to the constant spin of the wheel. On expansion of Eq. (6.5-14) in coordinates, $\mathbf{M}_C$ is obtained in gimbal-fixed coordinates.

Now taking a quasi-static point of view, we may reinterpret this equation as the following equilibrium relationship:

$$\mathbf{M}_C + (-\boldsymbol{\omega} \times \mathbf{h}_C) = \mathbf{0}$$

stating that the force moment $\mathbf{M}_C$ exerted by the gimbal on the gyro wheel and the gyroscopic moment $-\boldsymbol{\omega} \times \mathbf{h}_C$ exerted by the wheel on the frame are in equilibrium.

RATE-OF-TURN GYRO

One of the most useful and dependable gyro instruments is the turn indicator or rate-of-turn gyro (briefly called rate gyro). It is used, as the name implies, to measure the rate of turn of a vehicle (for example, an airplane or a rocket). Its basic functioning is very easily understood. Figure 6.5-13 shows a rate gyro mounted on a moving vehicle. The fast-spinning gyro wheel is mounted on a frame that is tied by springs to the vehicle in such a way that the rotor axis is forced to participate in the turn of the vehicle. We let its

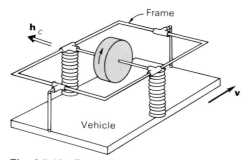

Fig. 6.5-13 Rate-of-turn gyro on vehicle moving along a straight line.

angular velocity be ω, as shown in Fig. 6.5-14, which is very small compared with the spin velocity of the wheel; then the gyro rotor exerts a gyroscopic moment $-\omega \times \mathbf{h}_C$ on the spring-supported frame, thereby causing an angular precessional displacement, as shown in Fig. 6.5-14. This angular

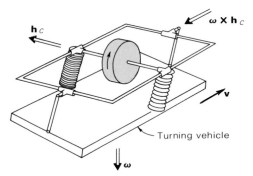

Fig. **6.5-14** Deflected position of rate-of-turn gyro on vehicle moving through a curve with angular velocity ω.

displacement is proportional to the angular speed ω of the vehicle. The sensitivity of the instrument obviously depends on the relationship between the gyroscopic moment and the spring stiffness. The larger, for a given rate of turn, the gyroscopic moment, the larger the angular momentum $\mathbf{h}_C$ of the gyro wheel, and the softer the springs, the larger the angular displacement of the spring-supported frame.

FLOATED INTEGRATING RATE GYRO

The sensitivity of the rate gyro is greatly enhanced when the springs are completely removed, and instead, the precessional rotation of the gyro-wheel frame is resisted by the torque caused by the shearing of a viscous fluid. A schematic representation of a conventional floated integrating gyro design is displayed in Fig. 6.5-15. Again the gyro wheel is mounted

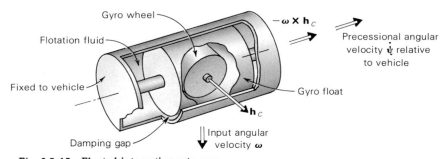

Fig. **6.5-15** Floated integrating rate gyro.

so that its axis has to participate in the turn of the vehicle.   The gyro wheel is enclosed in a cylindrical casing (gyro float), which is surrounded by a heavy viscous fluid in such a way that the gyro float is separated from the concentric outer vehicle-fixed cylindrical casing by a narrow gap.   The liquid in the gap serves, besides relieving the bearings carrying the gyro float, the purpose of providing a viscous torque proportional to the precessional velocity $\dot{\psi}$ in order to balance the gyroscopic moment $-\boldsymbol{\omega} \times \mathbf{h}_C$, so that we have the relationship

$$-\boldsymbol{\omega} \times \mathbf{h}_C + c\dot{\psi} = 0$$

We have, therefore, proportionality between the rate of turn ω and the precessional speed $\dot{\psi}$:

$$\dot{\psi} = k\omega$$

In other words, the precessional angle ψ through which the gyro float turns relative to the outer vehicle-fixed casing is proportional to the angle of turn of the vehicle, that is, to $\int_{t_0}^{t} \omega \, dt$.   An instrument constant k equal to 100 can easily be realized, and thus extreme sensitivity requirements may be satisfied.   Therefore the floated integrating gyro represents one of the most important sensing devices used in modern inertial navigation.

THE GYROCOMPASS

Among the gyroscopic instruments the gyrocompass is undoubtedly the most interesting from the point of view of mechanics, as well as an example of true engineering ingenuity.   Here we consider only the basic dynamical properties of this device, assuming, for the sake of simplicity, that it is installed at an earth-fixed location of latitude λ (see Fig. 6.5-16).   We first

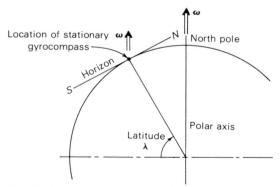

Fig. 6.5-16   Cross section through pole axis and location of gyrocompass; meridional plane.

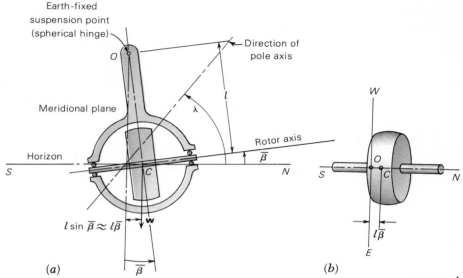

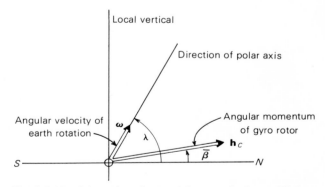

Fig. 6.5-17   Equilibrium position of pendulous gyrocompass.   (a) View normal to meridional[1] plane (angle $\bar{\beta}$ greatly exaggerated, actually little more than 10^{-3} rad).   (b) View looking down on horizontal plane (showing only the gyro rotor).

deal with the equilibrium position of a gyrocompass (see Fig. 6.5-17), consisting of a rotor, driven at high constant speed, suspended in the earth-fixed point O so that it can swing in all directions.[1]   Referring to Figs. 6.5-17 and 6.5-18 one can easily show that in its equilibrium position the gyro-rotor axis points north with a very small angle of elevation $\bar{\beta}$ above the horizon.   For actual gyrocompass designs the angle $\bar{\beta}$ is only little larger than 10^{-3} rad.   From Fig. 6.5-18 we immediately deduce that in

Fig. **6.5-18**   Orientation of essential vectors in the equilibrium position of the gyrocompass.

[1] Such suspension can, for example, be realized by a floating support, O being the metacenter of the floating gyrocompass assembly.

equilibrium the sum of the gravity force moment $wl\bar{\beta}$ (w = weight of the gyro-rotor assembly) and of the gyroscopic moment $-\boldsymbol{\omega} \times \mathbf{h}_C$ about O must be zero, the latter being caused by the fact that the angular-momentum vector $\mathbf{h}_C$ of the gyro rotor rotates about the pole axis with the angular velocity $\boldsymbol{\omega}$ of the earth. Hence with $h_C = Cn$, where C is the moment of inertia of the gyro rotor about its spin axis and n is its spin velocity,[1] we have

$$-\omega Cn \sin (\lambda - \bar{\beta}) + wl \sin \bar{\beta} = 0$$

or with $\cos \bar{\beta} \approx 1$ and $\sin \bar{\beta} \approx \bar{\beta}$

$$-\omega Cn \sin \lambda + \omega Cn\bar{\beta} \cos \lambda + wl\bar{\beta} = 0$$

Thus we find that in the equilibrium position the elevation angle is

$$\bar{\beta} = \frac{\omega Cn \sin \lambda}{\omega Cn \cos \lambda + wl}$$

Since in practical cases $wl/\omega Cn$ is of the order of magnitude 10^3, we may safely write

$$\bar{\beta} = \frac{\omega Cn \sin \lambda}{wl} \tag{6.5-15}$$

Somewhat more difficult is the investigation of the behavior of a gyrocompass when it is deflected from its equilibrium position. Then it carries out a periodic motion such that a point on the gyro-rotor axis describes an elongated ellipse about the equilibrium position in a plane normal to the meridional plane.

PROBLEMS

6.5-1   A toy top consists of a thin disk of radius r on a shaft that extends a distance l on each side of the disk. When spun to an angular speed ω_{spin} and set on an indentation on the floor so that the pivot point remains stationary, as shown in Fig. P 6.5-1, determine the conditions for steady precession. Choose $l = r = \frac{1}{2}$ ft and $\omega_{\text{spin}} = 20$ rps $= 126$ rad/sec, and plot $mgl/I_{\text{normal}} \cos \theta$ versus $\dot{\psi}$ for $\theta = 10$ and $30°$.

Fig. P 6.5-1

[1] Here we used a notation frequently used in the engineering literature on gyroscopes: $C \equiv I_{\text{spin}}$ and $n \equiv \omega_{\text{spin}} \approx \dot{\phi}$ for fast-spinning gyro rotors. Here $\omega_{\text{spin}} \approx \dot{\phi}$ is definitely allowed, since $\dot{\phi} \gg \omega_{\text{earth}}$.

6.5-2   A top spins on the floor of an elevator with its spin axis inclined at an angle θ with the vertical. If the elevator accelerates downward, discuss qualitatively what happens to the tilt angle and the precessional velocity.

6.5-3   For steady precession, show that the angle between the momentum vector $\mathbf{H}_0$ and the spin axis is given by the equation

$$\tan \alpha_{1,2} = \tfrac{1}{2} \tan \theta \left(1 \pm \sqrt{1 - \frac{4w\,Al\cos\theta}{C^2 n^2}} \right)$$

where the minus sign must be used for the slow precession. $C \equiv I_{\text{spin}}$ and $A = I_{\text{normal}}$.

6.5-4   Referring to Prob. 6.5-3, show that for large n, the angle α corresponding to the slow and fast precessional speeds is

$$\tan \alpha_1 = \frac{Awl \sin \theta}{C^2 n^2} \qquad \tan \alpha_2 = \tan \theta$$

6.5-5   A demonstration gyro wheel is pinned at O and can be made to precess about the z axis in either direction by adjusting the arm b of the balancing weight w (see Fig. P 6.5-5). Derive the equation for the steady precession of the system, and describe its motion.

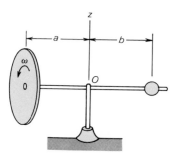

Fig. P 6.5-5

6.5-6   A top consists of a thin disk 4 in. in diameter weighing $\tfrac{1}{4}$ lb, with a thin pin of negligible weight that extends $1\tfrac{1}{2}$ in. from the center of the disk. If the axis of the top precesses steadily at an angle of 30° with the vertical, and at a rate of 1 revolution per 8 sec, determine the spin rate n. Is the precession direct or retrograde?

6.5-7   A symmetric body spins under a moment-free condition about its axis of symmetry, which rotates at a constant angle of 30° about the space-fixed z axis. The eigenspin of the body relative to the ζz plane is $\dot\phi = 100$ rpm, and the ζz plane rotates about the z axis at $\dot\psi = 10$ rpm. Determine the ratio $I_{\text{spin}}/I_{\text{normal}}$ of the body, and describe its shape.

6.5-8   Because of faulty initial conditions a rotating space station in the form of a large ring undergoes steady precession $\dot{\psi}$ at a constant angle θ, as shown in Fig. P 6.5-8, where the magnitude of the angle is shown greatly exaggerated. Determine the acceleration experienced by a crew member in the ring.

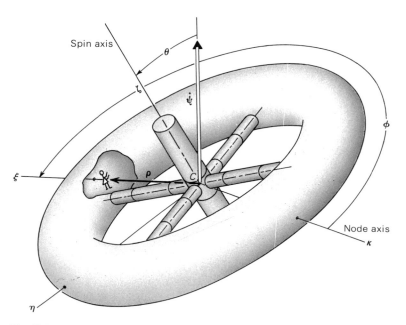

Fig. P 6.5-8

6.5-9   The following information is given for a rate-of-turn indicator. Rotor weight = 0.80 lb, radius of gyration of rotor = 1.0 in., spin = 18,000 rpm, $K = 1.3$ lb in./rad (see Fig. P 6.5-9). Determine the rotation about the output axis when the angular rotation of the input axis is 60°/min.

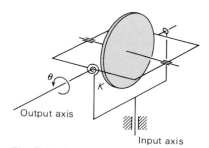

Fig. P 6.5-9

6.5-10 If a ship travels with velocity v due north, the angular velocity v/R (R = radius of earth) toward the west must be added to the horizontal component $\Omega \cos \lambda$ toward the north to give a resultant angular velocity deviating toward the west from the north. How does this affect the reading of the gyrocompass?

6.5-11 A ship travels due north with velocity v at latitude $\lambda = 60°$. If the axis of the gyrocompass shows that the ship is directed 3° east of north, how fast is the ship traveling?

6.5-12 A ship's gyrocompass has a rotor that runs at 8,000 rpm. The spin moment of inertia of the rotor is $C = 0.24$ lb ft sec², and the wl of the pendulous weight is 52 lb in. Determine the elevation setting $\bar{\beta}$ of the spin axis at latitude 32°N ($\Omega_{earth} = 7.27 \times 10^{-5}$ rad/sec).

6.5-13 Describe the motion of the gyro wheel of a pendulous gyrocompass when it is mounted on a vehicle accelerating in the east-west direction.

6.5-14 Show that the oscillation period of a pendulous gyrocompass mounted on a vehicle traveling with velocity v at an angle δ with apparent north must be $\tau = 2\pi \sqrt{R/g}$ in order that, even with an acceleration of the vehicle in the direction of apparent north, the gyro-wheel axis persists in pointing to the instantaneous apparent north.

6.5-15 Establish the differential equation of motion for the gyroscope in cardanic suspension, as shown in Fig. P 6.5-15 by means of Lagrange's equations. Consider that the pin on the outer gimbal transmits a small force in order to displace the pilot valve of a hydraulic control system.

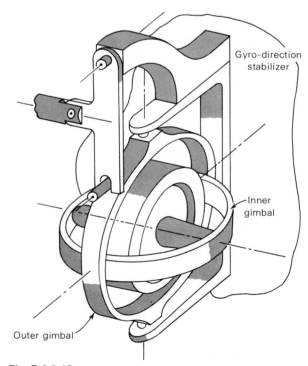

Gyro-direction stabilizer

Inner gimbal

Outer gimbal

Fig. P 6.5-15

Table A.1   Position of centroids and moments of inertia of areas

Form of area	Moment of inertia of area I	Position of centroid

Rectangular area

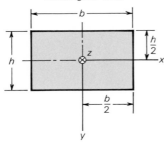

$$I_x = \frac{bh^3}{12}$$

$$I_y = \frac{b^3h}{12}$$

$$I_p = I_z = I_x + I_y$$

$$= \frac{bh}{12}(b^2 + h^2)$$

$x_C = y_C = z_C = 0$

Triangle

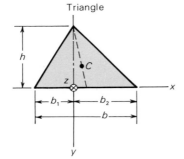

$$I_x = \frac{bh^3}{12}$$

$$I_y = \frac{h}{12}(b_1{}^3 + b_2{}^3)$$

$$I_p = I_z = I_x + I_y$$

$$= \frac{h}{12}(bh^2 + b_1{}^3 + b_2{}^3)$$

$$x_C = \frac{2b_2 - b}{3}$$

$$y_C = -\frac{h}{3}$$

$$z_C = 0$$

Special case: Isosceles triangle

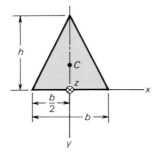

$$I_x = \frac{bh^3}{12}$$

$$I_y = \frac{b^3h}{48}$$

$$I_p = I_z = I_x + I_y$$

$$= \frac{bh}{48}(4h^2 + b^2)$$

$$x_C = 0$$

$$y_C = -\frac{h}{3}$$

$$z_C = 0$$

Table A.1   Position of centroids and moments of inertia of areas (continued)

Form of area	Moment of inertia of area I	Position of centroid

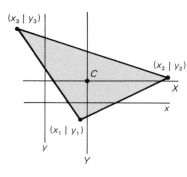

$$I_X = \frac{A}{12}(Y_1{}^2 + Y_2{}^2 + Y_3{}^2)$$

$$I_Y = \frac{A}{12}(X_1{}^2 + X_2{}^2 + X_3{}^2)$$

$$I_{XY} = \frac{A}{12}(X_1 Y_1 + X_2 Y_2$$

$$+ X_3 Y_3)$$

$$I_p = I_X + I_Y \qquad A = \text{area}$$

$x_C = \frac{1}{3}(x_1 + x_2 + x_3)$
$y_C = \frac{1}{3}(y_1 + y_2 + y_3)$
$A = \frac{1}{2}[x_1(y_2 - y_3)$
$\quad + x_2(y_3 - y_1)$
$\quad + x_3(y_1 - y_2)]$

Regular trapezoid

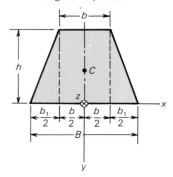

$$I_x = \frac{h^3}{12}(B + 3b)$$

$$I_y = \frac{h(B^4 - b^4)}{48(B - b)}$$

$$= -\frac{h}{48}(B^3 + B^2 b + Bb^2$$

$$+ b^3)$$

$$I_p = I_z = I_x + I_y$$

$x_C = 0$

$y_C = -\frac{3b + b_1}{2b + b_1}\frac{h}{3}$

$\quad = -\frac{B + 2b}{B + b}\frac{h}{3}$

$z_C = 0$

Regular polygon

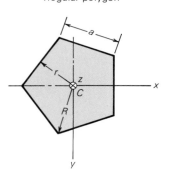

$$I_x = I_y = \frac{A}{24}(6R^2 - a^2)$$

$$= \frac{A}{48}(12r^2 + a^2)$$

$$I_p = I_z = I_x + I_y$$
$R = \text{radius of circumscribed circle}$

$r = \text{radius of inscribed circle}$
$A = \text{area}$

$x_C = y_C = z_C = 0$

Table A.1   Position of centroids and moments of inertia of areas (continued)

Form of area	Moment of inertia of area I	Position of centroid
Segment of a circle		

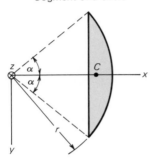

$$I_x = \frac{r^4}{8}(2\alpha - \tfrac{5}{3}\sin 2\alpha$$
$$\qquad\qquad + \tfrac{1}{6}\sin 4\alpha)$$
$$I_y = \frac{r^4}{8}(2\alpha - \tfrac{1}{2}\sin 4\alpha)$$
$$I_z = I_x + I_y$$
$$\quad = \frac{r^4}{4}(2\alpha - \tfrac{2}{3}\sin 2\alpha$$
$$\qquad\qquad - \tfrac{1}{6}\sin 4\alpha)$$

$$x_C = \frac{4r}{3}\frac{\sin^3\alpha}{2\alpha - \sin 2\alpha}$$
$$y_C = z_C = 0$$

Circular sector

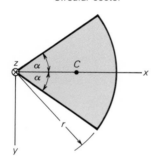

$$I_x = \frac{r^4}{8}(2\alpha - \sin 2\alpha)$$
$$I_y = \frac{r^4}{8}(2\alpha + \sin 2\alpha)$$
$$I_z = I_x + I_y = \frac{r^4}{2}\alpha$$

$$x_C = \frac{2}{3}\frac{r\sin\alpha}{\alpha}$$
$$y_C = z_C = 0$$

Special case: Semicircle

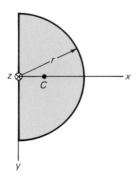

$$I_x = I_y = \frac{\pi}{8}r^4$$
$$I_z = I_x + I_y = \frac{\pi}{4}r^4$$

$$x_C = \frac{4}{3}\frac{r}{\pi}$$
$$y_C = z_C = 0$$

Table A.1   Position of centroids and moments of inertia of areas (continued)

Form of area	Moment of inertia of area I	Position of centroid

Circle

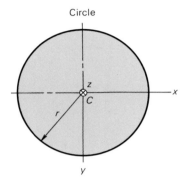

$$I_x = I_y = \frac{\pi}{4}\,r^4$$

$$I_z = I_x + I_y = \frac{\pi}{2}\,r^4$$

$$x_C = y_C = z_C = 0$$

Sector of annulus

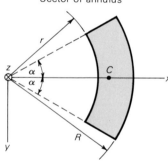

$$I_x = \frac{R^4 - r^4}{8}\,(2\alpha - \sin 2\alpha)$$

$$I_y = \frac{R^4 - r^4}{8}\,(2\alpha + \sin 2\alpha)$$

$$I_z = I_x + I_y = \frac{R^4 - r^4}{2}\,\alpha$$

$$x_C = \frac{2}{3}\,\frac{R^3 - r^3}{R^2 - r^2}\,\frac{\sin \alpha}{\alpha}$$

$$y_C = z_C = 0$$

Special case: Semiannulus $\left(\alpha = \dfrac{\pi}{2}\right)$

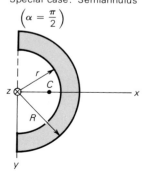

$$I_x = I_y = \pi\,\frac{R^4 - r^4}{8}$$

$$I_z = I_x + I_y = \pi\,\frac{R^4 - r^4}{4}$$

$$x_C = \frac{4}{3\pi}\,\frac{R^3 - r^3}{R^2 - r^2}$$

$$y_C = z_C = 0$$

Table A.1 Position of centroids and moments of inertia of areas (continued)

Form of area	Moment of inertia of area I	Position of centroid

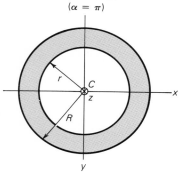

Total annulus
$(\alpha = \pi)$

$$I_x = I_y = \pi \frac{R^4 - r^4}{4}$$

$$I_z = I_x + I_y = \pi \frac{R^4 - r^4}{2}$$

$x_C = y_C = z_C = 0$

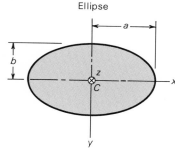

Ellipse

$$I_x = ab^3 \frac{\pi}{4}$$

$$I_y = a^3b \frac{\pi}{4}$$

$$I_z = I_x + I_y = \frac{\pi}{4} ab(a^2 + b^2)$$

$x_C = y_C = z_C = 0$

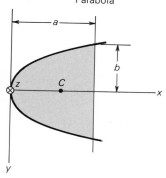

Parabola

$$I_x = \frac{4ab^3}{15}$$

$$I_y = \frac{4a^3b}{7}$$

$$I_z = I_x + I_y = {}^{88}\!/_{105}ab(a^2 + b^2)$$

$x_C = \frac{3}{5}a$
$y_C = z_C = 0$

Table A.2   Position of centroids and moments of inertia of mass

Form of mass	Moment of inertia of mass I	Position of centroid
Uniform slender rod		

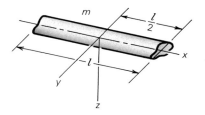

$$I_x = 0$$
$$I_y = I_z = m\,\frac{l^2}{12}$$

$$x_C = y_C = z_C = 0$$

Rectangular parallelepiped

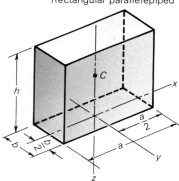

$$I_x = m\,\frac{b^2 + 4h^2}{12}$$
$$I_y = m\,\frac{a^2 + 4h^2}{12}$$
$$I_z = m\,\frac{a^2 + b^2}{12}$$

$$x_C = y_C = 0$$
$$z_C = -\frac{h}{2}$$

Rectangular pyramid

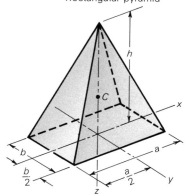

$$I_x = m\,\frac{b^2 + 2h^2}{20}$$
$$I_y = m\,\frac{a^2 + 2h^2}{20}$$
$$I_z = m\,\frac{a^2 + b^2}{20}$$

$$x_C = y_C = 0$$
$$z_C = -\frac{h}{4}$$

Table A.2   Position of centroids and moments of inertia of mass (continued)

Form of mass	Moment of inertia of mass I	Position of centroid
Right circular cone 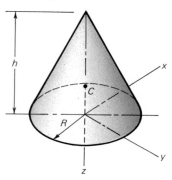	$I_x = I_y = \dfrac{m}{10}\left(\dfrac{3}{2}R^2 + h^2\right)$ $I_z = \tfrac{3}{10}mR^2$	$x_C = y_C = 0$ $z_C = -\dfrac{h}{4}$
Thin-arc segment 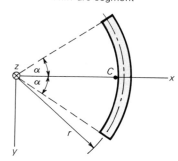	$I_x = m\dfrac{r^2}{2}\left(1 - \dfrac{\sin 2\alpha}{2\alpha}\right)$ $I_y = m\dfrac{r^2}{2}\left(1 + \dfrac{\sin 2\alpha}{2\alpha}\right)$ $I_z = mr^2$	$x_C = \dfrac{r \sin \alpha}{\alpha}$ $y_C = z_C = 0$
Right circular cylinder 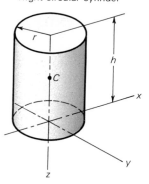	$I_x = I_y = \tfrac{1}{12}m(3r^2 + 4h^2)$ $I_z = m\dfrac{r^2}{2}$	$x_C = y_C = 0$ $z_C = -\dfrac{h}{2}$

Table A.2   Position of centroids and moments of inertia of mass (continued)

Form of mass	Moment of inertia of mass I	Position of centroid
Special case: Disk ($h \to 0$) 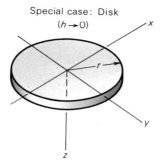	$I_x = I_y = m\,\dfrac{r^2}{4}$ $I_z = m\,\dfrac{r^2}{2}$	$x_C = y_C = z_C = 0$
Semicylinder 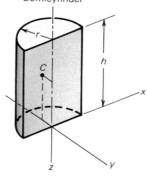	$I_x = I_y = \tfrac{1}{12}m(3r^2 + 4h^2)$ $I_z = m\,\dfrac{r^2}{2}$	$x_C = 0$ $y_C = -\dfrac{4}{3}\dfrac{r}{\pi}$ $z_C = -\dfrac{h}{2}$
Sphere 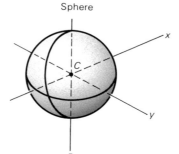	Hollow thin sphere: $I_x = I_y = I_z = m\,\dfrac{2r^2}{3}$ Solid sphere: $I_x = I_y = I_z = m\,\dfrac{2r^2}{5}$	$x_C = y_C = z_C = 0$ $x_C = y_C = z_C = 0$

Table A.2   Position of centroids and moments of inertia of mass (continued)

Form of mass	Moment of inertia of mass I	Position of centroid
Hemisphere	Solid hemisphere: $$I_x = I_y = I_z = m\,\frac{2r^2}{5}$$	$x_C = y_C = 0$ $z_C = -\tfrac{3}{8}r$

CHAPTER ONE

1.2-1 $r = 8.78$

1.2-3 $\cos \alpha = 0.303; \cos \beta = 0.505; \cos \gamma = 0.808$

1.2-5 $\mathbf{r} = \mathbf{r}_1 + \mathbf{r}_2 + \mathbf{r}_3 = 4\mathbf{i} + 3\mathbf{j} + 4\mathbf{k}$

   $\mathbf{1}_r = \dfrac{\mathbf{r}}{r} = 0.624\mathbf{i} + 0.468\mathbf{j} + 0.624\mathbf{k}$

1.2-7 $\mathbf{r} = 10\mathbf{i} \pm 10\mathbf{j} + 14.14\mathbf{k}$

1.2-9 $\phi = 56°45'$

1.2-11 $x = 1$

1.2-13 $x = 21.6 \text{ miles}; y = 37.2 \text{ miles}; z = 175.1 \text{ miles}$

1.2-15 $r(t = 0) = 5\mathbf{i} + 1\mathbf{j} + 4\mathbf{k}; r(t) = 3\mathbf{i} + 5\mathbf{j} + 8\mathbf{k}$

1.3-1 $h = 15.9 \text{ ft}$

1.3-2 $v = 2,570 \text{ ft/sec}; h = 51,500 \text{ ft}$

1.3-6 $x = 12 \text{ ft}; s = 15 \text{ ft}$

1.3-11 $v_{av} = 2.50 \text{ ft/sec}; \text{average speed} = 40.8 \text{ ft/sec}$

1.3-13 $v = 675 \text{ ft/sec} = 460 \text{ mph}; x = 2.43 \text{ miles}$

1.3-15 $H = \tfrac{3}{2}v_0{}^2/g$

1.3-17 $v_B = 30 \text{ mph}$

1.3-19 $s = 8,400 \text{ ft}; t = 2 \text{ min } 30 \text{ sec}$

1.3-21 $(a)\ t_{lost} = 112.5 \text{ sec}; (c)\ s_{min} = 5,390 \text{ ft}$

1.3-22 $t = 33.7 \text{ sec}$

1.3-25 $s = 6 \text{ in.}$

1.3-27 $x = 229 \text{ ft}; v_A = 23.2 \text{ ft/sec}; v_B = 28.6 \text{ ft/sec}$

1.3-29 $s_1 - s_n = 16.1[2(n - 1)t - (n - 1)^2]; t \geq n - 1$

1.3-32 $[12] = [L^{2/3}T^{-2}]; x = 2.82t^3$

1.4-1 $y = x(\tfrac{1}{2}x - 1) + 3$

1.4-3 $\dot{\mathbf{r}}_{t=2} = \tfrac{1}{2}\mathbf{i} + \mathbf{j}; \ddot{\mathbf{r}}_{t=2} = -\tfrac{1}{4}\mathbf{j}$

1.4-5 $\rho = 2.60$

1.4-7 $\dot{x} = -9 \text{ ft/sec}; \ddot{x} = -30 \text{ ft/sec}^2; \text{point assumed above horizontal diameter}$

1.4-9 $a_n = 9.73 \text{ ft/sec}^2$

1.4-11 $\tan \theta_0 = v_0{}^2/gR \pm \sqrt{(v_0{}^2/gR)^2 - 1}$

1.4-13 $R = 42.6 \text{ ft}; h_{max} = 14.5 \text{ ft}; t = 1.63 \text{ sec}$

1.4-15 $v_0 = 56.7 \text{ ft/sec}$

1.4-16 $x_{max} = 100.8 \text{ ft}; t = 1.285 \text{ sec}$

1.4-19 $\ddot{x} = g \sin \alpha; \dot{x} = gt \sin \alpha; x = \tfrac{1}{2}gt^2 \sin \alpha$

   $\ddot{y} = -g \cos \alpha; \dot{y} = v_0 - gt \cos \alpha; y = v_0t - \tfrac{1}{2}gt^2 \cos \alpha$

   $R = \dfrac{2v_0{}^2}{g} \dfrac{\sin \alpha}{\cos^2 \alpha}$

1.4-21 $a = \dfrac{b\omega_0{}^2}{2\pi}$

1.4-23 $a_n = 2,600 \text{ ft/sec}^2$

1.4-24 $\theta = 2,700 \text{ revolutions}$

1.4-27 $a = 40.5 \text{ ft/sec}^2$

1.4-28 $a_B = 24.0$ in./sec²

1.4-31 $\dot{\omega} = 0.624$ rad/sec² clockwise

1.4-33 $x = R \cos \omega_0 t$

1.4-34 $\tau = 2\pi/3$ sec

1.4-37 $\dot{\theta} = -\dfrac{v_A}{h} \sin^2 \theta$

1.4-40 $x = Ce^{\alpha\theta} \cos \theta; \dot{x} = Ce^{\alpha\theta}\dot{\theta}(\alpha \cos \theta - \sin \theta)$
$\ddot{x} = Ce^{\alpha\theta}\dot{\theta}^2[(\alpha^2 - 1) \cos \theta - 2\alpha \sin \theta]$

1.4-41 $b = -2\alpha\omega; c = \omega^2(\alpha^2 + 1)$

1.4-43 $\dot{x} = 942$ in./sec; $\ddot{x} = 3.02 \times 10^5$ in./sec²

1.4-46 $\dot{x} = -\dot{y} \tan \theta; \ddot{x} = -\dot{y}^2/R \cos^3 \theta$

1.4-47 $\mathbf{v} = -(r_0\dot{\theta} + b\dot{\theta} \sin \theta)\mathbf{i} + b\dot{\theta} \cos \theta \, \mathbf{j}$
$\mathbf{a} = -[b\dot{\theta}^2 \cos \theta + \ddot{\theta}(r_0 + b \sin \theta)]\mathbf{i} + b(\ddot{\theta} \cos \theta - \dot{\theta}^2 \sin \theta)\mathbf{j}$

1.4-49 $\mathbf{a} = v\dot{\gamma}\mathbf{1}_n; \rho = \dfrac{v}{\dot{\gamma}}$

1.4-51 $\dot{\mathbf{r}} = r\omega_0(b\mathbf{1}_r + \mathbf{1}_\theta)$
$\ddot{\mathbf{r}} = r\omega_0^2[(b^2 - 1)\mathbf{1}_r + 2b\mathbf{1}_\theta]; \rho = r\sqrt{1 + b^2}$

1.5-2 $\mathbf{v} = 8\mathbf{i} - 4\mathbf{j} + 12\mathbf{k}$

1.5-4 $\mathbf{v} = \sqrt{4 + 9t^2 + t^4}\,\mathbf{1}_r$

1.5-6 $\mathbf{a} = -20\mathbf{k}$ at $t = \pi/4$

1.5-8 $\mathbf{v} = 4t\mathbf{j} + 2t\mathbf{k}; \mathbf{a} = 4\mathbf{j} + 2\mathbf{k}$

1.5-10 $a_\tau = 3.37$ ft/sec²; $a_n = 2.14$ ft/sec²; $\rho = 6.50$ ft

1.5-12 $\rho = 24.5; \rho = {}^{25}\!/_{26}(4\mathbf{i} - 3\mathbf{j} - 25\mathbf{k})$

1.5-14 $\mathbf{v} = \mathbf{i} + 2t\mathbf{j} + 2\mathbf{k}$

$a_\tau = \dfrac{4t}{\sqrt{5 + 4t^2}}; a_n = \sqrt{\dfrac{20}{5 + 4t^2}}$

1.5-16 $\dot{x} = \dfrac{b\omega_0}{2\pi} \cos \alpha; \dot{y} = \omega_0\left(R_1 + \dfrac{b}{2}\right) + \dfrac{b\omega_0^2}{2\pi} t \sin \alpha$

$\dot{z} = \dfrac{b\omega_0}{2\pi}; \ddot{x} = \ddot{z} = 0; \ddot{y} = \dfrac{b\omega_0^2}{2\pi} \sin \alpha; \tan \alpha = \dfrac{R_2 - R_1}{l}$

1.5-18 $\mathbf{v} = (r\Omega \cos \Omega t)\mathbf{1}_R + \dot{\theta}(R_0 + r \sin \Omega t)\mathbf{1}_\theta + (\omega z_0 \cos \omega t)\mathbf{1}_z$
$\mathbf{a} = -[r\Omega^2 \sin \omega t + (R_0 + r \sin \Omega t)\dot{\theta}^2]\mathbf{1}_R + [(R_0 + r \sin \Omega t)\ddot{\theta}$
$+ (2r\Omega \cos \Omega t)\dot{\theta}]\mathbf{1}_\theta - (z_0\omega^2 \sin \omega t)\mathbf{1}_z$

1.5-20 $\mathbf{v} = R\dot{\theta}\mathbf{1}_\theta + R\dot{\phi} \sin \theta \, \mathbf{1}_\phi$
$\mathbf{a} = -R(\dot{\theta}^2 + \dot{\phi}^2 \sin^2 \theta)\mathbf{1}_r + R(\ddot{\theta} - \dot{\phi}^2 \sin \theta \cos \theta)\mathbf{1}_\theta$
$+ R(\ddot{\phi} \sin \theta + 2\dot{\theta}\dot{\phi} \cos \theta)\mathbf{1}_\phi$

$\dot{\theta} = \alpha\omega \cos \omega t$
$\ddot{\theta} = -\alpha\omega^2 \sin \omega t$

1.5-22 $\mathbf{a} = -(10\pi^2 \sin \pi t)\mathbf{i} - (10\pi^2 \cos \pi t)\mathbf{j}$

CHAPTER TWO

2.1-1 $\dot{x} = 20.4$ ft/sec

2.1-3 $v = \sqrt{v_0^2 + 4k/3mx_0}$

2.1-5 $\mu = 0.231$

2.1-8 $\Gamma m_e = 1.41 \times 10^{16}$ ft³/sec²

2.1-9 $g = 79.2 \times 10^3$ miles/hr²

2.1-11 $r_{e,p} = 215,100$ miles

2.1-13 $a_{max} = 2F_t/m$

2.2-1 $w_b = 2w_1 \dfrac{a/g}{1 + a/g}$; w_1 = initial weight before releasing ballast

2.2-3 $\rho = 10.4$ ft; $a_\tau = 104$ ft/sec^2

2.2-5 $\theta_{max} = \sqrt{\theta_0{}^2 + \dot{\theta}_0{}^2/p^2}$

2.2-7 $\sigma = 13{,}450$ lb/in.^{2}

2.2-9 $r = 8.56$ in.

2.2-11 $T = 6.22$ lb; $L = 4.33$ lb

2.2-13 $\theta = 22°10'$

2.2-15 (a) $\omega^2 = \dfrac{g}{r} \dfrac{\sin \theta + \mu \cos \theta}{\cos \theta - \mu \sin \theta}$; (b) $\omega = 5.84$ rad/sec

2.2-18 $\cos \theta = \dfrac{w_1 + w_2}{w_1 l \omega_0{}^2} g$

2.2-19 $\omega^2 = \dfrac{w_1 + w_2 + (kl/2) \cos \theta}{w_1(a + l \sin \theta)} g \tan \theta$

2.2-21 $\omega = 36.6$ rpm; 40-lb weight moves out

2.2-23 $v = 10.32$ ft/sec; $t = 0.773$ sec

2.2-25 $N_1 = w_B/\cos 20°$; $N_2 = w_B(\tan 20° + a/g)$

2.2-26 $F = 53.9$ lb

2.2-29 $\ddot{y} = -\dfrac{\dot{s}^2}{y} \left(\dfrac{l}{y}\right)^2$; $2s$ = length of rope

$T = \dfrac{w}{2y} \left[1 + \left(\dfrac{l}{y}\right)^2 \dfrac{\dot{s}^2}{yg}\right] \sqrt{l^2 + y^2}$

2.2-31 $t = 6.1$ sec

2.2-33 $F = \dfrac{w_1 w_2}{w_1 + w_2} (\mu_1 - \mu_2) \cos \theta$

2.2-35 $\Delta w = 0.30w$

2.2-37 $\ddot{x}_1 = g \dfrac{1 - 2w_1/w_2}{0.5 - 2w_1/w_2}$

2.2-39 $\ddot{x}_A = -1\frac{1}{49}g$; $\ddot{x}_B = \frac{9}{49}g$; $\ddot{x}_C = \frac{1}{49}g$

$x_A = -14.5$ ft; $x_B = 10.8$ ft; $x_C = 1.3$ ft

Positive direction downward

2.2-41 $x_0 = \dfrac{\mu}{1 + \mu} L$

$\dot{x} = \sqrt{gL \left[1 - \mu - (1 + \mu) \left(\dfrac{\xi_0}{L}\right)^2 + 2\mu \dfrac{\xi_0}{L}\right]}$

2.2-43 $a \geq 0.364g$

2.2-45 $\dfrac{k}{m} = 1.61$ sec^{-1}; $v = \dfrac{m}{k} g(1 - e^{-(k/m)t})$

2.2-47 $x = 14{,}120$ ft

2.2-49 $v = \sqrt{\dfrac{w}{k} \dfrac{e^{2g\sqrt{k/wt}} - 1}{e^{2g\sqrt{k/wt}} + 1}}$; $k = 0.00124w$

$v_{t \to \infty} = \sqrt{\dfrac{w}{k}} = 28.8$ ft/sec; $h \approx 12.9$ ft

2.2-51 $a_x = 5.45$ ft/sec^2; $a_y = 1.47$ ft/sec^2

2.2-53 (a) $k_{eq} = k_1 \dfrac{(1 + a/b)^2}{1 + k_1a^2/k_2b^2}$; (b) $k_{eq} = k_1 + k_2$; (c) $k_{eq} = \dfrac{k_1k_2}{k_1 + k_2}$

2.2-55 $\omega_n = \sqrt{4F_t/ml}$

2.2-57 $\ddot{\theta} + \dfrac{k}{m}\left(\dfrac{a}{b}\right)^2 \theta = 0$; $\omega_n = \dfrac{a}{b}\sqrt{\dfrac{k}{m}}$

2.2-59 $\omega_n = \sqrt{\dfrac{k}{m}\left(\dfrac{a}{l}\right)^2 - \dfrac{g}{l}}$; unstable if $\dfrac{k}{m}\left(\dfrac{a}{l}\right)^2 < \dfrac{g}{l}$

2.2-61 $\ddot{x} + \dfrac{\mu g}{c}x = 0$; $x = x_0 \cos t \sqrt{\dfrac{\mu g}{c}}$; if reversed, $x = x_0 \cosh t \sqrt{\dfrac{\mu g}{c}}$; $\therefore$ unstable

2.2-64 $|x| \le \sqrt{\dfrac{C}{k}}$

2.2-65 $v_{2,\max} = 1.14$ ft/sec

2.3-2 $F_P = 1,500$ lb

2.3-4 $R = 27.5$ lb

2.3-6 $F_{av} = 93$ lb

2.3-8 $F = -372,000$ lb

2.3-10 $\mathbf{v} = 333\mathbf{i} + 400\mathbf{j} + 4,000\mathbf{k}$

2.3-12 $\hat{\mathbf{F}} = (0.963\mathbf{i} + 0.388\mathbf{j} + 0.097\mathbf{k})$ lb sec

2.3-14 $v = 15.7$ ft/sec

2.4-2 $\mathbf{H}_0 = 6\mathbf{j} + 12\mathbf{k}$

2.4-4 $\dot{\omega} = \dfrac{-2vr_1{}^2\omega_1}{(r_1 + vt)^3}$

2.4-6 $\omega = \dfrac{1}{2mr^2}(5t^2 + 2mr_1{}^2\omega_1)$

2.4-8 $\omega = 8$ rad/sec

2.4-10 $v_B = 8.03$ ft/sec; $T = w$ lb

2.5-2 $t = \pi\sqrt{R/g}$; $v_{\max} = \sqrt{gR}\sin\alpha$

2.5-4 $P = 5.3 \times 10^{-5}v^3$ (kw); v in feet per second

2.5-6 $t = 66$ sec

2.5-8 $v = \sqrt{v_0{}^2 + 4k/3mx_0}$

2.5-10 $P = 4kr^2\omega \cos\dfrac{\theta}{2}\left(\sin\dfrac{\theta}{2} - \dfrac{l}{2r}\right)$

2.5-12 $\dot{s} = \sqrt{\dfrac{2gs}{w}\left[\dfrac{M_0}{r} - w(\sin\theta + \mu\cos\theta)\right]}$; r = radius of pulley

2.5-14 $k = 198,000$ lb/ft; rebound $= 7.42$ in. from maximum compression

2.5-16 $v_B = 27.8$ ft/sec

2.5-18 $P = \dfrac{\mu mgr\omega}{\sqrt{1 + \mu^2}}$

2.5-20 $s = \dfrac{w}{Pg}\dfrac{v^3}{3}$

2.5-22 $\mathbf{v}_1 = (20\,\mathbf{1}_x + 17.2\,\mathbf{1}_y)$ ft/sec
$\mathbf{v}_2 = (20\,\mathbf{1}_x - 47.2\,\mathbf{1}_y)$ ft/sec

2.6-5 $v = \sqrt{\dfrac{2gR}{\pi}}\,(\theta^2 + 2\sin\theta)$

2.6-7 $v = 12.7$ ft/sec

2.6-8 $mg(y_2 + y_1) - \frac{1}{2}k[y_2{}^2 - y_1{}^2 - 2l(\sqrt{l^2 + y_2{}^2} - \sqrt{l^2 + y_1{}^2})] = 0$

2.6-10 $\delta = \sqrt{\dfrac{wl}{k + w/l}}$

2.6-12 $F = 3{,}800$ lb

2.6-14 $h_{\min} = \frac{1}{2}R;\ v_B = \sqrt{5gR}$

2.6-15 $\cos\phi = \frac{2}{3} + \frac{1}{3}v_0{}^2/gR$

2.6-18 $\frac{1}{2}gt^2 = h + x_0(1 - \cos\omega t);\ \omega^2 = k/m$

$$\cos\omega t = \frac{g}{x_0\omega^2}\left[1 \pm \sqrt{\left(1 - \frac{x_0\omega^2}{g}\right)^2 - \frac{2h\omega^2}{g}}\,\right]$$

2.6-19 $y = \dfrac{w_2}{k}\,(1 - \cos\omega t) + \dfrac{w_2}{w_1 + w_2}\,\dfrac{\sqrt{2gh}}{\omega}\sin\omega t$

$\omega^2 = \dfrac{kg}{w_1 + w_2}$

2.6-22 $U = -(\ln\tan\frac{1}{2}\phi_2 - \ln\tan\frac{1}{2}\phi_1)\dfrac{\Gamma m_1 m_2}{l}$

$\phi_{1,2} = $ angle between bar and radius vector from point to ends of bar

2.7-2 $v_e = R\sqrt{\dfrac{2g}{R + h}}$

2.7-4 $\tau = 94$ min

2.7-5 $r = 26{,}200$ miles

2.7-7 $v = 5{,}380$ ft/sec

2.7-9 $e = 0.44;\ a = 1.96R;\ r_a = 2.83R$

2.7-11 $e = 0.00807$

2.7-15 $\bar{R}^2 = R^2(1 + \frac{1}{8}l^2/R^2)$

2.7-17   (a) $v = 35{,}820$ ft/sec; (b) $v = 36{,}200$ ft/sec

CHAPTER THREE

3.2-2 $v = 1{,}935$ ft/sec

3.2-4 $A_1 = \dfrac{m_2}{m_1 + m_2}\,r;\ A_2 = \dfrac{m_1}{m_1 + m_2}\,r$

3.2-6 $v_1 = \dfrac{-m_b}{m_1 + m_b}\,v_0;\ v_2 = \dfrac{m_1 m_b}{(m_1 + m_b)(m_2 + m_b)}\,v_0$

3.2-8   Scale must read less during acceleration of cork

3.2-10   (a) $v_2 = \dfrac{w_1 v_1}{w_2}$; (b) $t = \dfrac{w_2}{gc}\dfrac{v^{1-k}}{1 - k}$; (c) $s = \dfrac{w_2}{gc}\dfrac{v^{2-k}}{2 - k}$

3.2-11 $x = \dfrac{w_1 + w_2}{k}\,\mu$

3.2-13   Sliding distance $= v_0^2/2\mu g$

3.2-14 $s = \dfrac{v_0^2}{2\mu g} \dfrac{w_C/w}{1 + w_C/w}$

3.2-16 $x_1 = \dfrac{m_1}{m_1 + m_2} \dfrac{v_0}{\omega} \left(\omega t + \dfrac{m_2}{m_1} \sin \omega t \right)$

$x_2 = l + \dfrac{m_1}{m_1 + m_2} \dfrac{v_0}{\omega} (\omega t - \sin \omega t)$

$\omega^2 = \dfrac{k(m_1 + m_2)}{m_1 m_2}$

3.2-18 $r_{1,2} \approx r \left(1 \mp \delta \sqrt{\dfrac{2kr}{mgR_0^2}} \right); \ R_0 = $ radius of earth

$t_{1,2}^2 = \dfrac{4\pi^2}{gR_0^2} (r + r_{1,2})^3$

3.2-20 $\ddot{x} = \dfrac{g}{l} x; \ \dot{x}_l = \sqrt{\dfrac{g}{l} (l^2 - x_0^2)}; \ t_l = \sqrt{\dfrac{l}{g}} \ln \left[\dfrac{l}{x_0} + \sqrt{\left(\dfrac{l}{x}\right)^2 - 1} \right]$

3.2-22 $a = g \left(\sin \theta - \dfrac{\mu m_1}{m_1 + m_2} \cos \theta \right); \ v = at$

3.2-24 $t = \sqrt{\dfrac{2c/g}{(\mu_1 - \mu_2)(1 + m_2/m_1) \cos \theta}}$

3.2-25 $a_2 = \dfrac{g \tan \alpha}{w_2/w_1 + \tan^2 \alpha}$

3.3-2 $\ddot{x}_1 = g - 4g \dfrac{m_2(m_1 + m_2)}{4m_1m_2 + (m_1 + m_2)^2}$

$\ddot{x}_2 = g - 4g \dfrac{m_1(m_1 + m_2)}{4m_1m_2 + (m_1 + m_2)^2}$

$\ddot{x}_3 = g - 8g \dfrac{m_1 m_2}{4m_1m_2 + (m_1 + m_2)^2}$

3.3-4 $V = \dfrac{m_1 v_1 - m_2 v_2}{m_1 + m_2}$

3.3-6 $v_2 = [m_1 + m_2 + m_3(l_3/l)^2]c/m_2$

3.3-8 $c_1 = \dfrac{b}{l} \dfrac{v_3}{\dfrac{m_1}{m_3} + \dfrac{b^2}{l^2} + \dfrac{m_1}{m_2} \dfrac{a^2}{l^2}}$

$c_2 = \dfrac{m_1}{m_2} \dfrac{a}{l} \dfrac{v_3}{\dfrac{m_1}{m_3} + \dfrac{b^2}{l^2} + \dfrac{m_1}{m_2} \dfrac{a^2}{l^2}}$

$c_3 = \dfrac{b^2}{l^2} \left(1 + \dfrac{m_1}{m_2} \dfrac{a^2}{l^2} \right) \dfrac{v_3}{\dfrac{m_1}{m_3} + \dfrac{b^2}{l^2} + \dfrac{m_1}{m_2} \dfrac{a^2}{l^2}}$

3.3-10 $c_1 = \dfrac{m_3(v_3 - c_3)}{m_1(1 + a/b)}; \ c_2 = \dfrac{m_3}{m_2} \dfrac{a}{l} (v_3 - c_3)$

3.4-2 $v = \sqrt{0.134lg}$

3.4-4 $\quad \theta^2 = \dfrac{4g}{l}\,\dfrac{\sin\theta_0 - \sin\theta}{1 + \cos^2\theta}$

3.4-6 $\quad v_1 = \sqrt{2gh\left(1 - \dfrac{1}{1 + \dfrac{w_1}{w_2}\tan^2\alpha}\right)}$

3.4-8 $\quad x_{max} = v_0\sqrt{\dfrac{w_1}{kg}}$

3.4-10 $\quad \Delta E = \dfrac{1}{2}\dfrac{m_1 m_2}{m_1 + m_2}(v_1 + v_2)^2$

3.4-12 $\quad \Delta E = \frac{1}{2}c^2\left\{\dfrac{1}{m_2}\left[m_1 + m_2 + m_3\left(\dfrac{l_3}{l}\right)^2\right]^2 - \left[m_1 + m_2 + m_3\left(\dfrac{l_2}{l}\right)^2\right]\right\}$

3.4-14 $\quad \Delta E = \frac{1}{2}m_3 v_3{}^2 - \frac{1}{2}m_1 c_1{}^2 - \frac{1}{2}m_2 c_2{}^2 - \frac{1}{2}m_3\left[c_1 + \dfrac{a}{l}(c_2 - c_1)\right]^2$

3.4-16 $\quad \Delta E = \frac{1}{2}m_3\left[v_3{}^2 - c_3{}^2 - (v_3 - c_3)^2\left(\dfrac{m_3}{m_1}\dfrac{b^2}{l^2} + \dfrac{m_3}{m_2}\dfrac{a^2}{l^2}\right)\right]$

3.4-17 $\quad \cos\theta = 1 - \dfrac{c^2}{2g}\dfrac{m_1 + m_2 + m_3(l_3/l)^2}{(m_1 + m_2)l + m_3 l_3}$

$\quad c = \dfrac{(m_1 v_1 - m_2 v_2)l + m_3 v_1 l_3{}^2/l}{(m_1 + m_2)l + m_3 l_3{}^2/l}$

3.4-18 $\quad \cos\theta = 1 - \dfrac{1}{2gl}\dfrac{m_1{}^2}{m_2(m_2 + m_3)}(v_1 - c_1)^2$; makes complete turn when $\cos\theta < -1$

3.4-20 $\quad h_2 = h_1\dfrac{w_1 + w_2}{w_1 - w_2}\dfrac{w_2 + w_3 - w_1}{w_1 + w_2 + w_3}$; $h_3 = h_1\dfrac{(w_1 + w_2)^2}{(w_1 + w_2 + w_3)^2}$

3.5-2 $\quad v_1 = \dfrac{w_1 + w_2}{w_1}\sqrt{2gs(\sin\theta + \mu\cos\theta)}$; $s = 5$ ft

3.5-4 $\quad V = 38.4$ ft/sec; $\Delta E = 2{,}960$ ft lb; goes completely around

3.5-6 $\quad R = \dfrac{w_1{}^2}{w_1 + w_2}\dfrac{h}{\delta} + w_1 + w_2$

3.5-8 $\quad x = \dfrac{v^2}{2g\left(1 + \dfrac{w_p}{w_h}\right)\left[\dfrac{R}{w_h} - \left(1 + \dfrac{w_p}{w_h}\right)\right]}$

3.5-10 $\quad k = 99.7$ lb/ft

3.5-12 $\quad \mu = 0.671$

3.5-14 $\quad v = \dfrac{-(M - m)\sqrt{2gh}}{M + m}$; $V = \dfrac{2m\sqrt{2gh}}{M + m}$; $\Delta x = V\sqrt{\dfrac{M}{k}}$

3.5-16 $\quad x_{max} = \dfrac{m_1(1 + e)}{m_1 + m_2}v_1\sqrt{\dfrac{m_2}{k}}$; $e = \dfrac{m_1}{m_2}$

3.5-18 $\quad x = \dfrac{w_2}{k}(1 - \cos\omega t) + w_2\sqrt{\dfrac{2h}{k(w_1 + w_2)}}\sin\omega t$; $\omega^2 = \dfrac{kg}{w_1 + w_2}$

3.5-20 At each impact the striking ball stops and the struck ball continues with velocity v_1 of the first ball; if $d = 0$, this process still takes place, so that intermediate balls serve only to transmit to last ball

3.5-22   (a) $c_1 = \dfrac{m_1 - m_2}{m_1 + m_2} v_1$; (b) $c_2 = \dfrac{2m_1(m_2 - m_3)}{(m_1 + m_2)(m_2 + m_3)} v_1$

(c) $c_3 = \dfrac{4m_1 m_2}{(m_1 + m_2)(m_2 + m_3)} v_1$; $c_{3,\max} = \dfrac{4v_1}{(1 + \sqrt{m_3/m_1})^2}$

$m_{2,\max} = \sqrt{m_1 m_3}$

3.5-24 $s = \left(\dfrac{2m}{m + M}\right)^2 \dfrac{v^2}{2g} \dfrac{1}{\mu \cos \alpha - \sin \alpha}$; $h = \dfrac{v^2}{2g}\left(\dfrac{m - M}{m + M}\right)^2$

3.5-26 $V_2 = \dfrac{(1 + e) \sin 2\alpha}{2(\sin^2 \alpha + M/m)} v_0$; $h = \dfrac{v_0{}^2}{2g} \dfrac{\sin^2 \alpha}{\sin^2 \beta} \cos^2 (\alpha + \beta)$ if $\alpha + \beta \leq \dfrac{\pi}{2}$

$\tan \beta = \dfrac{\left(\dfrac{M}{m} + \sin^2 \alpha\right) \tan \alpha}{\left(e\dfrac{M}{m} - \sin^2 \alpha\right)}$; $\beta = $ rebound angle

3.6-2 $D = 8{,}350$ lb; hp $= 13{,}400$

3.6-4 $\dfrac{dv}{dt} = \dfrac{P - \dot{m}v}{w/g + \dot{m}t}$; $\dot{m} = \dfrac{100}{32.2}$

3.6-6 $\dot{x} = \sqrt{\tfrac{2}{3}gx}$; $\dot{x}_l = \sqrt{\tfrac{2}{3}gl}$; $t = \sqrt{\dfrac{6l}{g}}$

3.6-8 $(M + \mu x)\ddot{x} = (M - \mu x)g - \mu \dot{x}^2$

$\dot{x}^2 = \dfrac{2gx(M^2 - \tfrac{1}{3}\mu^2 x^2)}{(M + \mu x)^2}$

3.6-10 $v_2 = 6{,}710$ ft/sec; $h = 31.4$ miles

3.6-12 $v = u$

3.6-13 $\eta_{\text{mean}} = \dfrac{1}{r_1} \ln (1 + r_1{}^2)$; $r_1 = \dfrac{v_1}{u} = \ln \dfrac{m_0}{m_f}$

$(\eta_{\text{mean}})_{\max}$ at $r_1 \approx 2.0$ or $\dfrac{m_f}{m_0} = 0.693$

3.6-15   101.7 lb

3.7-2 $m_1 \ddot{x}_1 - k(x_2 - x_1) \dfrac{\sqrt{(x_2 - x_1)^2 + l^2} - l}{\sqrt{(x_2 - x_1)^2 + l^2}} = 0$; in equation for x_2 use $+$ after

$m_2 \ddot{x}_2$

3.7-4 $\left[m_2 + \left(\dfrac{l_3}{l}\right)^2 m_3\right]\ddot{x}_2 + k_2(x_2 - x_1) = \dfrac{l_3}{l} F_0 \sin \omega t$

$m_1 \ddot{x}_1 + k_1 x_1 - k^2(x_2 - x_1) = 0$

3.7-6 $\ddot{\theta}(1 + \cos^2 \theta) - \dot{\theta}^2 \sin \theta \cos \theta + \dfrac{2g}{l} \sin \theta + \dfrac{k}{m} (\sqrt{1 - \cos \theta} - \sqrt{1 + \cos \theta}) = 0$

3.7-8 $l_1(m_1 + m_2)(\ddot{x}_3 \cos \theta_1 + l_1\ddot{\theta}_1 + g \sin \theta_1)$
$\qquad\qquad + m_2 l_1 l_2 [\ddot{\theta}_2 \cos (\theta_2 - \theta_1) - \dot{\theta}_2{}^2 \sin (\theta_2 - \theta_1)] = 0$
$l_2 \ddot{\theta}_2 + \ddot{x}_3 \cos \theta_1 + l_1[\ddot{\theta}_1 \cos (\theta_2 - \theta_1) + \dot{\theta}_1{}^2 \sin (\theta_2 - \theta_1)] + g \sin \theta_2 = 0$
$(m_1 + m_2 + m_3)\ddot{x}_3 + l_1(m_1 + m_2)(\ddot{\theta}_1 \cos \theta_1 - \dot{\theta}_1{}^2 \sin \theta_1)$
$\qquad\qquad + m_2 l_2 (\ddot{\theta}_2 \cos \theta_2 - \dot{\theta}_2{}^2 \sin \theta_2) = F + f$

3.7-10 $x_1 = x_0 + c\theta_1 + d\theta_2$
$x_2 = x_0 - (a - c)\theta_1 + d\theta_2$

$$x_3 = x_0 - (a - c)\theta_1 - (b - d)\theta_2$$
$$x_4 = x_0 + c\theta_1 - (b - d)\theta_2$$

Variables are x_0, θ_1, θ_2

$$T = \frac{1}{2}\sum_{i=1}^{4} m_i \dot{x}_i^2; \quad U = \frac{1}{2}\sum_{i=1}^{4} k_i x_i^2$$

Equations of motion decoupled if

$$\frac{k_1}{m_1} = \frac{k_2}{m_2} = \frac{k_3}{m_3} = \frac{k_4}{m_4} = \omega^2$$

Then

$$\ddot{x}_0 + \omega^2 x_0 = 0$$
$$\ddot{\theta}_1 + \omega^2 \theta_1 = 0$$
$$\ddot{\theta}_2 + \omega^2 \theta_2 = 0$$

3.7-12 $T = \frac{1}{2}m_3\dot{x}^2 + \frac{1}{2}m_1(\dot{x} + \dot{\xi})^2 + \frac{1}{2}m_2(\dot{x}^2 + \dot{\xi}^2)$
$U = \frac{1}{2}k\xi^2 + m_2 g\xi$
$(m_1 + m_2 + m_3)\ddot{x} + m_1\ddot{\xi} = 0$
$(m_1 + m_2)\ddot{\xi} + m_1\ddot{x} + k\xi = -mg$

CHAPTER FOUR

4.2-1 $\omega = -0.386$ rad/sec ccw

4.2-3 $\omega_{AB} = 1.33$ rad/sec

4.2-5 $\omega_{AB} = 5$ rad/sec; $v_B = 20$ ft/sec

4.2-7 $\omega_{BC} = \frac{6}{7}$ rad/sec; $v_C = 4.85$ ft/sec; $\omega_{DC} = 2.43$ rad/sec

4.2-9 $\dot{\phi} = \dfrac{\sqrt{2}\cos\theta - 1}{3 - 2\sqrt{2}\cos\theta}\ \dot{\theta} \qquad +\phi$ cw, $+\theta$ ccw

4.2-11 $a_C = 72$ ft/sec² up incline
$\dot{\omega}_{CB} = 12.9$ rad/sec² cw

4.2-13 (a) $\omega_{AB} = 1$ rad/sec
(b) $\dot{\omega}_{AB} = \frac{1}{5}$ rad/sec² ccw; $a_B = 26.9$ in./sec² to left

4.2-15 (a) $v_{B/AC} = 15$ ft/sec; $\omega_{AC} = 3$ rad/sec
(b) $\dot{\omega}_{AC} = 5.75$ rad/sec² ccw

4.2-17 (a) $\omega_{BC} = 1$ rad/sec ccw; (b) $\omega_{DC} = 2$ rad/sec cw
(c) $\dot{\omega}_{DC} = 8$ rad/sec² ccw; (d) $\dot{\omega}_{BC} = 4$ rad/sec² cw

4.2-19 $\mathbf{a} = -5,000\mathbf{i} - 23\mathbf{j}$; $i \perp$ to slot and j along slot

4.2-21 $\omega_{AB} = \dfrac{r\dot{\theta}(r + c\sin\theta)}{r^2 + c^2 + 2rc\sin\theta}$

$v_{B,\text{rel}} = r\dot{\theta}\,\dfrac{c\cos\theta}{\sqrt{r^2 + c^2 + 2rc\sin\theta}}$

4.2-23 $\mathbf{v}_C = -r(\dot{\theta} + \omega)\sin\theta\,\mathbf{i} + [b\omega + r(\dot{\theta} + \omega)\cos\theta]\mathbf{j}$
$\mathbf{a}_C = -[\omega^2(b + r\cos\theta) + r(2\omega\dot{\theta} + \dot{\theta}^2)\cos\theta]\mathbf{i} - [\omega^2 r\sin\theta + r(2\omega\dot{\theta} + \dot{\theta}^2\sin\theta)]\mathbf{j}$

$\omega_{AB} = \omega + \dfrac{r\dot{\theta}(r + b\cos\theta)}{r^2 + b^2 + 2rb\cos\theta}$

$\dot{\omega}_{AB} = \dfrac{rb(r^2 - b^2)\dot{\theta}^2\sin\theta}{(r^2 + b^2 + 2rb\cos\theta)^2}$

4.2-25 $\dot{\omega}_{BC} = 2.0$ rad/sec² ccw

4.2-27 $\theta = \dfrac{\dot{s} \sin \phi}{l \cos (\phi - \theta)}$

4.2-29 $v_A = 2\omega(R + r) + R\dot{\phi}$ down
$v_B = R\dot{\phi}$ up
$v_C = \omega(R + r)$ down

$a_A = -\dfrac{R^2}{r}(\omega + \dot{\phi})^2 - 2\omega R(\omega + \dot{\phi}) - \omega^2(R + 2r)$

$a_B = \dfrac{R^2}{r}(\omega + \dot{\phi})^2 + 2\omega R(\omega + \dot{\phi}) - \omega^2 R$

$a_C = -\omega^2(R + r)$

4.2-30 $\mathbf{v}_P = (R - r)\theta[\sin \phi\, \mathbf{i} + (1 - \cos \phi)\mathbf{j}]$

$\mathbf{a}_P = -\theta^2(R - r)\left[\left(1 + \dfrac{R - r}{r}\cos \phi\right)\mathbf{i} + \dfrac{R - r}{r}\sin \phi\, \mathbf{j}\right]$

$\mathbf{i}$ through centers of circles; $\mathbf{j}$ tangent

4.2-32 $\omega_2 = -2\,\dfrac{R - r}{R - 2r}\,\omega_1$

4.2-34 $\omega_{\text{roller}} = \theta\,\dfrac{R_i}{2r}$ cw; $v_C = \frac{1}{2}\theta R_i$

4.2-35 $\omega_B = R\omega \sqrt{10}$; $a_B = R \sqrt{10(\dot{\omega}^2 + \omega^4) + 12\dot{\omega}\omega^2}$

4.3-2 $I = \frac{1}{2}\mu L(R_1^2 + R_2^2) \approx \mu L R_1 R_2$ for thin tube

4.3-4 $I_\xi = \frac{1}{4}\mu l(R_1^2 + R_2^2)$

4.3-6 $I = m\left(\dfrac{L^2}{3} + \dfrac{R^2}{4}\right)$

4.3-8 $I_\xi = 13\frac{3}{4}mR^2$

4.3-10 $I = 2m\,\dfrac{a}{2a + c}\left(\dfrac{a^2}{3} + \dfrac{c^2}{4}\right) + m\,\dfrac{c}{2a + c}\,\dfrac{c^2}{12}$

4.4-1 $t = 3$ sec

4.4-3 $h = 1.35$ ft; $F = 181.4$ lb

4.4-5 $v = \dfrac{g}{2}\,\dfrac{0.60tl}{l + 0.60h}$; $v = \dfrac{g}{2}\,\dfrac{0.60tl}{l - 0.60h}$; $v = 0.60gt$

4.4-7 $N_1\mu = \mu w\,\dfrac{C + ah/g}{c + b}$ front wheel

$N_2\mu = \mu w\,\dfrac{b - ah/g}{c + b}$

4.4-9 $a = \dfrac{g}{h}\sqrt{(l + b)^2 - h^2}$

4.4-11 $a = 23.9$ ft/sec²; $N_1 = 4.0$ lb; $N_2 = 20.1$ lb

4.4-13 $t = \sqrt{\dfrac{w}{k}\left(\dfrac{b}{h} - \mu\right)}$ if $\mu \le \dfrac{b}{2h}$

$t = \sqrt{\dfrac{w}{k}\,\dfrac{b}{2h}}$ if $\mu \ge \dfrac{b}{2h}$

4.4-15
$$\left\{ m_1 \left[\frac{l^2}{3} + r^2 - rl \cos \left(\frac{R}{R-r} \theta \right) \right] + m_2 \frac{3r^2}{2} \right\} \ddot{\theta} - \frac{1}{2}\dot{\theta}^2 m_1 rl \frac{R}{R-r} \sin \left(\frac{R}{R-r} \theta \right)$$

$$+ \frac{l}{2} m_1 g \sin \theta + (m_1 + m_2)gr \sin \left(\frac{r}{R-r} \theta \right) = 0$$

Reduces for small oscillations to:

$$\left[m_1 \left(r^2 - rl + \frac{l^2}{3} \right) + m_2 \frac{3r^2}{2} \right] \ddot{\theta} + \left[m_1 g \frac{l}{2} + (m_1 + m_2)g \frac{r^2}{R-r} \right] \theta = 0$$

4.4-17 $\ddot{\theta} \left[\frac{3}{2} m_1 r^2 + m_2 \left(r^2 - rl \cos \theta + \frac{l^2}{3} \right) \right] + \dot{\theta}^2 m_2 r \frac{l}{2} \sin \theta + m_2 g \frac{l}{2} \sin \theta = 0$

$$\tau = 2\pi \sqrt{\frac{\frac{3}{2} m_1 r^2 + m_2(r^2 - rl + l^2/3)}{m_2 gl/2}}$$

4.4-19 $(M+m)\ddot{x} + m(R-r)(\ddot{\theta} \cos \theta - \dot{\theta}^2 \sin \theta) + kx = 0$
$\ddot{x} \cos \theta + \frac{3}{2}(R-r)\ddot{\theta} + g \sin \theta = 0$
Reduces for small oscillations to:
$(M+m)\ddot{x} + m(R-r)\ddot{\theta} + kx = 0$
$\ddot{x} + \frac{3}{2}(R-r)\ddot{\theta} + g\theta = 0$
Frequency equation:
$\omega^4(3M+m)(R-r) - \omega^2[M+m+\frac{3}{2}k(R-r)] + kg = 0$

4.4-21 $n_2 = 45.3$ rpm

4.4-23 $a = \dfrac{g}{1 + \dfrac{w_2}{w_1} \left(\dfrac{k}{r} \right)^2}$

4.4-25 $\ddot{\theta} = \dfrac{4}{3\pi} \dfrac{g}{R}$

4.4-27 $\ddot{\theta} = \dfrac{g}{4R} \dfrac{2 \cos 2\theta - \cos \theta}{\frac{4}{3} - \cos \theta}$

4.4-29 $a = g \dfrac{1}{1 + \dfrac{w_2}{w_1} \dfrac{R^2 + k_C^2}{(R+r)^2}}$

4.4-31 $a = g \dfrac{1}{1 + \dfrac{3}{8} \dfrac{w_2}{w_1}}$

4.4-33 $a_1 = \dfrac{m_1 m_2 + (m_1 - m_2)I/R^2}{m_1 m_2 + (m_1 + m_2)I/R^2} g$

$a_2 = \dfrac{m_1 m_2 - (m_1 - m_2)I/R^2}{m_1 m_2 + (m_1 + m_2)I/R^2} g$

4.4-35 $a = 0.818$ ft/sec^2

4.4-37 $\ddot{\theta} = -\dfrac{\mu R w}{I_C} \dfrac{1 + (1/\mu) \cos \theta - \sin \theta}{(1/\mu + \mu) \cos \theta}$

4.4-40 $\mu \geq \dfrac{\tan \theta}{1 + (r/k_C)^2}$

4.4-41 $F = 15.2$ lb; $A = -3.88$ lb; $B = 2.49$ lb

4.4-43 $\mu = \left| \dfrac{3 \sin \theta (3 \cos \theta - 2)}{(3 \cos \theta - 1)^2} \right|$

4.4-45 $x_1 = \dfrac{\omega_0^2 R^2}{18\mu g}$

4.4-47 $a = 18.25 \text{ ft/sec}^2; f = 2.80 \text{ lb}$

4.4-49 $a = 23.7 \text{ ft/sec}^2; f = 0.020w$ to right; cylinder rolls

4.4-51 $A_x = -6.21 \text{ lb}; A_y = 1.86 \text{ lb}; B_y = 2.80 \text{ lb}$

4.4-53 $A_r = 0.233wR; A_t = 0.124wR; B = 0.171wR;$ w and R measured in pounds and feet

4.4-55 $h = \tfrac{3}{2}R$

4.4-57 $R = \dfrac{mg}{1 + 12 \left(\dfrac{l - 2a}{2l}\right)^2}$

4.4-59 $R = \dfrac{w}{1 + 12(a/l)^2}$

4.4-61 $B = \dfrac{w}{1 + \left(\dfrac{l - b}{k_C}\right)^2}$

4.4-63 $\theta_1 = \theta_2 = \tfrac{3}{5}\sqrt{2}\,\dfrac{\hat{F}}{ml}$

4.4-65 $\omega = \tfrac{5}{2}\sqrt{\tfrac{3}{2}g/l}; \ \tfrac{1}{4}\phi - \cos\phi = 1\tfrac{7}{8}; \ \therefore$ goes completely around

4.4-67 $M_B = \dfrac{\mu a(a + 2b)b^3 g}{2(a^3 + b^3 + 3a^2 b)}$

4.4-69 $x = \dfrac{2g \sin \alpha - a_B}{6} t^2 + \dot{x}_0 t;$ x positive down incline

4.4-71 Uniform bar

4.5-2 $T = 2mv_M^2 + \tfrac{1}{2}(I_M - mR^2)\left(\dfrac{v_M}{R}\right)^2$

4.5-4 $v = 19.9 \text{ ft/sec}$

4.5-6 $v^2 = g(l \sin \theta + l_2 - h)$

4.5-8 $\omega = \sqrt{4\tfrac{0}{3}} \text{ rad/sec}$

4.5-10 $\cos \theta = \tfrac{2}{3}$

4.5-12 $\omega = \dfrac{n_B}{n_C}\sqrt{\dfrac{k}{I}}$

4.5-14 $\omega = \sqrt{\dfrac{1}{I}\left(\dfrac{k_1 k_2}{k_1 + k_2} + k_3\right)}$

4.5-16 $\left[\dfrac{1}{g}(w_1 + 4w_2) + \dfrac{I}{R^2}\right]\ddot{x} + kx = 0$

$\tau = 2\pi \sqrt{\dfrac{\dfrac{w_1 + 4w_2}{g} + \dfrac{I}{R^2}}{k}}$

4.5-18 $\theta = \dfrac{v_A}{2l}; \ v_A = 2.06\sqrt{gl}$

4.5-20 $\tan \theta_0 = \tfrac{1}{4}; \ \theta_{\max} = 2 \tan^{-1} \tfrac{1}{4}$

4.5-22 $\quad \dot{\theta}^2 = \dfrac{gl(\sin \theta_0 - \sin \theta)}{\dfrac{l^2}{3} + \dfrac{h^2}{\sin^4 \theta} - \dfrac{lh}{\sin \theta}}$

$\qquad \ddot{\theta} = \dfrac{-(gl/2) \cos \theta}{\dfrac{l^2}{3} + \dfrac{h^2}{\sin^4 \theta} - \dfrac{lh}{\sin \theta}} \left[1 + \dfrac{h(l \sin^3 \theta - 4h)(\sin \theta_0 - \sin \theta)}{\sin^5 \theta \left(\dfrac{l^2}{3} + \dfrac{h^2}{\sin^4 \theta} - \dfrac{lh}{\sin \theta} \right)} \right]$

4.5-24 $\quad \dot{\theta}^2 = \dfrac{12g(1 - \sin \theta)}{l \left(4 - 3 \dfrac{w_1}{w_1 + w_2} \sin^2 \theta \right)}$

$\qquad = \dfrac{3g(1 - \sin \theta)}{l}$ if $w_3 \to \infty$ (hinge fixed)

4.5-26 If the two despinning masses do not fly off when $\phi = \phi_e$, then the centrifugal forces continue to exert on the satellite a force couple in the direction opposite to the original rotational direction of the satellite (cf. Fig. 4.5-4)

4.5-28 $\quad t = \dfrac{1}{\omega_0} \sqrt{\dfrac{I_C}{2mR^2} + 1}$

4.6-1 $\quad (R + r) \left[w_1 \left(1 + \dfrac{k^2}{r^2} \right) + \tfrac{1}{3}w_2 \right] \ddot{\theta} + (w_1 + \tfrac{1}{2}w_2)g \sin \theta = 0$

4.6-3 $\quad \tfrac{3}{2}m\ddot{x} + k \left(1 - \dfrac{3}{\sqrt{9 + x^2}} \right) x = 0$

4.6-5 $\quad [(4m + M)r^2 + Mkc^2]\ddot{\theta} + 8kr^2\theta = 0$

4.6-7 $\quad \left(\dfrac{l^2}{3} + \dfrac{h^2}{\sin^4 \theta} - \dfrac{lh}{\sin \theta} \right) \ddot{\theta} + \dfrac{h \cos \theta}{2 \sin^2 \theta} \left(l - \dfrac{4h}{\sin^3 \theta} \right) \dot{\theta}^2 + \tfrac{1}{2}gl \cos \theta = 0$

4.6-9 $\quad [I_C + m(R^2 + r^2 - 2Rr \cos \phi)]\ddot{\phi} + mRr\dot{\phi}^2 \sin \phi + mgr \sin (\phi + \theta)$
$\qquad\qquad\qquad\qquad\qquad\qquad\qquad\qquad\qquad\qquad\qquad - mgR \sin \theta = 0$

4.6-11 $\quad T = \tfrac{1}{2}m_1 R_1^2 \dot{\phi}_1^2 \left[\left(1 - \dfrac{2}{\pi} \cos \phi_1 \right)^2 + \left(\dfrac{2}{\pi} \sin \phi_1 \right)^2 + 1 \right]$

$\qquad\qquad + \tfrac{1}{2}m_2 \left\{ [R_1\dot{\phi}_1 - (R_1 - R_2)(\dot{\phi}_2 - \dot{\phi}_1) \cos (\phi_2 - \phi_1)]^2 \right.$

$\qquad\qquad\qquad + [(R_1 - R_2)(\dot{\phi}_2 - \dot{\phi}_1) \sin (\phi_2 - \phi_1)]^2 + \dfrac{R_2^2}{2} \left. \left(\dfrac{R_1 - R_2}{R_2} \dot{\phi}_2 + \dot{\phi}_1 \right)^2 \right\}$

$\qquad U = -m_1 g \dfrac{2R_1}{\pi} \cos \theta - m_2 g(R_1 - R_2) \cos (\phi_2 - \phi_1)$

$\qquad \phi_1$ measured from vertical to symmetry axis of half cylinder
$\qquad \phi_2$ measured from symmetry axis of half cylinder to line connecting centers

4.6-12 $\quad \ddot{x} - x\dot{\theta}^2 - g \sin \theta = 0$

$\qquad \left(x^2 + \dfrac{l^2}{12} \right) \ddot{\theta} + 2x\dot{x}\dot{\theta} - gx \cos \theta = 0$

$\qquad x =$ distance from edge to midpoint of bar
$\qquad \theta =$ angle of bar with horizontal

4.6-15 $\quad m\ddot{x} - mx\dot{\theta}^2 - mg \sin \theta = 0$

$\qquad m(x^2\ddot{\theta} + 2x\dot{x}\dot{\theta}) + \mu \dfrac{l^3}{3} \ddot{\theta} - \mu \dfrac{l^2}{2} g \cos \theta - mgx \cos \theta = 0$

4.7-2 x = axis between centers from 5- to 10-lb spheres
y = axis tangent
$c_{1y} = -18; c_{1z} = -9$
$c_{2y} = -12; c_{2z} = 7.50$

4.7-4   Each sphere rebounds in direction 151° ccw from initial direction of velocity

4.7-6 $\theta^2 = \dfrac{3g}{l}\left(\sin\theta_0 + \dfrac{6h}{l}\dfrac{\cos^2\theta_0}{1 + 3\cos^2\theta_0}\right)$

4.7-9 $T_{\text{rot}}/T_{\text{trans}} = 4.90e^2\tan^2\phi$

4.7-10 $\omega = \dfrac{3m(1 + e)}{3m + M}\dfrac{v}{l}; c_1 = \dfrac{3m - eM}{3m + M}v$

$v = \dfrac{3m + M}{3m(1 + e)}\sqrt{3gl}$ for 90° rotation of bar

$c_1 = 0$ if $e = \dfrac{3m}{M}$

CHAPTER FIVE

5.1-2 $\mathbf{v}_2 = 13\mathbf{i} - 7.5\mathbf{j} + 0\mathbf{k}$
$\mathbf{v}_3 = 1\mathbf{i} + 1.5\mathbf{j} + 1.5\mathbf{k}$

5.1-4 $\mathbf{v}_1 = \frac{1}{1.000}(3\mathbf{i} + 2\mathbf{j} - 4\mathbf{k})$ ft/sec
$\mathbf{v}_2 = \frac{1}{1.000}(3\mathbf{i} + 17\mathbf{j} + 16\mathbf{k})$ ft/sec
$\mathbf{v}_3 = \frac{1}{1.000}(11\mathbf{i} + 6\mathbf{j} - 4\mathbf{k})$ ft/sec

5.2-2   W11°30′S

5.2-4 $R = \dfrac{1}{g}(v_0\cos\theta_0 - v)(v_0\sin\theta_0 + \sqrt{2gh + v_0{}^2\sin^2\theta_0})$

$\cos\theta_0 = \dfrac{v}{4v_0} + \sqrt{\left(\dfrac{v}{4v_0}\right)^2 + \dfrac{1}{2}}$ if $h = 0$

5.2-6 $\mathbf{v}_{\text{rel}} = (-15.7\ \mathbf{1}_r + 12.9\ \mathbf{1}_\theta)$ mph if A moves to left
$\mathbf{v}_{\text{rel}} = (78.6\ \mathbf{1}_r - 61.8\ \mathbf{1}_\theta)$ mph if A moves to right
$\mathbf{1}_r$ along radius of curve
$\mathbf{1}_\theta \perp$ to $\mathbf{1}_r$ in direction of motion of B

5.2-8 $\tan\phi = \dfrac{20\sin\theta_0 + 15}{20\cos\theta_0}$

5.2-10

Position	x component (horizontal to right)	y component (vertical up)
A	$-(R + r)\omega^2$	$(R - r)\dot\omega$
B	$-(R\dot\omega + r\omega^2)$	$-(R\omega^2 + r\dot\omega)$
C	$(R - r)\omega^2$	$-(R + r)\dot\omega$
D	$R\dot\omega - r\omega^2$	$R\omega^2 - r\dot\omega$

5.2-12 $\mathbf{a} = -6\ \mathbf{1}_r - 8\ \mathbf{1}_\theta$

5.2-14 $\tan \theta = \dfrac{\omega t + \sin \omega t}{1 + \cos \omega t}$; $\omega t = \dfrac{D\omega}{2v_1} \sqrt{2(1 + \cos \omega t)}$

$v_1 = \sqrt{\left(\dfrac{D\omega}{2} - v_R \sin \theta\right)^2 + (v_R \cos \theta)^2}$ for $v_R \gg D\omega$, $\tan \theta \approx \omega D / v_R$, θ measured back

5.2-16 $\omega = 331$ rpm; $\alpha = 30°$ if channel width $=$ const

5.2-18 $\mathbf{v} = 92.7 \, \mathbf{1}_r - 9.2 \, \mathbf{1}_\phi$; $\alpha = 84°20'$ from $-\mathbf{1}_\phi$

5.2-23 $\mathbf{v} = 1.295(-\mathbf{i} + \mathbf{j} - \mathbf{k})$

5.2-24 $\mathbf{v} = -10 \, \mathbf{1}_\xi - 22.4 \, \mathbf{1}_\eta + 36.6 \, \mathbf{1}_\zeta$

5.2-26 $\mathbf{v} = 20.2 \, \mathbf{1}_y + 11.1 \, \mathbf{1}_z$
          $\mathbf{a} = -158 \, \mathbf{1}_y - 59 \, \mathbf{1}_z$

5.2-29 $\mathbf{v}_A = -5\mathbf{i} + 2\sqrt{3}\,\mathbf{j}$; x axis horizontal to right

5.2-30 $\mathbf{v} = \dot{\theta}(k - R \sin \theta)\mathbf{1}_r + \dot{\theta}(k\theta - R \cos \theta)\mathbf{1}_\theta$
          $\mathbf{a} = (k\ddot{\theta} - k\theta\dot{\theta}^2 - R\ddot{\theta} \sin \theta)\mathbf{1}_r + (k\theta\ddot{\theta} + 2k\dot{\theta}^2 - R\ddot{\theta} \cos \theta)\mathbf{1}_\theta$

5.2-32   With ξ normal to tail fan, η horizontal toward back, ζ vertical up
          $\mathbf{v}_p = -(l\omega + r\omega \cos \theta)\mathbf{1}_\xi - r\Omega \sin \theta \, \mathbf{1}_\eta + r\Omega \cos \theta \, \mathbf{1}_\zeta$
          $\mathbf{a}_p = 2r\omega\Omega \sin \theta \, \mathbf{1}_\xi - (l\omega^2 + r\omega^2 \cos \theta + r\Omega^2 \cos \theta)\mathbf{1}_\eta - r\Omega^2 \sin \theta \, \mathbf{1}_\zeta$

5.2-34   (a) $R = 5,000$ ft; (b) $\mathbf{v} = 299\mathbf{i} + 500\mathbf{j}$; $|v| = 583$ ft/sec
          (c) $\mathbf{a} = -50\mathbf{i} + 59.9\mathbf{j} - 30,000\mathbf{k}$; $|a| \approx 30,000$ ft/sec^2

5.2-36 $\mathbf{a} = -(0.0330 \, \mathbf{1}_\xi + 0.0393 \, \mathbf{1}_\zeta)$ ft/sec^2

5.3-2 $\mathbf{r} = v_0 t \sin \alpha \left(1 - \dfrac{\frac{1}{2}\mu g t}{\sqrt{v_0^2 - 2Vv_0 \cos \alpha + V^2}}\right)\mathbf{i}$

$+ v_0 t \left(\cos \alpha - \frac{1}{2}\mu g t \dfrac{\cos \alpha - V/v_0}{\sqrt{v_0^2 - 2Vv_0 \cos \alpha + V^2}}\right)\mathbf{j}$

where $\mathbf{i}$ is $\perp$ to belt motion, $\mathbf{j}$ along belt motion, $\mathbf{r} =$ absolute displacement

5.3-4 $F_s = mb\omega^2 h/c$; $P_x = -mb\omega^2$; $P_y = mg + F_s$

5.3-5 $\omega = \left[\left(\dfrac{g\mu}{r_0}\right)^2 - \dot{\omega}^2\right]^{1/4}$

5.3-6 $\mu g \sin \alpha = r\dot{\omega} + 2\omega\dot{r} - r\ddot{\theta}$ in θ direction
          $-\mu g \cos \alpha = -r\omega^2 + 2\omega r\dot{\theta} + \ddot{r} - r\dot{\theta}^2$ in r direction

$\tan \alpha = \dfrac{r\dot{\theta}}{\dot{r}} = \dfrac{\dot{\omega}}{\omega^2}$ initially

θ measured relative to radius in disk
α measured relative to radius in disk

5.3-8 $\delta = \dfrac{m\omega^2 b}{k - m\omega^2}$; $f = \dfrac{1}{2\pi}\sqrt{\dfrac{k}{m} - \omega^2}$; rotation direction has no effect

5.3-10 $\omega_r = \Omega\left(-1 \pm \sqrt{\dfrac{R}{r}}\right) = 0.732$ rad/sec if in same direction, 1.53 rad/sec if in opposite direction

5.3-12 $F_{Cor} = 2,360$ lb

5.3-14 $a_\xi = 2\Omega v_0 \cos \beta \sin \lambda$; neglect Ω^2 terms
          $a_\eta = -2\Omega[v_0 \cos \alpha \sin \lambda + (v_0 \cos \gamma - gt) \cos \lambda]$
          $a_\zeta = 2\Omega v_0 \cos \beta \cos \lambda - g$

5.3-18   Elevation $\theta_0 = 9°56'$; direction $\alpha = $ N3′W

5.3-20 ξ—east; η—north; ζ up $\perp$ to surface

$a_\eta = 2\Omega v \cos \alpha \sin \lambda$

$\eta = \Omega v t^2 \cos \alpha \sin \lambda$

5.3-22 $a_{\text{rel}} = -\mu(\dot\omega\eta + \omega^2 r_A + 2\omega v_{\text{rel}}) + \omega^2 \eta - \dot\omega r_A$

$\xi \perp$ to slot; η parallel to slot

5.4-2 $v_{\text{rel}} = \sqrt{2(a - \mu g)l}; \; \mu_0 = a/g$

5.4-4 $v_{\text{rel}} = \omega \xi_1 \sqrt{1 - \dfrac{k}{m\omega^2}\left(1 - 2\dfrac{\xi_0}{\xi_1}\right)}; \; \xi_{\max} = \dfrac{2\xi_0}{1 - m\omega^2/k}$

5.4-6   Condition for moving: $m_2\omega^2 \sqrt{h^2 + \xi_0^2} > m_1 g$

$$v_{\text{rel}} = \frac{m_2\omega^2(\xi_1^2 - \xi_0^2) - 2m_1 g(\sqrt{h^2 + \xi_1^2} - \sqrt{h^2 - \xi_0^2})}{m_2 + m_1 \dfrac{\xi_1^2}{h^2 + \xi_1^2}}$$

5.4-8 $v_{\text{rel}} = \omega \sqrt{(R^2 - R_0^2)\left[1 - \dfrac{2g \cot \alpha}{\omega^2(R + R_0)}\right]}$

5.4-10 $v_{\text{rel}} = \omega R \sqrt{\left(\dfrac{1}{\sqrt{3}} + \dfrac{2\pi}{g}\right)^2 - 1}$

$v_2 = \omega R \left[\dfrac{1}{\sqrt{3}} - \dfrac{2\pi}{g} + \sqrt{\left(\dfrac{1}{\sqrt{3}} + \dfrac{2\pi}{g}\right)^2 - 1}\right]$

5.4-12 $v_{\text{rel}} = \omega \theta_0 \sqrt{rl}$

CHAPTER SIX

6.1-2 $\omega_{AB} = \pi$ rad/sec; $\omega_\zeta = 1.414\pi$ rad/sec

6.1-4 $\omega = 2\Omega \cos \alpha$; $\omega_{\text{rel}} = \Omega$

6.1-6 $\dot\phi = 5.80$ rad/sec; $\omega_{\text{resultant}} = \pi$ rad/sec; $\dot\omega = 0$

6.1-8   Half angle of space cone $\begin{Bmatrix}27°22'\\2°38'\end{Bmatrix}$ or $\begin{Bmatrix}33°8.4'\\3°8.4'\end{Bmatrix}$
Half angle of body cone

6.1-10 $\mathbf{v}_A = r\omega_\zeta \mathbf{j}$; $\mathbf{a}_A = -r\omega_\zeta^2\mathbf{k} - 2\omega_z r\omega_\zeta\mathbf{i}$

$\mathbf{v}_B = -r\omega_\zeta \mathbf{j}$; $\mathbf{a}_B = r\omega_\zeta^2\mathbf{k} + 2\omega_z r\omega_\zeta\mathbf{i}$

$\mathbf{i}$ along spin axis; $\mathbf{k}$ along z axis

6.1-12 $\mathbf{r}_P = [R \cos \phi \cos \psi - (R \sin \phi \cos \theta - h \sin \theta) \sin \psi]\mathbf{i}$
$+ [R \cos \phi \sin \psi + (R \sin \phi \cos \theta - h \sin \theta) \cos \psi]\mathbf{j}$
$+ (R \sin \phi \sin \theta + h \cos \theta)\mathbf{k}$

6.1-14 $\mathbf{a}_P = -968\,\mathbf{1}_\xi - 13{,}000\,\mathbf{1}_\eta + 36\,\mathbf{1}_\zeta$

6.2-2 $J_z = \dfrac{mR^2}{2}(\sin^2 \theta + \tfrac{1}{2}\cos^2 \theta); J_{zz} = 0$

$J_{yz} = -\dfrac{mR^2}{4}\sin \theta \cos \theta$

6.2-4 $J_z = \dfrac{ml^2}{3}\cos^2 \theta; J_{yz} = \dfrac{ml^2}{3}\sin \theta \cos \theta \cos \alpha$

$J_{zz} = \dfrac{ml^2}{3}\sin \theta \cos \theta \sin \alpha$

6.2-6 $J_y = \rho \pi r^2 \left(\dfrac{l}{8} + \dfrac{h}{40} \right) d^2$

$J_x = J_z = \rho \pi r^2 l \left[\dfrac{l^2}{12} + \dfrac{d^2}{16} + \left(\dfrac{l}{2} - \bar{y} \right)^2 \right]$

$+ \rho \dfrac{\pi r^2 h}{3} \left[\tfrac{3}{80} d^2 + \tfrac{6}{160} h^2 + \left(\dfrac{h}{4} + l - \bar{y} \right)^2 \right]$

$\bar{y} = \dfrac{\dfrac{l^2}{2} + \dfrac{h}{3} \left(l + \dfrac{h}{4} \right)}{l + h/3}$

6.2-8 $J_{01} = \dfrac{m}{6} \dfrac{a^2 b^2 + b^2 h^2 + a^2 h^2}{a^2 + b^2 + h^2} = \tfrac{7}{2} \times 10^{-4}$ lb in. sec^2

$J_{02} = \dfrac{m}{6} \left(\dfrac{a^2 b^2}{a^2 + b^2} + 2h^2 \right) = \tfrac{9 \cdot 4}{5} \times 10^{-4}$ lb in. sec^2

6.2-10 $J_\xi = 3.42 \times 10^{-2}$ lb in. sec^2

6.2-13 $J_\eta = 3.313\pi \times 10^{-2}$ lb in. sec^2

6.2-14 $J_\zeta = \tfrac{19 \cdot 9}{6,000}$ lb in. sec^2

6.2-16 $J_\eta = \tfrac{61}{120} mD^2$ lb in. sec^2

$J_\zeta = \tfrac{71}{240} mD^2$ lb in. sec^2

$J_{\eta\zeta} = -\tfrac{17}{120} mD^2$ lb in. sec^2

6.2-18 $I_\zeta = \dfrac{m r^2 h^2}{r^2 + h^2} \left[1 + \dfrac{1}{4} \left(\dfrac{r}{h} \right)^2 \right]$

6.3-2 $\tan \theta = \dfrac{\omega^2 l}{g} \left(\dfrac{b}{l} + \dfrac{2}{3} \sin \theta \right)$

$\bar{x} = \dfrac{l}{2} \dfrac{(b/l + \tfrac{2}{3} \sin \theta) \cos \theta}{b/l + \tfrac{1}{2} \sin \theta}$

6.3-6 $\cos \theta = \dfrac{3g}{4\omega^2 b}; \quad \omega^2_{\min} = g \sqrt{\dfrac{1}{b^2 - (l/2)^2}}$

$\phi = 90°; \quad \sin \theta = \dfrac{l}{2b}$

6.3-8 $h^2 = A^2(\omega_\xi^2 + \omega_\eta^2) + C^2 \omega_\zeta^2$

$2T = A(\omega_\xi^2 + \omega_\eta^2) + C\omega_\zeta^2$

6.3-10 $\mathbf{H}_0 = (I_\eta \dot{\psi} \sin \theta) \mathbf{1}_\eta + I_\zeta (\dot{\phi} + \dot{\psi} \cos \theta) \mathbf{1}_\zeta$

$\dot{\mathbf{H}}_0 = [I_\zeta (\dot{\phi} + \dot{\psi} \cos \theta) \sin \theta - I_\eta \dot{\psi} \sin \theta \cos \theta] \psi \mathbf{1}_\xi = \tfrac{3}{4} mgh \sin \theta\ \mathbf{1}_\xi$

$2T = I_\zeta (\dot{\phi} + \dot{\psi} \cos \theta)^2 + I_\eta (\dot{x} \sin \theta)^2 = $ const

No energy is applied to the system.   Therefore $T + U =$ const. $U =$ const because of $\theta =$ const.   Consequently $T =$ const

6.4-2 $F = \dfrac{2}{3} \dfrac{w}{\pi R^2 g} \omega^2 (R^2 - x^2)^{3/2}$

6.4-4 $I_{\xi\zeta} = I_{\eta\zeta} = \dfrac{6}{g} = 0.0156$ lb in. sec^2

$A_\xi = A_\eta = B_\xi = \tfrac{1}{2} B_\eta = -\dfrac{\omega^2}{2g} = -0.0013\omega^2$

ω measured in radians per second

6.4-6 $M_\xi = -0.00136\omega^2$ lb in.; ω in radians per second
$M_\eta = 0.0045\omega^2$ lb in.
$A_\xi = -0.000278\omega^2$ lb
$A_\eta = 0.000085\omega^2$ lb
$B_\xi = 0.00161\omega^2$ lb
$B_\eta = 0.00095\omega^2$ lb

6.4-8 $R = \dfrac{m\omega^2}{2h}\left(\dfrac{l^2}{3} - \dfrac{R^2}{4}\right)\sin\alpha\cos\alpha$

6.4-10 $R = \dfrac{2m\omega^2}{l}\left(\dfrac{R^2}{4} + e^2\right)\sin\alpha\cos\alpha$

6.4-12 $R = 0.090\omega^2 = 985$ lb; $M = 0.81\omega^2 = 8{,}870$ lb ft

6.4-14 $R = \dfrac{m\omega^2}{12}\dfrac{ab}{l}\dfrac{b^2 - a^2}{a^2 + b^2}$

6.4-16 $R_{\max} = 82.7$ lb

6.4-18 $R = 10.8$ lb; increases pressure on front tires, decreases pressure on rear tires

6.4-20 $M = 74.2$ lb ft; tends to turn nose up; can be countered by downward deflection of tail elevators

6.4-22 $M = I\omega\Omega = 14.6/R$; R measured in miles; compensated by down elevators, right aileron down, left aileron up, rudder to left

6.4-24 $R = \dfrac{mr^2\omega_a\omega_b}{2L}$

6.4-26 $M_\xi = -194\sin\theta\cos\theta$
$M_\eta = -831\sin\theta$
$M_\zeta = 277\cos\theta$

6.4-28 $F = w\sin\theta + \frac{1}{2}\psi^2\left[\dfrac{C}{R}(1 - \cos 2\theta) + \dfrac{A}{l}\sin 2\theta\right]$

$C = \dfrac{mR^2}{2}$; $A = m\left(\dfrac{R^2}{4} + l^2\right)$

6.5-2   During acceleration, moment due to weight is reduced. The top motion θ and ψ undergo periodic change

6.5-6 $n = 58.8$ rps, direct precession

6.5-8   Coordinates i, j radial and k axial

$\mathbf{a} = [-\xi(\dot{\phi}^2 + \dot{\psi}^2) + \xi\dot{\psi}^2\sin^2\theta\sin^2\phi - 2\xi\dot{\phi}\dot{\psi}\cos\theta]\mathbf{i}$
$\qquad + (\xi\dot{\psi}^2\sin^2\theta\sin\phi\cos\phi)\mathbf{j} + (2\xi\dot{\phi}\dot{\psi}\sin\theta\sin\phi + \xi\dot{\psi}^2\sin\theta\cos\theta\sin\phi)\mathbf{k}$

6.5-10   Will point west of north by angle $\gamma = \tan^{-1}\dfrac{v}{R\Omega\cos\lambda}$

6.5-12 $\bar{\beta} = 0.00179$ rad

6.5-13   With x east, y north, z vertical up

$\ddot{\theta}_y + \dfrac{(mgl)^2}{h^2 + m^2gl^3}\theta_y = \dfrac{m^2gl^2}{h^2 + m^2gl^3}\ddot{x}$

h = angular momentum of wheel
l = length of pendulum